A LEVEL
GEOGRAPHY

Clifford Lines and Laurie Bolwell

EDUCATIONAL

Every effort has been made to trace copyright holders and to obtain
their permission for the use of copyright material. The author and
publishers will gladly receive information enabling them to rectify any
reference or credit in subsequent editions.

First published 1982
Reprinted 1983, 1984, 1986, 1988, 1991, 1994, 1995
Revised 1993

Letts Educational
Aldine House
Aldine Place
London W12 8AW

Text © C Lines and L Bolwell 1982, 1983, 1984, 1986, 1988, 1993

Design Watermark Communications Ltd (cover), Jonathan Barnard (text)

Illustrations Barbara Linton, Illustra Design Limited,
Peter McClure, Tek-Art
Design and illustrations © BPP (Letts Educational) Ltd

British Library Cataloguing in Publication Data
A CIP record for this book is available from the British Library

ISBN 1 85758 223 3

Printed and bound in Great Britain by
Ashford Colour Press Ltd, Gosport, Hants

Letts Educational is the trading name of BPP (Letts Educational) Ltd

PREFACE

One book cannot give you all the facts and techniques you will require for the examination. Your teacher will recommend a small group of specialist text books, and there will be many others you should dip into, as well as articles in journals and magazines like *The Geographical Magazine* and *New Scientist*. Television programmes such as *The World About Us* and *Fragile Earth* may also provide relevant and topical information. This book is not intended to be a substitute for these specialist text books and journals. We have written it to complement them and give you specific guidance on the examination.

The reports on past examinations issued by the various boards emphasise that many candidates have not been prepared adequately for the examination, and, through inexperience or lack of confidence, achieve poor results or fail. We have drawn on our own experience as examiners, as well as the comments of the Chief Examiners to describe the techniques and skills you will need for the examination. If this book is used as it has been designed, as a guide and companion throughout the A, AS or Scottish Higher Grade course, we are convinced you will increase your confidence to succeed, study Geography with more enthusiasm, and possess a deeper understanding of what the examiners expect from you.

C J Lines
L H Bolwell

CONTENTS

SECTION 1: STARTING POINTS

SECTION 2: GEOGRAPHY TOPICS

STARTING POINTS

In this section:

HOW TO USE THIS BOOK

THE STRUCTURE OF THIS BOOK

The key aim of this book is to guide you in the way you tackle A-level Geography. It should serve as a study guide, work book and revision aid throughout any A-level/AS-level Geography course, no matter what syllabus you are following. It is not intended to be a complete guide to the subject and should be used as a companion to your textbooks, which it is designed to complement rather than duplicate.

We have divided the book into three sections. Section One, Starting Points, contains study tips and syllabus information – all the material you need to get you started on your A-level study, together with advice on planning your revision and tips and tips on how to tackle the exam itself.

Section Two, the main body of the text, contains the core of A-level Geography. It has been devised to make study as easy – and enjoyable – as possible, and has been divided into chapters which cover the themes you will encounter on your syllabus. The chapters are split into units, each covering a topic of study.

A list of objectives at the beginning of each chapter directs you towards the key points of the chapter you are about to read. The chapter roundup at the end gives a summary of the text just covered, brings the topics of the chapter into focus and links them to other themes of study. To reinforce what you have just read and learned, there are Worked Questions and Answers at the end of each chapter. Recent examinations from all the examination boards (including Scottish Higher) provide the question practice. The tutorial notes and suggested answers give you practical guidance on how to answer A-level questions, and provide additional information relevant to that particular topic of study. There is also a Question Bank, with further examples of different types of A-level exam questions for you to attempt.

In Section Three, Test Run, we turn our attention to the examination you will face at the end of your course. First, you can assess your progress using the Test Your Knowledge Quiz and analysis chart. Then, as a final test, you should attempt the mock exam, under timed conditions. This will give you invaluable examination practice and, together with the specimen answers specially written by the author, will help you to judge how close you are to achieving your A-level pass.

USING YOUR SYLLABUS CHECKLIST

Whether you are using this book to work step-by-step through the syllabus or to structure your revision campaign, you will find it useful to keep a checklist of what you have covered – and how far you still have to go. Keep the checklist at hand when you are doing your revision, it will remind you of the chapters you have revised, and those still to be done.

The checklist for each examination – A, AS or Higher Grade – is in two parts. First there is a list of topics covered by this book which are part of the syllabus. A word of warning: the list covers both compulsory and optional topics so that you need to look carefully through the list and cross out any optional topics which you do not need to study, or revise. The optional topics have been marked with an asterisk. One topic which you should always include is Techniques and Skills. These help you to understand the maps and diagrams in your text books and you will need to use some of them when you prepare your coursework.

When you have revised a topic make a note of the date in the column provided and, if there are questions elsewhere in the book, try to answer them, putting the date or dates in the final column.

The second part of the checklist gives you information about the examination, providing useful details about the time allocated for each written paper and the weighting of the questions on each paper. The different types of questions which may be set are explained under the heading The Examination.

SYLLABUS CHECKLISTS AND PAPER ANALYSIS

ASSOCIATED EXAMINING BOARD
A-level Syllabus 626

Syllabus topic	Covered in Unit No	Completed on (date)	Questions attempted
Population	3.1, 3.2		
Physical processes	2.2, 2.3, 2.4, 2.6, 2.7		
Weather and climate	2.8		
Ecosystems	2.9, 2.10		
Agriculture	3.7		
Industry	3.8		
Transport	3.9		
Settlement	3.3, 3.4, 3.5, 3.6		
Developing countries	3.10		
Human and environmental conflicts	3.4, 4.6, 4.7		
Techniques and skills	1.1, 1.2		

Paper analysis

Number of written papers: 3, plus assessment of fieldwork.

Paper 1 *2 hours*   Short, structured questions
    14 questions set
    Any 8 questions to be answered
    20% of total marks

Paper 2 *3 hours*   Essay-type questions
    16 questions set in 4 sections
    4 questions to be answered, 1 from each section
    40% of total marks

Paper 3 *2 hours*   Data-response questions
    4 questions set
    2 to be answered
    20% of total marks

Paper 4   Submission of a fieldwork investigation
    20% of total marks

AS-level Syllabus 988

Syllabus topic	Covered in Unit No	Completed on (date)	Questions attempted
Population	3.1, 3.2		
Atmospheric processes	2.8		
Ecosystems	2.9, 2.10		
Industry	3.8		
Settlement	3.3, 3.4		
Development	3.10		
Urban problems*	3.5, 3.6		
Changing coastline*	2.6		
Ecosystem modification*	4.6, 4.7		
Techniques and skills	1.1, 1.2		

* optional topic

Paper analysis

Number of written papers: 1, plus a fieldwork essay.

Paper 1 *2½ hours*   Structured questions
                13 questions in Part A
                4 to be answered
                30% of total marks

                Essay-type questions
                13 questions in Part B
                2 to be answered
                40% of total marks

Paper 2   Fieldwork essay
                30% of total marks

UNIVERSITY OF CAMBRIDGE LOCAL EXAMINATIONS SYNDICATE
A-level Syllabus 9050

Syllabus topic	Covered in Unit No	Completed on (date)	Questions attempted
Fluvial systems	2.3, 2.4		
Ecosystems	2.9, 2.10		
Atmospheric systems	2.8		
Glaciation*	2.5		
Coastal environments*	2.6		
Arid and semi-arid environments	2.7		
The atmosphere*	4.7		
Population	3.1, 3.2		
Urbanisation	3.4, 3.5, 3.6, 3.8, 3.9		
Farming*	3.7		
The unequal world*	3.10, 4.2, 4.3, 4.4		
Data collection and analysis	1.1		

* optional topic

Paper analysis

Number of written papers: 3 (Papers 1, 2 and 3) or 2 (Papers 1, 2 and 4).

Paper 1 *3 hours*	Section A: each question consists of three parts: short-answer (7 marks) data-response (8 marks) free-response (10 marks) 4 questions set, 3 to be answered Section B: essay-type questions 8 questions set, 1 to be answered 37½% of total marks	
Paper 2 *3 hours*	Section A: each question will consist of three parts, as for Paper 1 3 questions set, 2 to be answered Section B: essay-type questions 9 questions set, 2 to be answered 37½% of total marks	
Paper 3 *2¼ hours*	Essay-type questions 3 questions set, 2 to be answered 25% of total marks	
Paper 4	Investigative study 25% of total marks	

AS-level Syllabus 8460

Syllabus topic	Covered in Unit No	Completed on (date)	Questions attempted
Atmospheric systems	1.3, 2.8		
Fluvial systems	2.3, 2.4		
Weathering	2.1		
Slopes	2.2		
Biosphere	2.9, 2.10		
Coastal studies*	2.6		
Glacial studies*	2.8		
Arid landscape studies*	2.7		

* optional topic

Paper analysis

Number of written papers: 2 (Papers 1 and 2) or 1 (Papers 1 and 3).

Paper 1   *2 hours 20 minutes*   4 data-response questions set, 3 essay-type set
4 data-response questions to be answered
1 essay-type to be answered
75% of total marks: data-response 50%, essay-type 25%

Paper 2   *40 minutes*   Essay-type questions
6 questions set, 3 to be answered
25% of total marks

Paper 3   Local geography study
25% of total marks

AS-level Syllabus 8461

Syllabus topic	Covered in Unit No	Completed on (date)	Questions attempted
Population	3.1, 3.2		
Settlement	3.3, 3.4, 3.5, 3.6		
Agricultural land use*	3.7		
Industry*	3.8		
Regional disparities and development*	4.2, 4.5		

* optional topic

Paper analysis

Number of written papers: 2 (Papers 1 and 2) or 1 (Papers 1 and 3).
Paper details as for syllabus 8460 above.

UNIVERSITY OF LONDON SCHOOL EXAMINATIONS BOARD
A-level Syllabus 9210

Syllabus topic	Covered in Unit No	Completed on (date)	Questions attempted
Biogeography	2.9, 2.10		
Fluvial processes	2.3, 2.4		
Coastal processes	2.6		
Aeolian processes	2.7		
Glacial and periglacial processes	2.5		
Hydrology	2.3		
Meteorology and climatology	1.3, 2.8		
Economic activity	3.7, 3.8, 3.9		
Population	3.1, 3.2		
Settlement	3.3, 3.4, 3.5, 3.6		
Area studies	3.10, 4.1, 4.2, 4.3, 4.4, 4.5, 4.6, 4.7		

Paper analysis

Number of written papers: 3, plus an optional geography project.

Paper 1   *2½ hours*   Short-answer questions, either structured or
data-response type
Section A: 6 questions set
Section B: 6 questions set
     6 questions to be answered
     3 from section A, 3 from section B
     33⅓% of total marks

Paper 2   *2¾ hours*   Essay-type questions
     Section A: 9 questions set
     Section B: 9 questions set
     4 questions to be answered: 2 from each section
     33⅓% of total marks

Paper 3   *2¼ hours*   Sections A and B: essay-type questions set
Section C: stimulus material questions set
     Section A: 5 questions set
     Section B: 5 questions set
     Section C: 3 questions set
     3 questions to be answered, 1 from each section
     33⅓% of total marks

A-level Syllabus 9219 (16-19 Project)

Syllabus topic	Covered in Unit No	Completed on (date)	Questions attempted
Managing landform systems	2.4, 2.6		
Ecosystems	2.10		
Urbanisation	3.4, 3.5, 3.6		
Manufacturing industry	3.8, 4.7		
Agricultural systems	3.7, 4.4		
Pollution*	4.7		
Natural resources*	3.7		
Global issues*	3.1, 3.2, 3.10		
Managing human environments*	3.5, 3.9, 3.10, 4.1, 4.2		

* optional topic

Paper analysis

Number of written papers: 2, plus coursework and an individual study.

Paper 1	2½ hours	Decision-making exercise 22% of total marks
Paper 2	3 hours	Resource-based questions requiring essay-type answers Section A: 6 questions set, Section B: 2 questions set Candidates must answer 4 questions, of which no more than one may be selected from Section B 43% of total marks
Coursework		24% of total marks
Individual study		11% of total marks

A-level Syllabus 8219 (16-19 Project)

Syllabus topic	Covered in Unit No	Completed on (date)	Questions attempted
Managing landform systems	2.4, 2.6		
Ecosystems	2.10		
Urbanisation	3.4, 3.5, 3.6		
Industrial change	3.8, 4.7		
Agricultural systems	3.7, 4.4		
Pollution*	4.7		
Natural resources*	3.7, 3.9		
Limits to growth*	3.1		
Migrations*	3.2		
Development*	3.10		
Regional disparities*	4.1, 4.2		
Changing urban environments*	3.5		
Rural management*	4.6		

* optional topic

Paper analysis

Number of written papers: 1, plus a decision-making exercise and an individual study.

Paper 1 *2¼ hours*	12 questions set, 2 for each of the 6 core modules 3 questions to be answered Candidates may answer no more than 1 question on each of the 6 core modules 64% of total marks
Decision-making exercise	Report to be written during 5 hours of supervised class time 16% of total marks
Individual study	20% of total marks

AS-level Syllabus 8210

Syllabus topic	Covered in Unit No	Completed on (date)	Questions attempted
Environmental systems	1.3, 2.3, 2.4, 2.8, 2.10		
Human systems	3.1, 3.3, 3.4, 3.5, 3.6, 3.8, 4.4		
Resource development	3.10, 4.1, 4.6, 4.7		

Paper analysis

Number of written papers: 2, plus a project.

Paper 1	*1½ hours*	Structured questions Section A: 9 questions set Section B: 9 questions set 4 questions to be answered: 2 from Section A; 2 from Section B. The questions will be based on environmental systems and human systems. 40% of total marks
Paper 2	*2 hours*	(you are advised to spend 15 minutes reading through the paper, especially Section A) Section A: the writing of a structured report based on a case study (you are advised to spend 1 hour on this question) Section B: 6 essay-type questions: 1 to be answered. Questions in Section B will be based on resource development. 40% of total marks
Individual project		20% of total marks

NORTHERN EXAMINATIONS AND ASSESSMENT BOARD
A-level Syllabus B

Syllabus topic	Covered in Unit No	Completed on (date)	Questions attempted
Chief types of landforms	2.1, 2.2, 2.3, 2.4, 2.5, 2.6, 2.7		
Weather and climate	2.8		
Soils and vegetation	2.9, 2.10		
Population	3.1, 3.2		
Rural and urban settlements	3.3, 3.4, 3.5		
Non-urban land use	3.7		
Industry	3.8		
Transport	3.9		
Regional interrelationships	4.1, 4.2, 4.5		
Practical Geography	1.1, 1.2, 1.3		

Paper analysis

Number of written papers: 2, or 3 if Practical Geography is not presented in the form of a project.

Paper 1	*3 hours*	Section A: 8 essay-type questions set
		Section B: 6 data-response questions set
		2 questions to be answered from each section
		40% of total marks
Paper 2	*3 hours*	As for Paper 1
Practical	*2¾ hours*	Assessment of project or practical examination
		20% of total marks. 3 questions to be answered
		or
		Assessment by teacher of project(s) caried out during course

A-level Syllabus C

Syllabus topic	Covered in Unit No	Completed on (date)	Questions attempted
Economic development	4.1, 4.2		
Urban development	3.4, 3.5, 3.6		
Agricultural development	4.3, 4.4, 4.5		
Economic growth	3.10		
Practical geography	1.1, 1.2, 1.3		

Paper analysis

As for Syllabus B

AS-level Syllabus

Syllabus topic	Covered in Unit No	Completed on (date)	Questions attempted
Rivers	2.3		
Coasts	2.6		
Atmosphere	2.8, 4.7		
Soils	2.9		
Agriculture	4.2, 4.4		
Industry	4.1, 4.5		
Large urban areas	3.6		

Paper analysis

Number of written papers: 1, plus a report on a geographical investigation.

Paper 1	*3 hours*	Section A: 4 essay-type questions set
		1 question to be answered
		Section B: 4 essay-type questions set
		1 question to be answered
		Section C: 4 data-response type questions set
		2 questions to be answered
		75% of total marks
Report		25% of total marks

NORTHERN IRELAND COUNCIL FOR THE
CURRICULUM EXAMINATIONS AND ASSESSMENT
A-level Syllabus

Syllabus topic	Covered in Unit No	Completed on (date)	Questions attempted
Fluvial systems	2.3, 2.4		
Coastal systems	2.6		
Atmospheric systems	2.8		
Weather systems	1.3		
Soil system	2.9		
Ecosystems	2.10		
Pollution*	4.7		
Population	3.1, 3.2		
Settlement	3.3, 3.4, 3.5, 3.6		
Development	3.10		
Industry*	3.8		
Agricultural systems*	3.7		
Techniques and skills	1.1, 1.2, 1.3		

* optional topic

Paper analysis

Number of written papers: 3, plus a geographical enquiry.

Paper 1 *3 hours*   Essay-type questions
                                       Section A: 6 questions set, 3 to be answered
                                       Section B: 6 questions set, 1 to be answered
                                       35% of total marks

Paper 2 *3 hours*   Essay-type questions
                                       Section A: 6 questions set, 3 to be answered
                                       Section B: 6 questions set, 1 to be answered
                                       35% of total marks

Paper 3 *1½ hours*   Decision-making exercise
                                       15% of total marks

Paper 4   Geographical enquiry
                                       15% of total marks

AS-level Human Geography

Syllabus topic	Covered in Unit No	Completed on (date)	Questions attempted
Techniques and skills	1.1, 1.2, 1.3		
Population	3.1, 3.2		
Settlement	3.3, 3.4, 3.5, 3.6		
Development	3.10		
Industry*	3.8		
Agricultural systems*	3.7		

* optional topic

Paper analysis

Number of written papers: 1, plus a geographical enquiry.

Paper 1   *3 hours*   Essay-type questions
                      Section A: 6 questions set, 3 to be answered
                      Section B: 6 questions set, 1 to be answered
                      70% of total marks

Paper 2   Geographical enquiry
                      30% of total marks

AS-level Physical Geography

Syllabus topic	Covered in Unit No	Completed on (date)	Questions attempted
Techniques and skills	1.1, 1.2, 1.3		
Fluvial systems	2.3, 2.4		
Coastal systems	2.6		
Atmospheric systems	2.8		
Weather systems	1.3		
Soil system	2.1		
Ecosystems	2.10		
Pollution*	3.1, 3.2		

* optional topic

Paper analysis

As for AS-level Human Geography above.

UNIVERSITY OF OXFORD DELEGACY OF LOCAL EXAMINATIONS
A-level Syllabus 9845

Syllabus topic	Covered in Unit No	Completed on (date)	Questions attempted
Atmospheric processes	1.3, 2.8		
Fluvial processes	2.2, 2.3, 2.4		
Glacial and periglacial processes	2.5		
Biogeography and soils	2.9, 2.10		
Arid and semi-arid environments*	2.7		
Coastal environments*	2.6		
Population	3.1, 3.2		
Settlement	3.3, 3.4, 3.5, 3.6		
Agriculture	3.7		
Manufacturing	3.8		
Communications, transport and trade*	3.9		
Techniques and skills	1.1		
Regional problem areas	4.2		

* optional topic

Paper analysis

Number of written papers: 2, plus an individual study.

Paper 1   *3 hours*   Essay-type or data-response questions
                            Section A: Question 1, compulsory
                            data-response question
                            3 other questions set, 1 to be answered
                            36% of total marks

Paper 2   *3 hours*   Essay-type or data-response questions
                            4 questions set: 2 to be answered, 1 from
                            each option
                            36% of total marks

Paper 3   Individual study
                            28% of total marks

AS-level Syllabus 8746 Human Geography

Syllabus topic	Covered in Unit No	Completed on (date)	Questions attempted
Population	3.1, 3.2		
Settlement	3.3, 3.4, 3.5, 3.6		
Agriculture	3.7		
Industry	3.8		
Interface of Human and Physical Geography	4.2, 4.3, 4.4, 4.5		
Techniques and skills	1.1		
Individual map study*	1.2		

* optional topic

Paper analysis

Number of written papers: 2, plus a field report or an individual map study.

Paper 1 *2½ hours*   Essay-type and data-response questions
                9 questions set
                3 questions to be answered, 1 from each section
                60% of total marks

Paper 2 *1 hour*   Essay-type and data-response questions
                Little choice
                Compulsory question based on one major region
                Compulsory data-response question
                20% of total marks

Paper 3   Practical or individual study
                20% of total marks

OXFORD AND CAMBRIDGE SCHOOLS EXAMINATION BOARD
A-level Syllabus 9630

Syllabus topic	Covered in Unit No	Completed on (date)	Questions attempted
Atmospheric systems	1.3, 2.8, 4.7		
Hydrological systems	2.3, 2.4		
Lithosphere	2.1, 2.2		
Soils*	2.9		
Ecological processes*	2.10		
Coastal landforms and processes*	2.6		
Glacial landforms and processes*	2.5		
Arid landforms and processes*	2.7		
Settlements and their functions	3.3, 3.4		
Agriculture*	3.7		
Communications*	3.9		
Manufacturing industry*	3.8		
Population*	3.1, 3.2		
Urban and industrial land use	3.5, 3.6		
Regional disparities and development	4.1, 4.2, 4.4, 4.5		
Techniques	1.1		

* optional topic

Paper analysis

Number of written papers: 5 or 6, plus a local geography essay.
Physical geography (2), human geography (2), applied geography (1) plus a local geography essay; *or* physical geography (2), human geography (2), applied geography (1) and geographical techniques (1), to which may be added the local geography essay.

Papers 1 and 2   *2¾ hours*

Paper 1   Compulsory structured questions
                           Approximately 1¼ hours should be spent
                           on this paper
                           16⅔% of total marks

Paper 2   Essay-type questions
                           14 questions set
                           2 questions from different options to be answered
                           Approximately 1½ hours should be spent on
                           this paper
                           16⅔% of total marks

Papers 3 and 4   *2¾ hours*

Paper 3   Compulsory structured questions
                           Approximately 1¼ hours should be spent on
                           this paper
                           16⅔% of total marks

Paper 4   Essay-type questions
                           12 questions set
                           Any 2 to be answered
                           Approximately 1½ hours should be spent on
                           this paper
                           16⅔% of total marks

Paper 5   *1½ hours*   Most questions of essay-type
                           15 questions set
                           2 questions to be answered, each from a
                           different section
                           16⅔% of total marks

Paper 6   *1½ hours*   Essay-type questions
                           8 questions will be set
                           2 questions must be answered
                           16⅔% of total marks

Paper 7   Local geography essay
                           16⅔% of total marks

AS-level Syllabus 8461

Syllabus topic	Covered in Unit No	Completed on (date)	Questions attempted
Population	3.1, 3.2		
Settlement	3.3, 3.4, 3.5, 3.6		
Agricultural land use*	3.7		
Manufacturing industry*	3.8		
Regions*	4.1, 4.2, 4.4, 4.5		
Local geography study*	1.1		

* optional topic

Paper analysis

Number of written papers: 1 or 2. Either 1 paper plus a local geography study or 2 papers (core studies and associated studies).

Paper 1 *2 hours 20 minutes* 4 compulsory data-response questions
1 essay-type question chosen from 3
Data-response: 50% of total marks
Essay: 25% of total marks

Paper 2 *40 minutes* Essay-type questions
2 set for each of the 3 associated studies
1 to be answered
25% of total marks

Paper 3 Local geography study
25% of total marks

AS-level Syllabus 8460

Syllabus topic	Covered in Unit No	Completed on (date)	Questions attempted
Atmosphere	1.3, 2.8		
Hydrosphere	2.3, 2.4		
Lithosphere	2.1, 2.2		
Biosphere	2.9, 2.10, 4.6		
Coastal studies*	2.6, 4.7		
Glacial and periglacial studies*	2.5		
Arid landscape studies*	2.7		
Local geography study*	1.1		

* optional topic

Paper analysis

As for AS-level 8461

SCOTTISH EXAMINATION BOARD
Higher Grade

Syllabus topic	Covered in Unit No	Completed on (date)	Questions attempted
Atmosphere	2.8		
Hydrosphere	2.3, 2.4		
Lithosphere	2.1, 2.2, 2.5		
Biosphere	2.9, 2.10		
Population	3.1, 3.2		
Rural geography	3.3, 3.7		
Industrial geography	3.8		
Urban geography	3.4, 3.5, 3.6		
Rural land resources*	4.1, 4.5, 4.6		
European regional inequalities*	4.1, 4.2		
Development and health*	3.10		

* optional topic

Paper analysis

Number of written papers: 2, plus an investigation.

Paper 1 *2½ hours*		Short-response questions. Questions involving the use of an Ordnance Survey map: within most questions there will be a choice 35% of total marks
Paper 2 *2¾ hours*		Extended-response questions 6 questions set, grouped in 2 sections 3 questions to be answered: 1 from each section and 1 other 45% of total marks
Investigation		20% of total marks

WELSH JOINT EDUCATION COMMITTEE
A-level Syllabus

Syllabus topic	Covered in Unit No	Completed on (date)	Questions attempted
Landforms	2.2, 2.3, 2.4		
Weather and climate	1.3, 2.8		
Ecosystems	2.9, 2.10		
Agricultural systems	3.7, 4.4, 4.5, 4.6		
Manufacturing	3.8		
Urban world	3.4, 3.5, 3.6		
Water resource management*	2.4		
Population and food*	3.1, 3.2, 4.3, 4.4		
Regional differentiation*	4.1, 4.2		
Spatial inequalities*	3.10		
Skills and techniques	1.1, 1.2		

* optional topic

Paper analysis

Number of written papers: 3, plus an individual study.

Paper 1   *3 hours*   Essay-type and data-response questions
                                   12 questions set
                                   6 questions to be answered
                                   30% of total marks

Paper 2   *2½ hours*   Essay-type or structured questions
                                   6 questions set with either/or choice in each
                                   3 questions to be answered
                                   30% of total marks

Paper 3   *2 hours*   Essay-type or structured questions
                                   6 questions set, 3 for each optional module
                                   2 questions to be answered
                                   25% of total marks

Individual study   15% of total marks

AS-level Syllabus

Syllabus topic	Covered in Unit No	Completed on (date)	Questions attempted
Landforms	2.2, 2.3, 2.4		
Weather and climate	1.3, 2.8		
Ecosystems	2.9, 2.10		
Agricultural systems	3.7, 4.4, 4.5, 4.6		
Manufacturing	3.8		
Urban world	3.4, 3.5, 3.6		
Water resource management	2.4		
Skills and techniques	1.1, 1.2		

Paper analysis

Number of written papers: 2, plus an individual study

Paper 1   *1½ hours*   Data-response type questions
                                          6 questions set, 2 from each module
                                          3 questions to be answered, 1 from each module
                                          40% of total marks

Paper 2   *2½ hours*   Essay-type questions
                                          6 questions set, 2 from each module
                                          3 questions to be answered, 1 from each module
                                          40% of total marks

Individual study   20% of total marks

EXAMINATION BOARDS AND ADDRESSES

AEB The Associated Examining Board
Stag Hill House, Guildford, Surrey GU2 5XJ

Cambridge University of Cambridge Local Examinations Syndicate
Syndicate Buildings, 1 Hills Road, Cambridge CB1 2EU

NEAB Northern Examinations and Assessment Board
Devas Street, Manchester M15 6EX

NICCEA Northern Ireland Council for the
Curriculum Examinations and Assessment
Beechill House, 42 Beechill Road, Belfast BT8 4RS

Oxford University of Oxford Delegacy of Local Examinations
Ewert House, Ewert Place, Summertown, Oxford OX2 7BZ

Oxford and Cambridge Oxford and Cambridge Schools Examination Board
(a) Purbeck House, Purbeck Road, Cambridge CB2 1PU
(b) Elsfield Way, Oxford OX2 7BZ

Scottish Scottish Examinations Board
Ironmills Road, Dalkeith, Midlothian EH22 1LE

ULEAC University of London Examinations and Assessment Council
Stewart House, 32 Russell Square, London WC1 5DN

WJEC Welsh Joint Education Committee
245 Western Avenue, Cardiff CF5 2YX

STUDYING AND REVISING GEOGRAPHY

THE DIFFERENCE BETWEEN GCSE AND A/AS LEVEL

When you were studying for GCSE you may have thought that A level was rather similar but more difficult. This is an easy trap to fall into since at first sight there are some similarities in the syllabuses. For example, many aspects of physical and human geography, map work and regional studies are common to both GCSE and A-level syllabuses. Moreover the central concern, that of the interaction of man with his physical environment, is evident at both levels.

The similarity is, however, superficial and your A-level studies will have a greater significance if you fully appreciate what is expected of you and the approach which is required at this level. Just as there are differences between the GCSE and A-level syllabuses, differences also occur when the examination questions are analysed. One of the functions of this book is to consider a variety of questions, to identify what is required by the examiner and to suggest suitable structures for the answers.

What the examiner will expect

Most GCSE candidates take seven or more subjects in the examination. A-level subjects are selected more carefully since most candidates find that three subjects are as many as they can cope with. Consequestly, the A-level examiner will expect more of you in terms of breadth and depth of knowledge as well as in your ability to apply this knowledge and related concepts to specific situations or problems.

The successful A-level answer paper is one which convinces the examiner that you have a good grasp of the geographical facts, and an understanding of the processes involved and the related problems which exist. It should also demonstrate your ability to understand and use geographical models, statistical data and a comprehensive range of skills and techniques.

Quantitative differences

When GCSE and A-level examinations are compared there are some obvious quantitative differences. Most examining boards set two papers at GCSE, each designed to last for 2 hours. At A level there are usually three papers, each one being timed for 2½ hours. Not only are the examinations longer but also more time is provided to answer each question. Whereas a GCSE paper may require four questions to be answered in 2 hours, A-level papers may require only three questions to be answered in 2½ hours, giving 50 minutes for each question.

The AS level examination consists of one or two papers lasting 2½ to 3 hours.

These quantitative differences are not as formidable as they may appear at first sight. The normal two-year time span between GCSE and A level gives you the opportunity to study geography in depth as well as breadth, and there should be no difficulty in writing answers in the time provided. If there is any difficulty it is likely to be in deciding what should be included and what excluded in the time available. The selection and presentation of material in a manner which will demonstrate your ability to be succinct as well as erudite is of considerable importance.

The significance of facts

Some GCSE questions test your knowledge of geographical facts and little else. You may have spent many hours of revision before the exams learning sketch maps, climatic statistics, industries associated with particular cities, crop requirements and many other parcels of facts. These facts are required to answer questions like this one.
(i)   On the outline map of the USA which is provided, show the main areas of corn (maize) cultivation.
(ii) State the conditions under which corn is grown in the region.
(iii) Describe the major changes in agricultural land use in the Corn Belt.

By contrast, an A-level question on the same subject reads:

> Outline and explain the changes which have taken place in farming in the corn belt over the last forty years.

This question requires the candidate to make intelligent use of the knowledge at his or her disposal rather than to test a number of memorised facts. Moreover it concentrates on the concept of change over a period of time, a concept rarely considered at GCSE, where the emphasis is on understanding skills, values and issues as well as on knowledge. You will still need a wide range of facts to answer many A-level questions but the facts are not the final product. They are required to support ideas and arguments and to substantiate hypotheses.

A more analytical approach

A-level exams demand a much more analytical approach than GCSE. This becomes apparent when sets of questions at both levels are examined. The repeated use of certain verbs is common in both GCSE and A-level questions but there is a difference between those used at each level. In GCSE the most common directions are *describe*, *write an account of*, *explain*, *locate and describe*, *define*, *account for* and *what is meant by*. At A level *explain* and *account for* recur but they are joined by others such as *assess, discuss, justify, analyse, consider, compare, comment on, critically examine* and *to what extent would you agree with...?*

The A- and AS-level approach expects the candidate to have acquired sets of values; to appreciate the dynamic character of the environment in time and space, to weigh up the available evidence and make informed judgements about problems and issues, to understand the geographical processes, concepts and general principles by which spatial patterns may be explained and not to be content with straightforward descriptions.

A more mature approach

The increased sophistication required at A and AS level is evident from the wording of the questions and analysis of a large number of questions reveals certain recurring themes.

Interrelationships

Some questions examine the interrelationships which exist within the physical environment or between the physical and human aspects of the environment. The candidate is expected to link one aspect with another even though they may have been taught as separate units. For example:

> How far is the transport network more closely related to the distribution of population than to relief and drainage? Give examples from one or more developed countries to illustrate your answer.

Problem analysis

Instead of asking for descriptions or factual statements, some questions focus on problems which have geographical implications. For example:

> Examine the problems of siting new airports in developed countries.

To answer this type of question it is necessary to have a detailed knowledge of specific siting problems which have arisen and then to be able to summarise them in general terms. Relevant factual evidence is essential and the examiner will give high marks to the candidate who can show an ability to categorise the factors involved.

Use of models and concepts

Models, which are generalisations of some significant features or relationships in geography, are frequently used in A-level studies. In the examination a diagrammatic form of a model may be given which must then be explained and sometimes related to a particular situation. Alternatively a particular model is referred to, as in this question:

> Describe Weber's model of industrial location. Show how far the model can be used to explain the location of **either** the iron and steel industry of one country, **or** motor car manufacturing in one country.

An understanding of concepts is also important at A level, as this question illustrates:

> With reference to specific examples discuss the concept of the urban hierarchy.

Advanced skills and techniques

Many questions are set to test your ability to use geographical skills and techniques. Sometimes the questions give you the opportunity to write about practical experience, describing skills and techniques which have been gained during field work.

A-level questions reflect the trend in geography towards a more scientific and statistical approach which requires objectivity and rigour in collecting, measuring and interpreting data in physical and human geography. This question typifies the A-level emphasis on quantitative methods:

> Discuss the methods you would use and the problems involved in identifying and mapping **either** (a) a Central Business District, **or** (b) rural land use.

A systems approach

All the examination boards require a systems approach. The emphasis in this approach is on the interrelationships between variables such as vegetation, land and capital. These variables interact with one another and are influenced by such features as energy flows. Changes in one variable set in train changes throughout the system. These changes may be brought about by human activities such as cutting down rain forests or damming a river. As geographers, we are concerned with the processes by which changes occur in a system and in the complex interrelationships which exist between the variables. References to systems, including explanatory diagrams, occur where appropriate throughout this book. Here is an example of an A-level question which requires a knowledge of interaction within a system:

> Discuss the ways in which human activity in agriculture and forestry may affect the hydrological characteristics of a drainage basin.

Emphasis on process

Whereas GCSE is concerned with knowledge of physical and man-made phenomena such as corrie lakes and the location of nuclear power stations, A and AS levels are more concerned with causes and the processes of development and change. This is clearly evident in many questions on landforms. At GCSE the questions are concerned mainly with identification and the basic reasons for the formation of the landforms, whereas A-level questions require a detailed account of the process at work. For example:

> Analyse the processes that have led to the formation of two of the following: loess; drumlin; corrie (cirque); inselberg; meander.

STUDY STRATEGIES AND TECHNIQUES

At least 80% of your time as a student will be spent on private study so it is very important for you to acquire those skills which enable you to study effectively. Many hours can be wasted reading books from which you learn very little, or drawing elaborate maps and diagrams which are soon forgotten.

Study will involve you in collecting information, analysing it, clarifying your thinking, assimilating knowledge and expressing yourself clearly. No one is born with these skills, nor are they obtained accidentally: they must be acquired by conscious effort and practice. Here are some suggestions which will help you to develop these skills and make the most of your study time.

Establish targets

Research has shown that a learning period of about 45 minutes produces the best relationship between understanding and remembering. Set yourself study tasks which can be achieved in this period of time and then take a break for 15 minutes or longer before attempting another period of work. Plan reasonable targets which you can achieve in each study session, e.g. to read twenty pages and make notes.

Focus on essentials

There are large numbers of books and articles which deal with topics in the A-

or AS-level syllabuses. Some of this material is inappropriate or duplicates what is written better elsewhere. Try to focus on sections of books, avoid extraneous material and select what you read intelligently.

Select key words and phrases

When you read a section of a book, select words or phrases which will help you to remember what the section is about. These words can be written down for reference and used as personal notes. Many of the words you select will be important terms such as 'nitrification', 'intensive agriculture' and 'isodapanes'. Phrases selected will include definitions such as 'Bed load – that part of a stream's load which is moved along the bed of a stream by sliding, rolling and saltation.'

Note taking

Far too many students write notes as they write essays, in linear sentences. About 90% of what is written is wasted material and will never be remembered. It is the key words, concepts and phrases which need to be remembered and with practice you can abandon linear notes and learn more effectively by recording only the key words. This skill takes some time to acquire and can best be learned in stages by first writing down long phrases but not sentences and then, after a time, reducing your notes to just the key words and phrases. This form of note taking is suitable for notes made while reading or during a lecture. Remember to record the author and title. Sometimes the page number is also useful for future reference. A fluorescent highlighting pen is useful for identifying key words and phrases. These are not, of course, to be used on text books or journals but on notes you have made or been given.

Subject-specific skills

Three units in this book (1.1, 1.2 and 1.3) deal with specific skills and techniques and you will need to study them carefully. There are some additional tips that will help you to improve your planning and revision.

Make a topic summary

When you need to plan an essay or summarise a topic, the most effective method is by making a topic summary. First, print in the centre of a sheet of paper the core theme or topic title. Then draw lines from this centre, making as many lines as the number of sub-themes you can distinguish. Print the titles of the sub-themes at the end of the lines. Along each line print key words or phrases which are associated with the sub-theme. You can always add new lines as you go along and use arrows to show relationships between different sub-themes on the diagram. This topic summary, or web as it is sometimes called, will help you when planning an essay (the sub-themes could become sections or paragraphs), when revising a particular topic or as a summary of a chapter in a book. Printing the words will produce a diagram which can be referred to with ease at a later date.

Here is an example of a topic summary which was prepared by a student before answering the following question:

> For any one country of your choice, describe and account for the major patterns of internal migration since 1950.

The student chose Brazil for his answer.

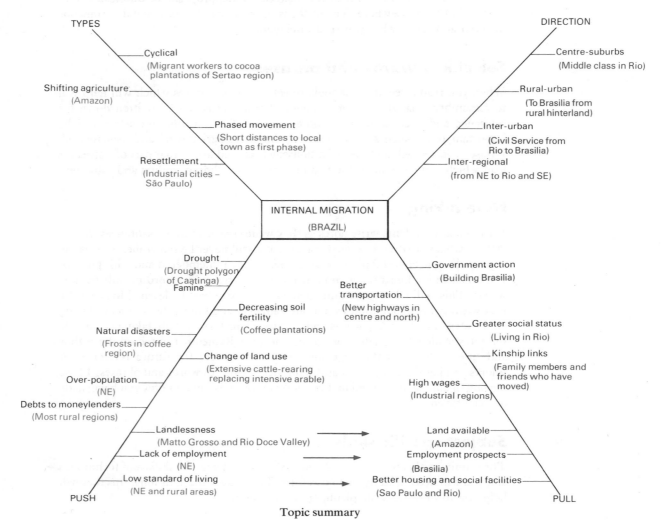

Topic summary

Practising techniques

Many aspects of practical geography and statistical data cannot be learned effectively by seeing examples or reading about them in books. To understand the techniques involved, it is essential to practise such things as using formulae, drawing sketch maps, compiling charts and plotting graphs. You will find suitable exercises in some text books and in past examination papers. Always try to reproduce diagrams and sketch maps neatly since marks are not awarded for untidy work.

COURSEWORK

Background information

Most examining boards include coursework as a part of the examination. Look at the syllabus checklists in Section 1 of this book if you are not sure whether your board requires coursework. Each board has its own terminology for coursework. Some call it an Investigative Study or an Individual Study, AEB refers to it as a Fieldwork Investigation, while Oxford and Cambridge uses the term Local Geography Study.

Whatever term is used, the end product takes the form of a written account, normally not exceeding 3 or 4000 words, containing data, illustrations, maps and, where relevant, photographs. This individual investigation must be planned with great care and each board gives very helpful advice in the printed syllabus which you can buy or look at in the reference section of some libraries. You will need to consult with your teacher about the title and objectives of your study. Titles and outlines must be submitted several months (sometimes a year or more) before the exam and unsuitable titles are referred back by the board. Once your teacher has given you guidance about a suitable topic to investigate and provided you with sources and background skills and techniques, you are on your own. No help will be given with investigations in the field or primary sources, or with writing the report. You will be told the date by which the report must be handed in – usually about two or three months before the written examination is taken. Avoid last-minute preparation by starting the investigation as early as possible and get on with it on a regular basis. Many students leave gaps of several weeks between one part of the work and another. Try to plan your study so that something is done each week, or most of it is done during one of the holidays.

What the examiners are looking for

Marks are awarded for the individual study using the following criteria:
- The appropriateness of the aims or hypothesis and the subject chosen for study.
- The clarity with which the problem or issue is described and the structure of the report.
- The candidate's ability to set the study into its broader geographical context, including the use of references.
- The suitability and quality of the data used and the quality of its analysis.
- The overall quality of the presentation, including the illustrative material.
- The extent to which the study achieves what it set out to do.
- The validity of the interpretation of the data and the conclusions reached.
- Evidence of the candidate's ability to see the limitations of his or her work.

Keep any field notes you may have made during the investigation because these must be available at the interview which most boards arrange. This interview is normally with an external examiner who will question you about the work, mainly to check that you did it by yourself and that you understand what you have found out.

REVISION TECHNIQUES

A revision schedule

It is essential to plan a revision schedule for the weeks leading up to the examination. Bearing this in mind, the timetable which follows has been prepared assuming that the examination will take place during the first week in June. A similar timescale would apply if you were sitting the exam in other months of the year.

Mid-March Draw up a revision schedule, planning weekly programmes for late March, April and May and increasing the workload for the Easter holiday period. Review weaknesses which may have shown up at the mock examination and allocate additional time in the schedule to weak areas. Plan the schedule so that there is at least a week available before the examination to refresh your memory of the most important points.

Late March, April and May Follow your revision schedule, allocating an hour or more each day with an increased revision workload during the Easter vacation and on some weekends. Don't forget to practise your skills during this period. Draw sketch maps, use the formulae in Unit 1.1 and look at data response/stimulus questions in previous papers and in the chapters of this book.

THE EXAMINATION

QUESTION STYLES

There are two major styles of questions on the A-level, AS-level and Higher Grade examination papers, structured questions and data-response or stimulus-response questions. You are likely to find both types on your question papers because the examiners like to include a variety of question styles to test the range of your techniques and skills.

Structured questions

Questions of this type examine a topic by asking a question or a series of sub-questions. They do not ask you to select an answer from a range of possibilities as do objective tests. The most common type of structured question is the essay topic. For example:

> Discuss the factors which affect the location of either the the iron and steel industry or the high-technology industries.

An essay question tests not only your knowledge, but also your ability to organise ideas and statements in sentences which make a coherent and lucid piece of prose. As part of your revision you must practise writing answers to essay type questions. Very few candidates are natural essay writers. The skill is learned by constant practice and criticism of what you have written.

Watch out for the key verb, probably to be found at the beginning of the question. In the example above it is *Discuss*. Other combinations include *Describe and account for...*, *Explain...* and *Compare...* It is worthwhile underlining or highlighting these key words on the examination paper so that they constantly remind you of the approach required in your answer. One of the problems of essay type questions is that you can wander off the subject.

Short, structured questions are popular with the examiners. They require only a few words or sentences as answers and marks can be allocated with some precision. For example:

> What is meant by the term soil erosion? (2 marks)
> List four ways in which soil may be eroded. (8 marks)
> Give three examples of areas which have suffered from soil erosion and, for each one, explain what caused the erosion. (6 marks)
> Describe two methods used to check soil erosion. (4 marks)

Data- and stimulus-response questions

There are an increasing number of questions in which information is given as a set of statistics (data), or as a map, diagram, photo, quotation or some other form (stimulus). You are required to interpret the data and also answer other sections of the question.

Here is an example of a data-response question:

> Table 1 opposite shows the percentage of the employed population of a number of European community countries working in the three employment sectors.
>
> (a)   What is meant by the term 'service sector'?
> (b)   How has the rapid increase in recent years in the percentage of people employed in the service sector influenced the distribution of population in Western Europe?

Table 1

Country	Primary sector	Manufacturing sector	Service sector
Denmark	8.5%	26.3%	65.2%
France	8.4%	34.6%	57.0%
Italy	12.4%	37.0%	50.6%
Netherlands	5.0%	28.7%	66.3%
Republic of Ireland	17.3%	31.1%	51.6%
United Kingdom	2.7%	34.7%	62.6%

Here is a stimulus-response question with a diagram as the stimulus:

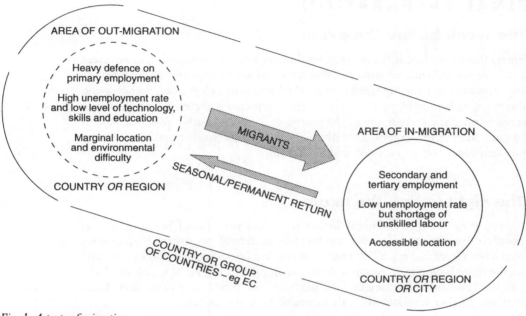

Fig. 1 Aspects of migration

Study Fig. 1 which shows aspects of migration.

Either (a) Referring to specific areas and/or countries which you have studied describe and explain the pattern of migration shown in the model.

Or (b) Explain the consequences which this pattern of migration creates for the area of out- migration and area of in- migration.

(Scottish Certificate, Higher Grade, specimen question)

There are many more examples of the various question styles throughout this book.

EXAMINATION TECHNIQUES

When you practise answering questions and when you are taking the examination there are two key words to remember: **read** and **time**. Make sure you read the question paper carefully, noting key words and the information in the rubric. Each question must also be read carefully, again noting key words and what you have been asked to do. If a question says 'Analyse' you must not limit your answer to a description. Analysis involves looking at causes and assessing their significance as well as reaching conclusions.

Secondly, it is essential to time yourself. Answering four questions in three hours gives you approximately 45 minutes for each question. If you are running more than five to ten minutes over this time-scale abandon the question, but leave a space in case you have time at the end to return to it. Marks cannot be awarded for parts of questions you have not answered, so check that when you answer short, structured questions you answer all the sections.

Essay-type questions should not be plunged into without first drawing up an answer plan. Jot down the main points you want to make, grouping them if possible, so that you have a paragraph structure for your answer. Do not forget your essay may need a concluding paragraph which sums up your findings, but beware of repeating yourself. Marks are only awarded once for points you have made: repeating these points at the end is a waste of time.

FINAL PREPARATION

The week before the exam

Spend this week glancing back over your notes at some of the most important areas you have revised and the maps and diagrams you need to remember. As it is very important to enter the examination refreshed and with a clear head, do not spend this week at late-night parties (reserve these until after the exams are over), or revising until the early hours of the morning. Revision is often more valuable if you are sharing the experience with a friend. Test each other and then discuss problem areas you still do not understand fully.

The night before the exam

Everyone agrees that the night before the exam you should be as relaxed as possible, but some people insist that you will be mentally reassured if you glance over a few topics you are still not happy about. We do not recommend any revision on the night before the exam, nor do we recommend a late night which will leave you tired and jaded for the exam the next day. Go to bed early in the knowledge that any further revision will only diminish your performance.

The day of the exam

Before the exam starts, check that you have all the pencils and other equipment you will need, plus some reserves in case of breakage. Make sure you arrive at least 20 minutes before the exam starts so that you can be seated and settled down on time by the invigilator.

When the exam starts

When you turn over your exam paper, spend some time selecting which questions you are going to answer.
❶ Read the rubric at the top of the paper.
❷ Read all the questions carefully.
❸ Mark all the questions you might be able to answer.
❹ Reduce the number of questions you have marked to the number required by the rubric.
❺ Read again the questions you will attempt, underline key words and ensure that you appreciate exactly what is involved in answering each one.
❻ Choose the order in which you will answer them, leaving the weakest until last.
❼ Allocate the remaining time available for each question, allowing ten minutes at the end of the exam for checking and revision. (Do not allow

yousluf to overwrite for more than five minutes on any one question. Space can always be left for additional material to be added later, if time permits.)

❽ Check once more that you are following the rubric and have chosen wisely.

Before you begin to answer the questions you have selected, bear these points in mind:

❶ Read the questions carefully, noting the key words you have underlined.

❷ Check whether the question falls into sections which can be dealt with separately. Decide whether maps and diagrams will be included in your answer.

❸ Draft a brief answer plan, listing the main sections of your answer and noting down key words, concepts and examples. Judge approximately how much time you should allow for each section.

❹ Read the question once more to ensure that your plan answers all the points required by the question.

Common faults

If this procedure seems tortuous and repetitive to you, here is a summary of criticisms made by the chief examiners about the A-level answer papers they have read:

❶ Time is wasted writing plans which are then ignored.

❷ Candidates fail to answer the question as it was asked.

❸ Answers are unstructured or do not keep to the structure of the question.

❹ There is a failure to concentrate on the main theme of the question.

❺ Some students write overlong introductions.

❻ Many candidates write a conclusion which does not add to the answer but only summarises points already made. Marks are not awarded for repetition of information.

❼ Key instructions, e.g. *describe*, *explain*, *compare*, are ignored.

❽ Some answers are presented untidily.

❾ There is an inadequate use of sketch-maps and diagrams.

❿ Many candidates make a poor choice of specific examples and locations are often imprecise, e.g. *chalk cliffs on the south coast*.

These comments should underline the need for a carefully planned approach to the examination papers and to each question you answer.

GEOGRAPHY TOPICS

In this section:

Chapter 1: Practical Geography

Chapter 2: Physical Geography

Chapter 3: Human Geography

Chapter 4: Regional and Environmental Issues

Each chapter features:

- *Units in this chapter:* a list of the main topic heads to follow.

- *Chapter objectives:* a brief comment on how the topics relate to what has gone before, and to the syllabus. Key ideas and skills which are covered in the chapter are introduced.

- *The main text:* divided into numbered topic units for ease of reference.

- *Chapter roundup:* a brief summary of the chapter.

- *A worked question:* a typical exam question, with tutorial notes and our suggested answer.

- *Question bank:* further questions, with tutorial comments on the pitfalls to avoid and points to include in framing your own answers.

PRACTICAL GEOGRAPHY

Units in this chapter

1.1 *Statistical methods*
1.2 *Ordnance Survey maps*
1.3 *Weather systems and synoptic charts*

Chapter objectives

When you have studied the units in this chapter you should be able to:

• understand the different types of data used by geographers;

• understand the techniques of data collection used by official organisations;

• use techniques which enable you to collect data and information from primary sources such as weather observations and vegetation mapping;

• use information and data from secondary sources such as census returns, maps and atlases;

• analyse data using statistical techniques such as measures of central tendency;

• identify a variety of methods by which data and information can be presented and select the most suitable method for each presentation;

• analyse and interpret Ordnance Survey maps;

• make an annotated sketch map of part of a printed map;

• interpret aerial photographs, and, if necessary, relate them to the information on a map;

• understand the causes responsible for the formation of and principal weather associated with northern hemisphere mid-latitude depressions and anticyclones;

• relate this knowledge to the information contained on synoptic charts;

• analyse and interpret mid-latitude synoptic charts.

Relevance of the units

The basic geographical skills illustrated in the next three units are essential to the understanding of geography. They underpin what you will read in text books, the methods you will use in field work and your understanding of maps at all scales. With these skills and techniques you can think and work as a geographer: without them the subject is meaningless. The use of data–

response and stimulus-response questions gives the examiner the opportunity to test your knowledge of specific skills and techniques – hence the popularity of this question style. Map or synoptic chart interpretation questions are frequently set and give you the chance to obtain high marks, provided you have prepared thoroughly.

You will depend heavily on statistical methods and map interpretation for your field work and individual study because this part of your examination is based on the practical application of these techniques and skills. There are many opportunities throughout this book to draw sketch maps, use the skills of graphicacy and interpret data. The more you practise, the more competent and confident you will become. Whenever you attempt a piece of coursework, or practise answering questions, refer back to these three units if you are in doubt about the techniques and skills to be used.

Key ideas and concepts

- Specific skills and techniques are essential to the understanding of geography.
- Application of these skills and techniqes will arise throughout the course and the various examination papers, especially the individual study.
- The map is a record of distributions and patterns in a space. It is a two-dimensional record of spatial phenomena. It is an essential part of the geographer's role to recognise, analyse and describe the distributing trends and relationships which map evidence provides.

1.1 STATISTICAL METHODS

SOME BASIC TERMS

Normal distribution

This is a bell-shaped or symmetrical frequency curve. Observations equidistant from the central maximum have the same frequency. The three values of the plotted data – the average, the median and the mode (see below) all coincide at the same central point in this distribution.

Given a normal distribution curve it is possible to postulate the number of occurrences at any given value or between given values (Fig. 2). Approximately 68% of the values lie less than one standard deviation from the mean and 95% less than two standard deviations from the mean (a definition of standard deviation is given later in this unit).

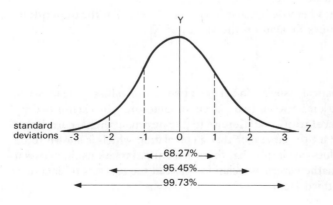

The normal curve is also known as the **Gaussian distribution**. It is important to note that statistical normality is a property of a distribution *not* of individual values. So one value cannot be said to be normal, but a set of values may be said to be normally distributed.

Fig. 2 The normal distribution curve

Skew (or skewness)

This term is used to describe the extent to which a frequency curve is asymmetrical (Fig. 3). When the modal class, i.e. the class containing the largest number of values, lies off-centre to the left when the data are plotted the distribution is said to have a **positive skew**. A **negative skew** exists when the modal class lies towards the upper end of the range, i.e. off-centre to the right when the data are plotted. Generally speaking the greater the skew the less representative is the average (the arithmetic mean value). Skewness may in fact be defined as the extent to which the mean differs from the median.

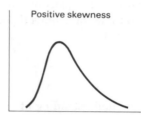 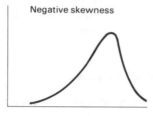

Positive skewness   Negative skewness

Fig. 3 Skew

Error

The difference between observed and calculated values. See, for example, **sampling error** below.

Significance

When statistical difference is **significant** it is extremely improbable that it occurred by chance. A geographer has to be concerned with probability – the probability that a particular conclusion based upon the interpretation of collected data is correct; the probability that a hypothesis is justified. So it is necessary to establish tests of significance.

A particular hypothesis may be assumed to be true and data are collected to test it. If the results observed in a random sample are markedly different from those expected in the context of the hypothesis and are not the result of pure chance, it is said that the observed differences are significant. The original hypothesis would then be rejected. If, on the other hand, the results correlate with those expected, the observed correlations are significant and the hypothesis is accepted. Tests of significance are therefore procedures which enable us to judge whether hypotheses should be accepted or rejected.

Dependent and independent variables

A variable is an item which can have several values. If to each value that can be assumed by a variable X there corresponds one or more values of a variable Y, we say that Y is a **function** of X i.e. Y = F(X).

X is the **independent variable** because it may vary freely. Y is the **dependent variable** because its values depend on the values of X.

Correlation

Correlation is a mathematical association between two sets of values. The measure of the degree of association between two paired variables may be established by the calculation of a **correlation coefficient** (e.g. Spearman's rank correlation coefficient). It is important to remember that a correlation which is shown to be statistically significant does not imply that there is a **causal** relationship between both sets of data. The mathematical association between the two sets of data may have been caused by a third factor.

DATA COLLECTION

Sampling

This is a means of obtaining a set of data of the smallest size that is representative of the total population or the whole area being studied. The set of data is within a desired degree of reliability.

When the data which has been collected to test a particular hypothesis has been identified, it may be found to be so large in volume that there are practical problems of time, cost or effort (workload). It therefore becomes important to select a sample representative of the total information available. A sample is a subset of the total population (**population** – a set of items or phenomena). It is the correct choice of a representative sample from the total population because the total population is, in practical terms, beyond reach.

Random sampling

Random sampling techniques are used to obtain as true and representative a cross-section of population as is permitted by the size of the sample. Random number tables are usually used to select the sample in a way which ensures that each member of the population has as much chance of being selected as part of the sample as any other. This makes it possible to generalise from the characteristics (mean, standard deviation, probability, etc.) of the sample, i.e. the statistical inferences made from the data are valid for the total population.

Stratified sampling

At times it may be best to collect and analyse data in a less general way than random sampling allows. For example, instead of assessing the characteristics for the whole population or whole body of data it may be preferable to examine individual groups separately. When data are grouped and a sample is randomly picked from within each group, the process is known as stratified sampling, i.e. each group is known as a stratum.

Systematic sampling

In systematic sampling an item is selected at some regular interval e.g. every tenth item on a list. It is important, however, that the sample interval does not coincide with any periodic repetition of conditions. For example, a systematic sample of firms arranged in alphabetical order is more acceptable than a systematic sample for the analysis of climatic data which fluctuates periodically.

Sampling error

Provided that a sample is truly random it is possible, given the sampling mean, to assess the limits within which the true mean falls with a known percentage probability. The value which controls these limits is known as the **standard error of the mean**. The formula for calculating it is:

$$SE\% = \sqrt{\frac{pq}{n}}$$

p = % of items in a given category
q = % not in this category
n = number of points in the sample

This calculation not only provides an estimate of the limits of the true mean, it also emphasises the limitations implicit in a sample mean. By calculating the sample error it is possible to calculate how an increase in sample size reduces the error. It is important in sampling because the art of sampling lies in choosing a sample size that will give an answer with the desired degree of accuracy and probability.

It also shows that if a certain degree of accuracy is required a minimum sample size is essential.

Point sampling

Random sampling can also be applied to data which has an areal distribution, e.g. farms. In order to achieve random sampling in a particular area the area under study is usually gridded and the grid numbered. The co-ordinates compiled from the numbers can apply either to a grid line or to the spaces between lines. A survey of farms is usually made using a sample of points. Land-use sampling is better based on areal sampling, i.e. the spaces between the lines (Fig. 4).

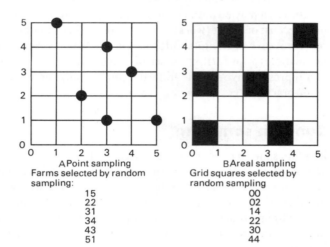

A Point sampling
Farms selected by random sampling:
15
22
31
34
43
51

B Areal sampling
Grid squares selected by random sampling
00
02
14
22
30
44

Fig. 4 Sampling

STATISTICAL MEASURES OF CENTRAL TENDENCY

The **central tendency** of data is the tendency of values of individual items within a set of data to cluster about a particular value such as the arithmetic mean.

Mean

The arithmetic mean or average is obtained by the formula:

$$\overline{x} = \frac{\sum x}{n}$$

$\sum x$ = sum of values making up set

n = number of values being considered

$\overline{x}$ = mean

Median

The central value of an ordered series i.e. the value which, when the items have been ordered (ascending or descending) has an equal number of values above and below it.

$$\text{Median} = \frac{n+1}{2}$$ where n is the number of values or occurrences.

If there is an odd number of occurrences the median is one of the values. If there is an even number of occurrences the median lies between two of the values recorded.

Mode

The value or class which occurs most often. Distributions may be unimodal (with 1 modal class), bimodal (2 modal classes), etc.

MEASURES OF DISPERSION

The degree to which numerical data tend to spread about an average value is called the dispersion (or variation) of the data.

Range

The range of a set of numbers is the difference between the largest and smallest numbers in the set. The range is often given by quoting the largest and smallest numbers, e.g. 2–12.

Quartile range

A percentile is the value below which lies a particular percentage of an ordered distribution of values. The percentiles which divide the distribution into quarters (the 25th, 50th and 75th percentiles) are called quartiles. The 25th percentile is the lower quartile, the 50th is the median and the 75th the upper quartile. The **inter-quartile range** is the difference between the 25th and 75th percentiles. This is a crude but useful measure of the spread of data. The smaller the inter-quartile range, the more closely the data clusters around the median. This range lies astride the median and if the values are normally distributed each of the quartiles (upper and lower) would lie half of the inter-quartile range away from the median. This value is called the **quartile deviation**. It is expressed as:

$$\frac{\text{upper quartile} - \text{lower quartile}}{2}$$

This value gives an indication of the range of the central 50 % of the occurrences above and below the median.

Mean deviation

This is a way of summarising the difference of each occurrence in a set of data from the average (or another constant such as the median). The difference between the size of any one value and the average value indicates the **deviation** of the unit from the average. The mean deviation is the mean value of all individual deviations from a given value, i.e.

$$\text{Mean deviation} = \frac{\Sigma \left| x - \bar{x} \right|}{n}$$

$\left| x - \bar{x} \right|$ is the difference irrespective of sign (+ or −).

It is therefore a simple way of assessing the scatter of data.

Standard deviation

The standard deviation is the square root of the average of the squares of the deviations from the arithmetic average. It indicates the degree to which individual values cluster around the mean and it may be used as a measure of variability of a frequency distribution (see normal distribution above). The formula which expresses this is:

$$\text{Standard deviation} = \sqrt{\frac{\Sigma \left(x - \bar{x} \right)^2}{n}}$$

where $\left(x - \bar{x} \right)^2$ is the square of the difference between individual values;

n is the number of occurrences in the set of data.

Running means

Some sets of data (e.g. agricultural production) consist of values which change over time. A central concern with such data is to reduce or eliminate the detailed differences between one particular value and another in order to identify and understand the overall characteristics. The running mean is a smoothing device designed to eliminate erratic or shorter movements in a time series. This succeeds in throwing into emphasis the major fluctuations in the data.

If a 5-year running mean is being used, for example, the first value will be the mean for years 1–5, the second value will be the mean for the years 2–6, etc.

Histograms

A histogram is a graph which displays the frequency of items within classes. So it is a graphical representation of frequency distributions.

DESCRIPTIONS OF SPATIAL DISTRIBUTIONS

Location quotient

See Unit 3.5.

Lorenz curve

(See Fig. 5). This curve is used to compare an uneven distribution with an even one. The location quotient is based on this curve. The curve is drawn on a square graph with the X and Y axes having comparable scales. An even distribution results in the curve being a straight line at 45° to the horizontal. The more uneven the distribution, the more concave will be the curve. The unevenness of a distribution represented by a Lorenz curve can be indicated by expressing the area under the curve as a percentage of that under the perfectly even theoretical distribution (the straight line). The curve is not an exact device but is an approximate visual method of representing a distribution.

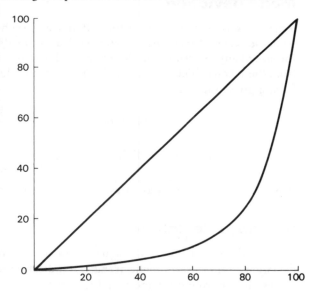

Fig. 5 Lorenz Curve

Mean centre

The mean centre is a measure of concentration. It is used, for example, to establish the position around which a set of factories is clustered. The location of a point can be defined accurately by means of two coordinates (x,y) which represent the distance of that point horizontally and vertically from a fixed reference point (e.g. the National Grid).

The mean centre of a point pattern is the point which has as its x,y coordinates the mean values of all the x and y coordinates in the distribution respectively. This is the mean centre of a spatial distribution.

Points are sometimes weighted according to their significance (e.g. the output of the factory) and the weighted mean centre is then calculated.

Nearest neighbour analysis

This technique considers the location of individual points in a distribution in relation to others. The formula for the analysis is:

$$N.N.A. = 2\bar{d}o\sqrt{\frac{n}{A}}$$

$\bar{d}o$ is the observed mean distance (i.e. the measured distance between each town and its nearest neighbour);

n is the number of points in the pattern;

A is the area over which the points are distributed.

This method enables geographers to make simple objective comparisons between distributions.

Cumulative frequency graphs

A cumulative frequency curve shows the number of occurrences or values above or below a particular level. The absolute numbers in each class are converted into percentages of the total. The number in each class is added to the classes above it until 100% is achieved.

Measuring networks

See Unit 3.9.

Measuring shape

Traditionally, shapes have been described subjectively, often by comparison with other objects, e.g. bell-shaped. Indices have been developed to provide a precise basis for comparison. The basic parameters used in measuring shape are: area, length of longest axis, radius of the largest inscribing circle, the radius of the smallest subscribing circle, the length of the perimeter. Ratios have been constructed so that a circle would have a value of 1.0 and the more linear the shape the more the ratio approaches zero. An example of a shape index is:

$$s = \frac{A}{0.282p}$$

A = area
p = length of perimeter

RELATIONSHIPS BETWEEN DATA

Scatter diagrams

The drawing of scatter diagrams is part of the process of finding equations for approximating curves which fit given sets of data. The process is known as curve fitting. In order to express the relationship between two variables in mathematical form, the first step is to collect data showing corresponding values of the variables being examined. These points are then plotted on a rectangular coordinate system. The resulting set of points is a scatter diagram.

The drawing of a scatter diagram is used to investigate the relationship between two sets of data between which it is logical to assume there is a relationship. Usually there is a cause and effect association between the two sets of data which are plotted. If a causal factor (the independent variable) can be identified it is usually scaled along the horizontal axis. If values range widely the data may be plotted on a logarithmic scale. The diagram which results from plotting the data then allows the relationship between the two variables to be judged subjectively. If a definite trend in the distribution of points can be seen, a relationship of some sort exists. The more closely the points on a scatter diagram conform to a straight line the stronger is the relationship (correlation) between the two variables. Objective tests of correlation then need to be applied (see Spearman's rank correlation coefficient below).

Spearman's rank correlation coefficient

This is a fairly quick method of assessing correlation. The coefficient is based not upon the actual values but on their rank order. It is useful because only rank order may be available for some data. Despite the fact that it is a crude index of correlation it makes a generalised estimate of correlation possible by using a simple formula.

The formula for its calculation is:

$$r_s = 1 - \frac{6 \Sigma d^2}{n(n^2 - 1)}$$

r_s = Spearman's rank correlation
d = difference in rank value of 2 sets of data
n = numbers of pairs being compared

Chi-square

This is a non-parametric test. It tests whether the observed frequency of a given phenomenon differs significantly from the frequencies which might be expected according to the hypothesis which is being examined.

The data is processed in the form of frequencies and not in absolute values. In order that the test may be used it is necessary to set the hypothesis in precise terms. Usually this is done by formulating a **null hypothesis** (no) which postulates that two samples form part of the same population and that there is a high probability that the observed variations are the result of chance. The alternative hypothesis (H_1) being examined is that the observed differences are so great that they are unlikely to be the result of chance and the two samples must therefore be regarded as coming from different populations.

Observed values are values which actually occur (O).
Expected values are values which would occur if the null hypothesis applied completely (E).

The value of chi-square, x^2 is obtained by the formula:

$$x^2 = \frac{(O-E)^2}{E}$$

This value can be referred to a table or graph and a probability value read off.

MAPS AND GRAPHS

Cartographic methods

It is not possible to describe the methods of construction of the various cartographic methods, and techniques listed in this section. It is important therefore that you read up construction methods.

The interpretation of diagrams and assessment of the advantages and disadvantages of using a particular method needs practice. You should look through the geography books you are using which identify examples of a range of cartographic methods. For each of the diagrams you identify try to answer these questions:

- What is the particular technique used?
- Why was this particular method used?
- What are the advantages/disadvantages of this method in illustrating this set of data?
- What other method(s) might have been used?
- How may the diagram be interpreted? (i.e. what is the significance of what it shows?)

Methods of cartographic representation of distribution and spatial patterns

Methods	Examples in this book (by unit)
Isopleths	1.3, 3.7
Choropleths	4.1, 4.2, 4.3

The **isopleth** map is composed of lines of equal values (isolines). The patterns of the lines illustrate the distribution of the phenomena mapped (e.g. contours, isobars). The **choropleth** or colour patch map may be a density shading map. Given areas are coloured or shaded according to the values or densities relating to each area. **Dot maps** are maps on which values are represented by dots which are as precisely located as possible.

Advantages of the methods

Isopleth maps allow data to be plotted for a region without internal boundaries (e.g. of parishes) interrupting the pattern. They therefore illustrate general trends with changes in values shown smoothly rather than abruptly.

Choropleth maps give an immediate impression of variations in values. They can also be quantitatively interpreted in terms of the areas on which the data is based.

Dot maps are simple to construct and enable values to be precisely located in space. They can be interpreted quantitatively.

Disadvantages of the methods

Isopleth maps can disguise abrupt changes which may occur in features of human geography from one locality to another. There is a degree of subjectivity both in deciding where to locate the values within areas and in the interpolation of the isolines.

Since the shading in **choropleth maps** is related to specific areas, distributions may be shown in a disjointed way and gradual trends may appear as a series of steps. The shading relates to an average figure for each area so variations within the area are not shown.

With **dot maps** the selection of the dot value is critical – wrong visual impressions may be given by choosing too high or too low a dot value. If values vary widely the map can become rather confusing unless proportional circles are used to represent the highest values. Constructing a dot map accurately can be very time-consuming.

Magnitude symbols

Symbols/methods	Examples in this book (by unit)
Proportional circles	4.2
Pie graphs (divided proportional circles)	4.2
Bar graphs	3.7, 4.1
Divided bar graphs	4.2
Population pyramids	3.2

Proportional circles The radius of each circle is made proportional to the square root of the quantity it represents.

Pie graphs The quantities represented by the proportional circles are subdivided into component parts.

Proportional squares Squares are drawn instead of circles. The size of the square is proportional to the square root of the value.

Bar graphs Variable data are represented by bars or columns of different lengths.

Divided bar graphs These show the components which make up the total represented by the whole bar or column.

Population pyramids A special type of bar graph. Adjoined horizontal bars are placed on either side of a central vertical axis which represents age categories and is usually graduated in units of five years. The length of each column varies with either the number or the percentage of the total population in each group.

Symbolic representation Data are represented by symbols, e.g. car silhouettes to represent vehicle manufacturing. Variations in value are shown either by the number of symbols or by drawing the symbols proportionally.

Advantages of the methods

Proportional circles Because the square roots of the crude values are used, the size of the symbols can be kept within reasonable limits. Each symbol can be located precisely on a base map.

Divided proportional circles These share the advantages of the proportional circles with the added advantage of showing how total values are made up by different components. Pie graphs need not be located on a base map and can illustrate non-spatial data.

Proportional squares Again the use of square roots means that the size of symbols can be kept within reasonable limits. Comparison of data is easy because of the ease of comparing the areas of the squares.

Bar graphs An extremely versatile technique for representing data. The bars are simple to construct and give an immediate visual impression.

Divided bar graphs Share the advantages of the bar graph with the added bonus of showing the component parts. May be used for non-spatial data or located on base maps.

Population pyramids Can be interpreted quantitatively. Provide a good basis for comparing male with female population characteristics and for comparing age structures over time. The overall shape of the pyramid is indicative of a range of socioeconomic factors (see Unit 3.10).

Symbolic representation Gives a good visual impression.

Disadvantages of the methods

Proportional circles and divided proportional circles It is not easy to estimate the differences in value by comparing the areas of the circles.

Proportional squares These are not as easy to locate precisely as circles. If they are divided to show components the division is laborious and untidier in appearance than pie graph divisions.

Bar graphs, divided bar graphs and **population pyramids** When located on maps the symbols may be bulky and extend beyond the boundaries of the areas to which they relate.

Proportional symbols The major difficulty is that they are very difficult to draw accurately.

Graphs and flow-lines

Method	*Examples in this book* (by unit)
Line graph	3.9
Segmented bar graph (transect graph)	2.3
Flow-line	2.9

For **line graphs**, values are plotted on the vertical axis against (for example) time on the longitudinal axis. Points are connected by lines to indicate fluctuations in value through time. **Segmented line graphs**, e.g. the relief cross-section, represent variations in values or quantity along a line which may or may not be straight. A **flow-line** is a map in which lines vary in width according to the quantities of goods, vehicles, etc. which move along the routes represented by the lines. Values are usually grouped into classes and the width of the lines then varies according to a regularly increasing scale.

Advantages of the methods

Line graphs give a good visual impression of changes in value over time and identify peaks and troughs in trends. Composite data may be shown by the superimposition of a number of sets of data (i.e. a number of lines) on the same graph.

A great advantage of **transect graphs** is that they need not be straight lines so, for instance, the key features of a slope or of an urban area may be included in one diagram.

Flow-lines effectively relate quantity or volume to a direction of movement. They give an excellent visual impression and clearly show the relative significance of individual routes or paths. They may be used to show two-way flow and if multiple lines are used instead of solid bands it is possible to indicate the relative importance of components of the flow.

Disadvantages of the methods

Line graphs It is not possible to determine intermediate values from line graphs. It is not easy to interpret the fluctuations because the factors to which the fluctuations relate are not shown.

Transect graphs The decision as to what is shown on the diagram and where the transect is to be made is essentially subjective.

Flow-lines The choice of scale is critical, an evenly graduated scale may hide significant variations in volume or frequency. Too generous a scale may lead to the obliteration of key details of the map.

1.2 ORDNANCE SURVEY MAPS

ORDNANCE SURVEY MAPS

These are essential tools for the geographer. You should be familiar with 1:25 000 and 1:50 000 Second Series maps. Questions may be based on evidence provided by an OS map extract. A-level map questions are not concerned with testing your knowledge of the conventional symbols or your ability to measure distances. It is assumed you already have this information and these skills and can use them to describe, analyse, compare and comment on various aspects of the physical and man-made patterns discernible on the map extract.

Here are some examples of the types of questions which are asked.

Describe in detail the physical features of the area west of easting 84 and suggest possible origins for these features.

Analyse the pattern of settlement to be seen on the map extract.

Compare the patterns of settlement and communications in the area north of northing 20 with that to the south.

Comment on the nature and location of the land use types in the area of the map extract.

From these examples it should be evident that A level is concerned more with broad patterns and less with fine detail. Descriptions are required but they are linked with interpretation and as a result the map is used to test your knowledge of various aspects of physical and human geography as well as your ability to interpret OS maps.

ANNOTATED SKETCH MAPS

Sometimes A-level questions ask you to draw an annotated sketch map of all or part of the map extract to illustrate selected features such as physical regions and

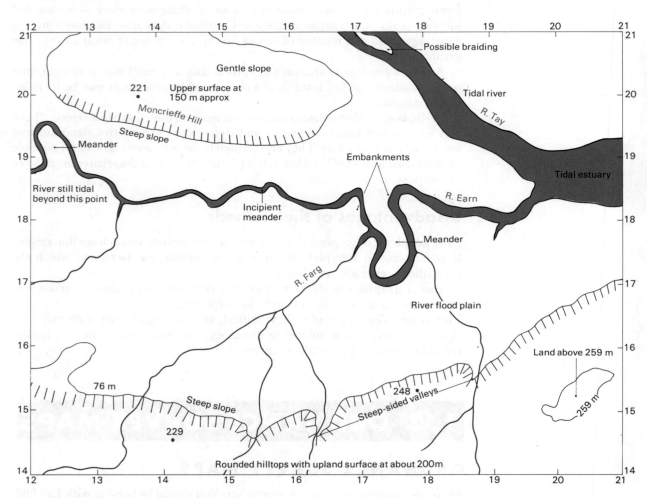

Fig. 6 Annotated sketch map of the map area south of northing 21

town sites. At the back of this book there is a 1: 50 000 map extract of the Perth area of Scotland. It is for use with this unit and you will need to refer to it while reading the rest of this chapter.

Fig. 6 has been drawn as an example of an annotated sketch map of the area east of easting 12 and south of northing 21.

It would be impossible in the time available in the examination to reproduce a sketch map as accurate as Fig. 6, but you should make your sketch as accurate and neat as possible. A few minutes spent drawing the grid lines before you sketch in the detail will help you to achieve a high standard of accuracy. All annotations should be clearly printed and, if necessary, arrows used to identify precisely to what the annotation refers.

Very often you will find it both convenient and time-saving to include small sketch maps or diagrams even though these have not been requested in the question. Settlement sites, situations and patterns as well as communications and land use can often be shown better by well-annotated sketch maps and diagrams than by lengthy descriptions.

Sketch maps alone are not, however, an adequate substitute for a written answer. Examiners will only award additional marks for sketch maps if they contain extra material not already referred to in the written answer. But sketch maps will help to clarify the written answer.

Examiners often express concern at the quality of many of the sketch maps submitted by candidates. Untidily scribbled maps are the result of haste and lack of practice at map drawing. Good sketch maps can be drawn quickly and accurately only after continuous practice so take advantage of any opportunities available to develop this useful skill.

AERIAL PHOTOGRAPHS

Sometimes the OS map question includes an oblique aerial photograph of part of the map. The photograph is used to test your ability in interpreting an aerial photograph and also to see how far you are able to relate photographic and map evidence.

Fig. 7 shows an oblique view of part of the Perth map. When you are given questions about a photograph first locate the part of the map which appears on the photograph. Clues such as large buildings, bridges, rivers, roads and railways will help you. When Fig. 7 is compared with the map extract the river is an obvious starting point in locating the area. Other clearly defined landmarks such as the river bridges and the island in the foreground help to relate the photograph more precisely with the map.

Having identified the area, find other landmarks on the photograph which also appear on the map. On Fig. 7 the railway can be seen running through the city area with a branch crossing the river. Many other locations can be similarly compared. It should also be possible to identify the area of the map over which the aircraft was flying when the photograph was taken. On the Perth map it is the southern part of GR 1221. In which direction was the camera pointing? Do not expect the map to match the aerial photograph precisely. There could be several years' difference between the map survey and the taking of the aerial photo.

SETTLEMENT

There are a number of features concerning settlement on maps which you must understand and be able to interpret.

Site The actual area upon which the settlement is built. The site of Perth, for example, is an area of level ground close to the River Tay at a point where the river is narrow and easily crossed.

Situation The position of the settlement in relation to its surroundings. Perth is a centre for the farmland of the Tay valley.

Fig. 7 An oblique view of part of the Perth OS map

Pattern of settlement OS maps show the distribution of settlements in considerable detail ranging from individual houses in country areas to the built-up areas of towns and cities.

When examining settlement patterns on a map, first distinguish the areas where settlement is sparse or non-existent. Find two such areas on the Perth sheet, then look for village sites. In the valley of the River Earn there are a number of villages on the south side below the high ground. What are their names? Other villages like Bridge of Earn may be near river crossings or route centres. Finally, examine the urban distribution and note any distinctive features, e.g. the development of New Scone (1326) close to Perth. You should summarise your analysis of the settlement pattern on a sketch map with the main features such as sparse settlement delineated and suitably annotated.

LAND USE

Ordnance Survey maps are not specialist land-use maps but they do contain a great deal of information about land use. You should be able to distinguish a number of features which indicate how the land is used. At the same time you must appreciate that the information is limited and on no account should you attempt to fill in the gaps with guesswork. Use only the evidence supplied by the map.

The 1: 50 000 map shows such types of land use as woodland, orchards, parks, quarries and heathland (although in the latter case the same symbol may also mean rough grassland). Routeways and associated services such as railway sidings are also shown, as well as large industrial units, hospitals and schools. In urban areas it is possible to distinguish a limited number of land use types. Broad categories can be identified but no precision can be given to the boundaries of the morphological zones. For example, the Central Business District of Perth can be identified in GR 1123 between the railway station and the river where there is a focus of routes but the limits of the CBD cannot be accurately drawn (see Unit 3.5). Residential areas and small industrial plants are not identified separately but some large industrial sites such as the distillery (GR 098259) are named. Recreational areas such as golf courses are marked, as well as hospitals, prisons and cemeteries. Newer housing estates can be recognised by their layout and crescent-shaped road pattern. Find these and other land use types in Perth and then make a sketch map of the morphological zones of the city as far as you can identify them.

1.3 WEATHER SYSTEMS AND SYNOPTIC CHARTS

DEFINITIONS – DEPRESSIONS

Depressions are areas of low pressure which can vary considerably in size. There are several different types.

Tornadoes Very low pressure systems only a few hundred metres across. They are common in the centre of continents in spring and summer.

Tropical storms These vary from 80 to 800 km across (50 to 500 miles). They usually originate over oceans and can do extensive damage. At their centres there are calm areas or 'eyes' where the sky is clear and the winds light. They occur most

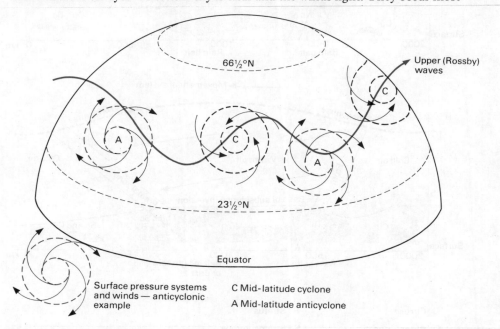

Fig. 8 Mid-latitude winds and pressure systems

frequently in late summer or autumn and are most pronounced in the China Seas where they are called typhoons and in the Caribbean where they are known as hurricanes.

Frontal depressions These occur in middle latitudes where the westerly winds above the earth's surface move from west to east in a series of waves. Long waves (called **Rossby waves**) contain shorter waves, and it is the air streams of the shorter waves which produce the high and low pressure systems of the mid-latitudes. The location of the pressure systems in relation to the long wave pattern is shown on Fig. 8.

In a depression the pressure decreases towards the centre with air streams converging and revolving anti-clockwise around the centre in the northern hemisphere. The convergence of the air streams leads to a concentration of the isotherms between cold north-westerly air and warm south-westerly air with the boundaries between these air streams forming **fronts**. The convergence produces vertical movement of the air which results in cooling, condensation and precipitation.

Non-frontal depressions These can be formed by pressure changes brought about by local heating. They vary in size. Another form of non-frontal depression is the lee depression which is formed by air rising over mountains and descending on the lee side.

ANA- AND KATA-FRONTS

Meteorologists distinguish two main types of frontal depression; those in which

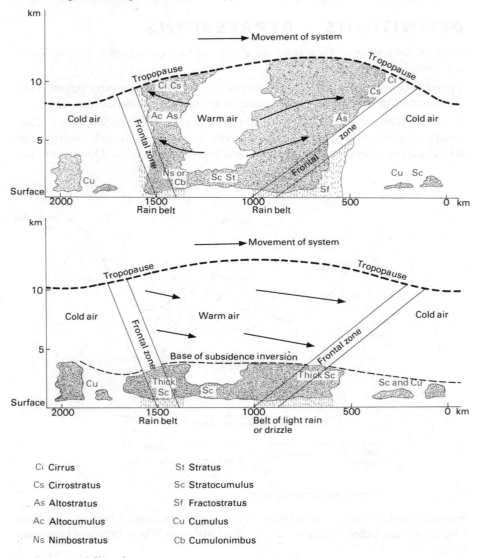

Ci	Cirrus	St	Stratus
Cs	Cirrostratus	Sc	Stratocumulus
As	Altostratus	Sf	Fractostratus
Ac	Altocumulus	Cu	Cumulus
Ns	Nimbostratus	Cb	Cumulonimbus

Fig. 9 Ana- and Kata-fronts

the air in the centre is generally rising are called **ana-fronts**. Those in which the air in the centre is generally sinking are called **kata-fronts** (Fig. 9). In a depression with ana-fronts the rising air results in instability and precipitation. In kata-fronts sinking air is warmed by compression and produces more stable conditions. An inversion layer forms, holding down the layer of cloud and, in the more stable conditions, producing only light rainfall.

Occlusion

In a depression the warm front and the cold front are separated by the warm sector. The area of this warm sector at the surface is gradually reduced as the cold front moves faster than the warm front and eventually catches up with it. The boundary between the two air streams is known as an occlusion. If the air behind the cold front is colder than the air ahead of the warm front it will cut under it and lift the warm air above the ground forming a cold occlusion. If the air behind the cold front is warmer than the air ahead of the warm front it will rise over the warm front to form a warm occlusion. Cloud and sometimes rain may result from the vertical displacement of some of the air in the occlusion.

Anticyclones

Anticyclones – regions of high pressure – usually cover large areas. Their winds are light and rotate clockwise and outwards from the centre. Anticyclones may be cold-centred or warm-centred. Cold-centred anticyclones are shallow and often move swiftly. Warm-centred anticyclones are deep and move slowly. The subsiding air near the centre of an anticyclone can give clear skies and much sunshine. However, if temperatures are low and humidities high, there may be condensation giving fog or low cloud and a temperature inversion may become established in the lower air layers.

Troposphere

The layers of the atmosphere nearest to the earth in which temperatures generally decrease with height are known as the **troposphere**. At about 8 km (5 miles) above Polar regions and 16 km (10 miles) above the Equator the **tropopause** marks the end of the troposphere and the beginnings of the stratosphere. In the stratosphere temperatures increase with height.

Jet stream

At the level of the tropopause wind speeds up to 500 km/h (310 mph) are reached. In the northern hemisphere there is one jet stream related to the Polar front which is discontinuous. The other is the sub-tropical jet lying between the Equator and approximately latitude 30°N.

GENERAL CONCEPTS

Air moves in a series of waves, known as Rossby waves, in mid-latitudes (see Fig. 8). Air flowing northwards at high altitudes from the Equator is deflected to the right in the northern hemisphere as the earth rotates in an anti-clockwise direction. This is known as the **Coriolis force**. Waves form in this air stream as the result of vorticity which is explained below. The ridges and troughs of these waves cause smaller waves to form on which originate the anticyclones and depressions which influence weather conditions in mid-latitudes.

Vorticity is the rotation or spinning of a column of air. It acts like water as it drains out of a bath. A column of air spinning of its own accord without regard for the rotation of the earth is said to have **relative vorticity**. A column of air can also spin as a result of the earth's rotation. This is called **global vorticity** and is strongest at the Poles and non-existent at the Equator.

The two forms of vorticity give the column of air an **absolute vorticity** – global vorticity increases and relative vorticity decreases towards the Poles. Relative vorticity increases and global vorticity decreases towards the Equator. This increase in one form of vorticity and decrease in another which is most intense in mid-latitudes sets up a wave pattern in the movement of the air stream, hence the development of the waves.

Convergence and divergence In mid-latitudes, warm tropical air from the Equator meets cold Polar air and the two mix in vortices induced by the spinning earth. If the area in the centre of the vortice is relatively cold and pressure decreases with height, the air streams converge near the ground, rise vertically and then diverge near the tropopause. This produces the **cyclone** or low pressure system which affects Britain and northern Europe.

If there is relatively high pressure and a warm core to the vortice the air flows will converge above the earth, descend and diverge at the earth's surface. This produces anticyclonic or high pressure systems.

UNDERSTANDING SYNOPTIC CHARTS

Make a habit when interpreting a synoptic chart of proceeding as follows.
- Check the time of the day and month of the year for which the information on the chart relates. This is very important because the conditions during a high pressure system in January will be totally different for those in July. A chart for midday will show different information to that for 6 a.m.
- Get a general impression of what the chart shows. Is the area predominantly under a low pressure system or a high? Are there any features on part of the chart which are significant, such as an occluded front over part of the land area?
- What are the predominant weather symbols which occur over a large area of the chart? The symbols may show a predominance of clear skies, strong winds, rain or some other feature which is affecting the weather pattern at a number of stations.
- Having familiarised yourself with the chart, go back to the question and relate it to the symbols and patterns made by the isobars and fronts. Then draft your answer.

Examiners sometimes provide two synoptic charts which show the changes that have taken place over a short period of time, such as twelve hours. Symbols are normally provided in a key but the more you are familiar with weather symbols the less time you will waste looking at the key, and the more confident you will feel.

Fig. 10 shows the weather pattern over north-west Europe and part of the Mediterranean at 6 p.m. on 14th May. North-west Europe is dominated by high pressure centred over Poland with shallow lows over southern France, southern Italy and the Iberian Peninsula. A cold front stretches across Scotland and Norway. The clear skies over central Europe and parts of southern England contrast with the cloud and associated rain or drizzle near the fronts. Temperatures over southern England, northern France and the Benelux countries are high for the time of year. They are higher than in the Mediterranean region where cloud will have reduced the amount of sunshine. Winds are light and variable in the high pressure area and very much stronger north of the cold front in the Orkneys and off the coast of central Norway. The whole of continental Europe shown on the chart is rain free, as are England and Wales. The rain and drizzle are limited to northern Ireland, northern Scotland and the Norwegian coast. In southern Ireland, north Wales and the Baltic coast region of Latvia and Estonia there are patches of mist.

Fig. 11 shows the same area 12 hours later, at 6 a.m. on May 15th. You would expect the temperature readings to be lower in view of the hour and the contrasts in temperature close to the cold front compared with further south in central

KEY

Cloud (amount in oktas)

- ◯ 0
- ◗ 1 or less
- ◗ 2
- ◗ 3
- ◗ 4
- ◗ 5
- ◗ 6
- ◖ 7 or more
- ● 8
- ⊗ Sky obscured
- ⊠ Missing or doubtful data

Weather

- ═ Mist
- ≡ Fog
- , Drizzle
- ⦁ Rain and drizzle
- ● Rain
- ✶ Rain and snow
- ＊ Snow
- ▽ Rain shower
- ▽ Rain and snow shower
- ▽ Snow shower
- △ Hail shower
- ☇ Thunderstorm

Wind (speed in knots)

- ◯ Calm
- ◯— 1-2
- ◯—⌐ 3-7
- ◯—┐ 8-12
- ◯—╕ 13-17

For each additional half-feather add 5 knots

- ◯—╗ 48-52

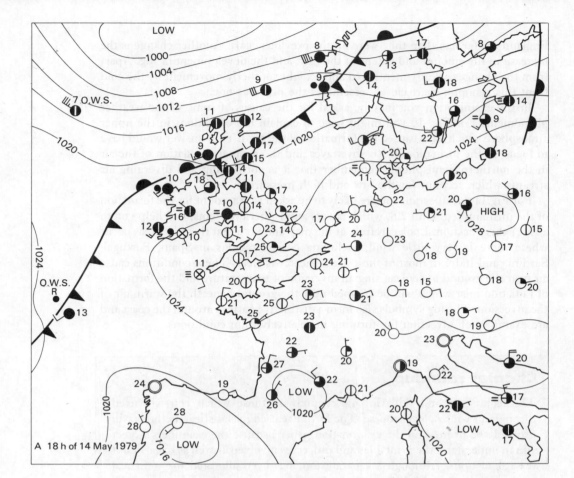

A 18 h of 14 May 1979

Fig. 10

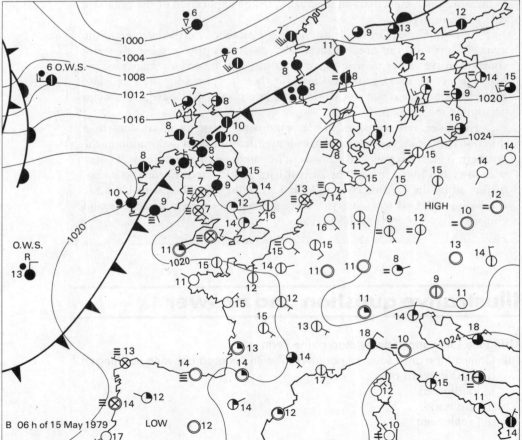

B 06 h of 15 May 1979

Fig. 11

England are far less than they were on the previous chart. Another change is the increase in the amount and extent of the mist and the development of fog. Apart from the changes already mentioned and a slight southerly movement by the cold front this synoptic chart closely resembles the previous one.

In the examination you may be asked for the causes of some of the weather phenomena. For Fig. 10 you might have to explain the conditions in the upper atmosphere which have caused the formation of the high. Your answer would have to focus on the formation of Rossby waves and the general circulation of the air in the northern hemisphere. Remember that it is converging and diverging air streams which account for the low and high pressure.

For Fig.11 one question you are likely to be asked is to account for the formation of the mist and fog. Unit 2.8, which covers atmospheric systems, will help you to answer this question. Look carefully at the map and note that the mist areas occur where there is very little wind, including coastal regions in Spain, Portugal, Sardinia and Italy. In most of these areas the sky is clear. These conditions cause air near the ground to cool causing an inversion of temperature and the formation of radiation mist which will be trapped near the ground beneath the warm air of the inversion. The fog symbols also form a distinctive pattern around the coast and are examples of advection fog forming in relatively calm conditions.

Chapter roundup

The techniques and skills in this chapter are those which you will need throughout your A-level course. The formulae used in statistical methods will probably be printed on the examination paper because the examiners expect you to understand the principles and processes involved as well as to carry out the calculations. Although a separate unit has been allocated for statistical methods you are unlikely to be given a question which is limited to using the formulae. Questions will require you to use data in a certain context, such as to measure the connectivity of a network, or the application of the rank-size rule to a country.

Remember that Ordnance Survey maps present a detailed survey of the main features in the areas which they cover. In this respect they are comprehensive rather than selective. You may also be given a map which is highly selective, like a geological map, or those prepared for the Land Use Survey. These maps are not difficult to interpret if you have a thorough grounding in OS maps.

Examiners are surprised when candidates write poor answers to a question containing a synoptic chart for another mid-latitude location in the northern hemisphere such as Canada. The same weather features will occur with lows and highs as over the British Isles and Western Europe so do not be put off by the location chosen. Unit 1.3 should be studied with Unit 2.8, combining the two will give you a comprehensive survey of weather and climate.

Illustrative question and answer

Using the Ordnance Survey map of the Perth area:
(a) Contrast the area south of northing 17 with the area between northings 17 and 20 in terms of:
    (i) landforms;
    (ii) drainage;
    (iii) settlement.

(b) Outline map evidence for the choice of route taken by the M90 motorway.

(c) Using map evidence, suggest contrasting reactions to the building of the M90 motorway likely to have been voiced by local people at different locations in the area.

(in the style of the Associated Examining Board, A Level)

Tutorial note

The key word in part (a) is *contrast* and it would be quite wrong to confine your answer to two descriptions, one for south of northing 17 and the other for the area between northings 17 and 20.

In part (b) you are asked to outline map evidence for the choice of route. This means you must look closely at contours, rivers, valleys and other physical features. Having done that you must also look at human aspects of the landscape, such as settlement because it is very expensive and socially very undesirable to demolish housing and other settlement features on a large scale to build a new road.

Again in part (c) you are asked for map evidence and contrasting reactions. These key words and phrases are extremely important in framing your answer.

Suggested answer

(a) (i) There is a sharp contrast in the landforms south of northing 17 with those to the north. Whereas the area between northing 17 and 20 is mainly lowland, the flood plain of the River Earn, to the south the land rises steeply to heights over 200 metres and reaching 313 metres at the highest point in the west of the area. By contrast the land north of northing 17 is mainly low lying, only a few metres above sea level. There is one exception, a ridge of higher land, Moncreiffe Hill to the north of the River Earn and Bridge of Earn.

(ii) South of northing 17 the streams cut steep valleys northwards through the higher ground to reach the flood plain. They are small tributaries of the River Earn running downhill to join the river. The drainage pattern north of northing 17 is that of a meandering river with evidence of oxbow lakes and cut-offs as well as of levées or embankments to contain the river.

(iii) Settlement south of northing 17 is very sparse. There is no settlement on the high land, it is to be found below the steep north facing slope of the hills where it takes the form of isolated houses or small clusters such as Abernethy and Dron. By contrast there is a greater extent of settlement between northing 17 and 20. The largest site is Bridge of Earn, a nucleated settlement with a hospital. There are other settlements to the west but little to the east near the mouth of the River Earn.

(b) The route taken by the M90 avoids the higher land and built-up areas where possible. It also avoids steep gradients by following the contours, for example in the south in square 1514. It crosses the flood plain, sometimes on embankments and crosses the River Earn at Bridge of Earn before swinging west to avoid the high land of Moncreiffe Hill and the outskirts of Perth. It uses valleys where possible to cross the higher land, as in squares 2011 and 2110. The junction with the M85 is at a break in the higher ground where a gap leads north to the crossing of the River Tay. Both physical and human factors have helped to determine the route of the M90.

(c) The building of a motorway involves a considerable change to local land use and can increase noise levels as well as air pollution in the vicinity. A motorway can also bring advantages such as better access for road traffic to other centres. No doubt many people in Bridge of Earn were concerned at the passing of the motorway through the outskirts of their village, effectively forming a semi-barrier between the village and the hospital to the east. At the same time the settlement has its own exit and entrance to the motorway which would please those people who travel regularly to other places in the area and who might wish to shop or work in Perth. No doubt local farmers on the lower ground were concerned at the loss of some of their land to the motorway, or the fragmenting of their farms. This cannot be proved from map evidence since farm boundaries are not marked. The settlement near Moncreiffe House and the house itself may not be able to see the motorway which at this point is in a cutting, but on the outskirts of Perth in square 2209 the motorway is raised on an embankment and could cause noise to reach the nearby housing. The same problem of an embankment occurs to the south in square 1713 where the A912 road joins the motorway. As in most major land use changes of this type, some local people will benefit, others will not and may voice their protests.

Question bank

1 (Time allowed: 50 mins)

(a)

Table 2   Traffic flow in both directions at census points on motorways 1987

Motorway	Census point (North side of junction)	Average number of vehicles (000's) in 24-hour period
M1	10	105.9
M1	26	53.3
M1	37	43.7
M6	3	75.1
M6	15	68.7
M6	23	64.8
M6	34	43.5
M6	40	28.7

(i)   So far as the data in Table 2 allow, construct a flow-line map on Fig. 12 to show volume of traffic on the motorways indicated.

(ii)   Justify your choice of scale for the flow lines.

(iii)   Discuss the limitations imposed by **both** the data **and** the means by which you have dealt with them in the construction of the map.   (10)

(b)

Table 3   Number of cars and heavy goods vehicles on M1 at census points 1987 (average number of vehicles (000's) in both directions in 24-hour period)

Count North side of junction	Cars	Heavy goods	All vehicles
10	77.3	18.8	105.9
26	40.7	8.6	53.3
37	31.0	8.2	43.7

Showing all your working, construct on the map provided (Fig. 12) proportional diagrams to show total traffic and the proportions of cars and heavy vehicles passing each of the junctions shown in Table 3.

Compare this method of showing the traffic census data with the flow line method used in (a). (10)

(University of Cambridge Local Examinations Syndicate, A Level, June 1990)

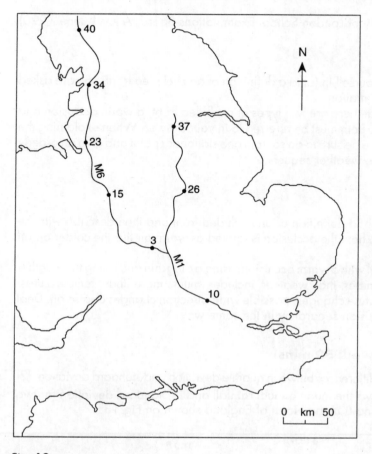

Fig. 12

Pitfalls

This question is not as easy as it looks. The flow line must follow the route and a scale is essential.

In part (b) make sure you calculate percentages for both vehicle types and remember that there must be a third group of 'Other vehicles' to make up the totals in the total column. Drawings need to be clear and either shaded or coloured with a key.

Points

(a) Work out the scale you will use on the map to show the number of vehicles. Do not classify your scales into groups but increase the scale width in units of 10 or similar to avoid standard widths.

When you consider limitations note the significance of the junction of the M1 and M6.

(b) Decide whether to use divided circles or columns to display the information. Look at the total for each junction and then decide on circle sizes if you are using divided circles, or column heights if you are using columns. When using divided circles calculate the proportion of each circle for each of the two vehicle types, remembering that part of the circle will be needed for other types of vehicles. Make neat drawings and shade or colour them in.

2   (Time allowed: 40 mins)

(a) Explain the formation of an occluded front. (10)

(b) Outline the weather sequence associated with the passage of an occluded front. (15)

(University of London School Examinations Board, A level, June 1990)

Pitfalls

Do not confine yourself in (a) to a definition of an occluded front, you are asked to explain the formation.

Remember that there are two types of occluded front, a warm occlusion and a cold occlusion. Both must be referred to in your answer. When explaining the weather sequence be sure to do so from one stationary point and give an orderly description of the weather sequence.

Points

Start off with a short definition of an occluded front and then describe with the aid of diagrams, how the occlusion is formed as warm air lifts the colder air off the ground.

In (b), first deal with a warm occlusion, using a diagram and listing the weather changes. Remember that weather includes much more than temperatures. Suggest temperature changes, possible wind direction changes and so on. Deal with a cold occlusion separately in the same way.

3   (Time allowed: 50 mins)

(a) Discuss the differences between quartile deviation and standard deviation. (2)

(b) Table 4 shows the mean annual rainfall and its standard deviation for two stations A and B in the North of England shown on Fig.13.

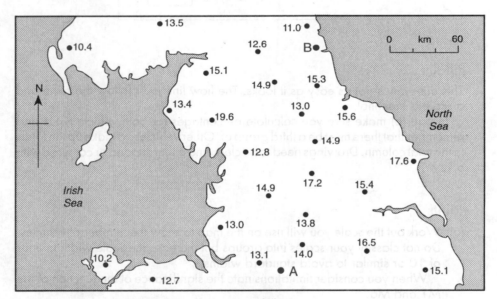

Fig. 13   Coefficient of variation of annual rainfall

Table 4

Station	Mean	Standard Deviation
A	124.9	14.8
B	69.9	9.7

(i) Calculate the coefficient of variation of annual rainfall at A and B. (2)
(ii) Plot these values on the map, Fig. 13. Construct isolines for 12%, 14%, 16% and 18%. Draw a choropleth map and provide a key to the shading you have used. (8)

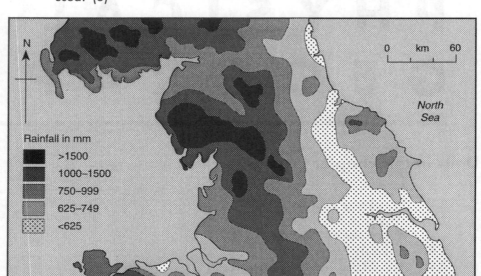

Fig. 14 Average annual rainfall

(c) Fig.14 shows mean annual rainfall for the same area.
  (i) Compare this with the map you have constructed on Fig.13. (4)
  (ii) Discuss the uses to which your map of the coefficient of variation could be applied. (4)

(University of Cambridge Local Examinations Syndicate, A Level, June 1991)

Pitfalls

Look carefully at the distribution of marks. Part (b)(ii) receives 8 whereas (b) (i) only merits 2. Do not draw the choropleth lines in ink: use pencil as you may wish to adjust them. Remember they are for specific values so you will need to interpolate between the percentage numbers. Do not draw the lines over the sea and start with the lowest line required, 12%. These lines must never cross one another.

Points

Show the working of your calculation for each of the stations A and B. Plot them on the map and then begin to carefully interpolate between the percentage figures for the places shown on the map.

The shading should be carefully scaled to show the progression of 2% in each case. Make the shading visually accurate – this can be done best by using lines and cross-hatching rather than by increasing the intensity of solid shading.

When you make your comparison, identify any correlation between high rainfall and coefficient of variation. Look similarly at low-rainfall areas.

You should be able to discuss two good uses of your map, each of which is worth two marks.

CHAPTER 2

PHYSICAL GEOGRAPHY

Units in this chapter

Chapter objectives

When you have studied the units in this chapter you should be able to:

- differentiate between landform processes which 'build up' and those which 'wear down' the landscape;

- describe and explain the movement of water and materials on slopes;

- describe the processes at work in the hydrological cycle;

- describe the orders of streams and rainfall/discharge relationships within a drainage basin;

- recognise the characteristics of ice movement and the landforms of glaciation;

- identify the distinctive features of periglacial environments and the processes involved;

- understand the processes at work in a coastal environment and identify the associated landforms;

- understand the processes at work in an arid environment and the associated landforms;

- describe the main features of the major soil types;

- understand how plant communities develop and the importance of ecosystems;

- appreciate that there are human implications resulting from physical changes such as wave erosion of a coastline;

- appreciate that people are an integral part of the physical environment and that they can alter, modify and control features within it.

Relevance of the units

The natural environment is the starting point for geographical studies and it is essential to understand the elements which make up this environment. The core areas of the syllabuses comprise the characteristics of the lithosphere, atmosphere, hydrosphere and biosphere and you will be expected to have a broad working knowledge of the main features of each of these areas.

At the same time you must appreciate that human activities have a significant influence on the natural world. This influence can be direct or indirect. There is a direct influence through interventions in physical processes, such as the building of a dam across a river valley. Indirectly, humans can unintentionally modify physical processes as, for example, by the desertification of semi-arid marginal lands. To understand the interactions of humans with the processes of the natural environment it is essential to have a clear understanding of the processes themselves. The first part of each of the units is concerned, therefore, with physical processes. These descriptions are followed with examples of human intervention and its consequences.

Many contemporary environmental problems are closely associated with the natural environment and you should keep newspaper cuttings of case studies which occur, as well as studying problems in your own locality. Natural hazards such as earthquakes, volcanic eruptions and severe flooding regularly make the headlines and provide topical examples to help your understanding of physical geography.

Key ideas and concepts

The basic concept underlying the A-level syllabuses is that of interrelationships. These interrelationships are between man and the natural environment, and between elements within the natural environment such as that between soils and vegetation.

Interrelationships are best understood within a systems approach. This is an attempt to provide a framework which explains the complexities of the connections between humans and the natural world.

A system is a combination of elements usually called components or variables. Components are such things as water, vegetation, buildings, and some forms of energy like solar radiation and electricity. Other components are dimensions such as distance, area, density and time.

Within a system the interacting variables are held together by flows of energy, water, goods, ideas, information and so on. We see this as a process whereby a change in one variable communicates itself to the rest of the system

Many systems are self-regulating, so that changes in one variable beyond a certain point set in train changes throughout the system, restoring the original balance. This happens in the relationship between stream discharge and channel form. Of course, humans can interfere with these natural forces, as happens, for example, when a river is diverted.

All systems contain sub-systems and these may have a distinct hierarchy, such as exists, for example, in the stream orders of a drainage system.

Examples of systems which you will study are the hydrological cycle and the plant-soil system.

2.1 WEATHERING PROCESSES

DEFINITIONS

Weathering

Weathering is the process of rock destruction. It is the breakdown (mechanical fracturing) or decay (chemical decomposition) of rocks *in situ* by natural agents. It is essentially a static process.

Weathering is therefore the first phase in the denudation of any landscape. Rocks must be weathered before there is debris to be transported and the effectiveness of the agents of transport (water, ice, wind) as agents of erosion depends upon the carrying of this debris.

There are three main types of weathering – physical, chemical and organic.

Physical weathering

This is also called **mechanical weathering**. It is the process of the loosening of the surface of rocks and the gradual reduction of the rocks into fragments under the influence of atmospheric forces without chemical change taking place. The products of this process are usually coarse and angular.

Chemical weathering

This is the process of the rotting of rocks. Minerals within the rocks are decomposed by agents such as water, carbon dioxide and various organic acids. Since minerals vary in their resistance to chemical agents this type of weathering attacks rocks selectively and may penetrate them deeply in places. The products of chemical weathering are generally 'finer' than those of mechanical weathering.

Organic weathering

This consists of both mechanical and chemical weathering. Flora and fauna increase the carbon dioxide content of soil and this increases the weathering potential of the biosphere. Various organisms may also cause reactions with minerals in particular rocks, e.g. guano weathers limestones; chemotrophic bacteria oxidise minerals such as sulphur and iron.

AGENTS OF WEATHERING

In mechanical weathering there are two main processes at work: temperature change and crystallisation. Mechanical weathering may also be assisted by the action of plant roots which penetrate and widen joints in rocks and expose a greater surface area to weathering.

Temperature changes produce the disintegration of rocks in a number of ways:

- Rocks are generally poor conductors of heat. The effect of daily heating and cooling is confined to surface layers of the rock. So the surface expands more than the interior and this sets up stresses which may lead to the fracturing of the rock in places roughly parallel to the surface. This is called **exfoliation**.
- Igneous and metamorphic rocks are made up of different minerals which expand at different rates when heated. Minute internal fracturing occurs within crystals and at their edges. Eventually the rock fractures.
- The **pressure release hypothesis** explains that many metamorphic rocks were crystallised under temperature and pressure conditions which were

very different from those found at the surface of the earth. So minerals may be less stable at surface temperatures and pressures. As the rocks are exposed as the result of erosion, stresses are caused, fracturing the rock surface.

- When polycrystalline (many crystals) rocks are buried, grains of the rock may be deformed at the interfaces between them. In sedimentary rocks the cement between the grains may be affected. As the surface is eroded the load is taken off the rock and this release of energy can cause faulting which weakens the rock as it is exposed on the surface and weathering starts. So there is **granular disintegration**.

- Temperature changes can also encourage **wetting and drying** weathering e.g., high temperatures cause evaporation of rock moisture. If rocks are alternatively soaked and dried they are more easily weathered.

CRYSTALLISATION

- **Freeze-thaw** When water is turned into ice its volume increases by about 10 per cent. The freeze-thaw process is a very effective means of weathering in rocks which are fractured. The process cannot cause fractures but can widen them. The freeze-thaw process is especially effective in rocks such as cellular limestone in which the water collects in enclosed cavities from which it cannot escape as it expands.

- **Crystallisation of salts** Salts are dissolved in the moisture which penetrates rocks e.g. sodium chloride (common salt), calcium sulphate (gypsum).

CHEMICAL WEATHERING

- **Hydration** Certain minerals take up water and expand. This causes additional stresses within the rock e.g. Anhydrite takes up water to become gypsum.

- **Oxidation** This is the process of taking up oxygen from the air. For example, below the water table gault clay is blue or grey but above the water table where the water and clay are replaced by air it is oxidized into red or brown ferric compounds.

- **Hydrolysis** Felspars are important constituents of igneous rocks. Hydrolysis is a process which leads to the breakdown of felspars. It is caused by a chemical reaction with the water which involves H and OH ions.

- **Solution** This is not a very common process because few minerals are soluble. Solution may help weathering by removing the products resulting from other types of chemical weathering.

- **Carbonation** This occurs when carbonate ions combine with minerals. Carbon dioxide solution in the atmosphere converts calcium carbonate into the much more soluble calcium bicarbonate. This process is important in limestones and chalk.

FACTORS AFFECTING THE TYPE AND RATE OF WEATHERING

The main factors are the hardness of the rocks (mineral composition), the texture of rocks (their crystalline state), rock jointing, relief and climate.

Rock resistance

Rocks vary significantly in resistance to weathering. Resistance depends on the constituent minerals of the rock, the coherence of these minerals (how they are cemented together in the rocks), and the extent to which the minerals have been compressed.

The hardness of the minerals in the rock is measured by **Moh's scale of hardness**. This scale ranges from 10 (extremely hard) to 1 (very soft). Quartz, for example, is classified at 7, gypsum at 2. Most igneous rocks are hard. This is partly because of their mineral constituents e.g. quartz and felspar. It is also because as the minerals cooled and crystallised they were tightly bonded together. Sedimentary rocks tend to be softer because even those composed of hard quartz grains are often cemented together by a soft cement. If the cement is hard then the rock is very resistant to weathering e.g. quartzite which has a hard silica cement.

As far as the igneous rocks are concerned minerals which determine the rate of weathering may be divided into light-coloured (felspars and quartz) and dark-coloured (ferromagnesian minerals, e.g. mica). Light-coloured minerals have greater acidity.

Rates of weathering of minerals in igneous rocks

	Dark coloured minerals	Light coloured
Most susceptible to weathering	Olivine	Lime plagioclase
	Augite	Lime-soda plagioclase
↑	Hornblende	Soda plagioclase
↓	Biotite	Orthoclase
Least susceptible to weathering		Muscovite
		Quartz

The texture of rocks (i.e. the crystalline state)

Under most conditions coarse-grained rocks are likely to weather more rapidly than fine-grained rocks which are composed of the same minerals. Although in fine-grained rocks the mineral grains have a greater surface area exposed, these surfaces are not open to weathering. Susceptibility to weathering of one of the minerals is a more important factor than the surface area exposed.

Usually one mineral in a rock is weathered more rapidly than others. The weathering of this mineral loosens the whole fabric of the portion of the rock exposed to weathering.

Rock jointing

As far as both chemical and mechanical weathering are concerned the jointing of rocks is a vital factor influencing the nature and rate of weathering. Its importance is due to the fact that jointing increases the surface area exposed for attack by agents of weathering. It is very clear, particularly in limestone areas, that chemical weathering concentrates along joints and bedding planes. The joints allow acidic solutions, oxygen and carbon dioxide to enter the rocks and so encourage chemical rotting.

The pattern of jointing determines the character of the landforms produced. For example, plutonic rocks (the most common being granite) have a jointing system which divides the rock into rectangular blocks. As they are chemically weathered they are reduced to piles of partly rounded boulders such as the Tors of Dartmoor. Basalt, a volcanic rock, often has a well-defined jointing pattern which forms vertical polygonal columns. Weathering of such rock has produced the Giant's Causeway in Northern Ireland.

Relief

This is a factor which is often undervalued. If mechanical weathering is to continue, fresh exposure of the unweathered rock is vital. In areas of high land and steep slopes, such phenomena as landslides, slumps and solifluction result in the fresh exposure of bare rock. In lowland areas in contrast a thick layer of soil and weathered material protects the unweathered rock (although in others, e.g.

limestone areas, soil accelerates weathering).

Climate

The processes of weathering are dependent upon particular climatic conditions. For example, particular climatic conditions make the freeze-thaw a dominant weathering process. In the Tundra, for instance, the seasonal spring thaw and autumn freeze together with the likelihood of frost all through the year provide suitable conditions. In cool, temperate, humid regions there is also sufficient rainfall for water to penetrate joints and fissures and winters are cold enough to induce regular freeze-thaw.

Exfoliation and granular disintegration are most effective in regions with a large diurnal range of temperatures, for example, continental desert regions. On the other hand, wetting and drying needs sufficient precipitation to wet the rocks and temperatures which are warm enough to evaporate the moisture.

Chemical weathering is generally most effective in hot, humid climates. Equatorial climates provide ideal conditions for the rotting of rock masses.

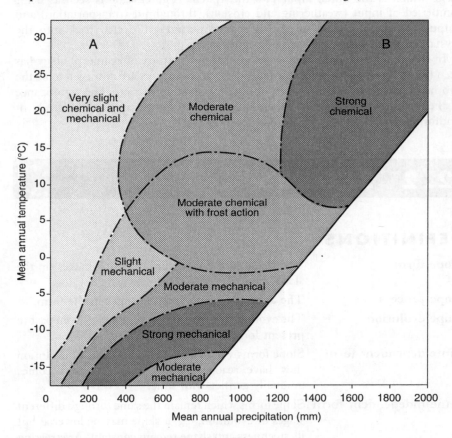

Fig. 15 Climatic controls of weathering (after Peltier)

Fig. 15 shows how different weather and climate create conditions under which chemical and mechanical weathering become significantly more or less important. For example, at point A the high temperatures and very little moisture in the atmosphere means that mechanical weathering is almost non-existent. At B, chemical weathering is powerful because the hot, humid conditions encourage rich vegetation which increases the amount of humic acid present. Water flowing through the soil sustains a continuous weathering process.

Human activity

The process of weathering and the rates at which its effects become evident have been intensified by human activities which result in the introduction of large quantities of gases, car emissions and other pollutants into the atmosphere. In Britain the long-term effects of chemical weathering on the sandstones used to build ancient churches and cathedrals is seen on figures and statues that have been disfigured as they disintegrate. Restoration of weathered stonework is a massive problem for the Church of England. Elsewhere the damage is even more serious.

WEATHERING AS A SYSTEM

At one time, weathering was seen as a distinctive and separate process of landscape formation. In the same way, mechanical and chemical weathering processes were regarded as separate types of weathering. Today the process of weathering is placed in the broader context of landform development and various types of weathering are seen as simultaneous and interrelated influences.

In the systems analysis of landscape formation known as the **rock material cascade**, for example, weathering is seen as contributing to the formation of rock waste which is the initial input into the system. The cascade is seen as being comprised of input (weathering and erosion), throughput (transportation) and output (deposition). Parts of the deposited output are cycled back into the crystalline rocks where the cascade begins again.

In recent years an important development in the study of geomorphology has been the study of slopes. Weathering and surface transport are now seen to be the two main groups of processes responsible for slope formation. The significance of the weathering process has therefore increased appreciably in the study of landforms.

2.2 SLOPES

DEFINITIONS

Slope form	The shape of the land surface which makes up the slope.
Slope process	The agents bringing about changes in the form.
Slope evolution	The evolution of the slope is the change from past to present form.
Time dependent form	Slope forms which depend on the stage of evolution they have reached, e.g. a slope which becomes gradually gentler with time.
Time independent form	Slope forms which remain the same through different stages of evolution, e.g. a slope may be lowered but its steepness and shape remain constant. A retreating escarpment may retain the same form.
Slope retreat	The wasting back of slopes by weathering and surface wash.
Regolith	A covering of waste material composed of soil and weathered rock which lies beneath the soil. Its composition is constantly being changed by weathering as it moves down the slope.
Soil creep	The gradual movement of the regolith down the slope. It is a slow process but it affects the whole slope. It is caused by the expansion and contraction of the soil combined with the effect of gravity (see **heave** below). Rates of creep vary with climate –

maximum rates (5 mm per annum) being in humid tropical areas.

Solifluction   A more rapid form of soil flow which occurs mainly in periglacial areas.

Throughflow (sometimes soil throughflow)   The downhill movement of water through the soil. It is significant in humid tropical areas, e.g. clay particles are removed from slopes and concentrated in the valley floor.

Surface wash   The transport of soil by water flowing across the ground surface. There are two processes involved:

❶ *Raindrop impact* when raindrops hit bare regolith soil, detaching soil particles. This produces miniature craters. In some instances this can lead to the formation of earth pillars when soil is washed away except for pillars protected · by resistant caps.

❷ *Surface flow* occurs when rainfall intensity is greater than the rate at which the soil can absorb water. The ground is saturated and the rain no longer percolates into it. Surface flow also occurs at the base of slopes where the water table rises to the surface because the soil is saturated.

The rate of surface wash varies with rainfall, vegetation cover, slope angle, distance from the crest of the slope.

Mass movement   The movement of soil and parts of the regolith down the slope. It can be classified as follows.

slow or gradual movements	*rapid mass movements (landslides)*
solution	rockfall
soil creep (heave)	soil slip
solifluction – frost creep, gelifluction	mudflow
surface wash – surface flow, raindrop impact	debris avalanche
	rotational slip

Heave (see Fig. 16)   The heave mechanism is the process whereby rock waste moves downhill. It is caused by freeze-thaw processes of wetting and drying, etc., which cause clay particles to swell and shrink and the expansion and contraction of loose rock fragments as a result of temperature changes. As material moves it shifts upwards towards the surface of the slopes and settles back vertically. The net result is downward movement.

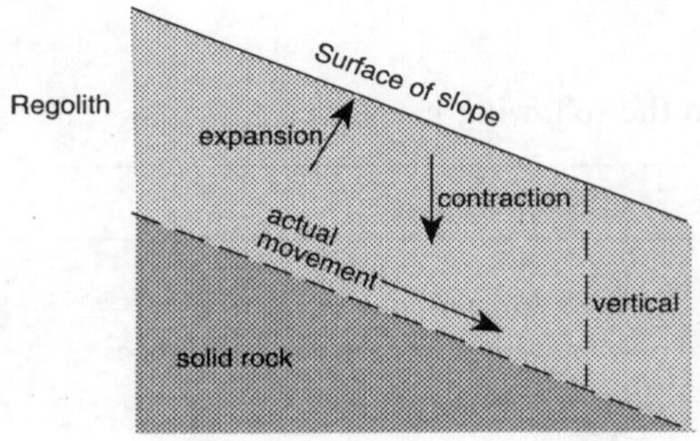

Fig. 16 Heave

Stable slope   A slope or part of a slope on which rapid mass movements do not occur. The rock and regolith possess sufficient strength to resist the forces tending to cause mass movement. A stable slope has a smooth surface.

Unstable slope   A slope on which mass movements occur because the rock or regolith is not strong enough to resist the forces which cause them. Active landslides and scars of past ones are evidence that the slope is unstable.

Landslide — A particular kind of rapid mass movement on slopes. Landslides usually affect only a very small part of the slope and occur infrequently. A frequent cause is the saturation of the regolith by very heavy rain.

Free face — A steep slope or part of a slope formed of bare rock.

Cliff — A slope which consists mainly or entirely of a free face.

Scree — An accumulation of rock fragments at the foot of a free face. The steepness of the slope of the scree depends on the **angle of repose** (usually 32°–38°). This is the maximum angle at which the fragments will accumulate without sliding further downhill.

Slope angle — The angle made with the horizontal, it expresses the steepness of the slope. **Percentage grade** is the vertical rise in metres per 100 metres horizontal distance. Percentage grade = $100 \cdot \tan \theta$, where θ is the angle in degrees.

SLOPE FORM

The **slope profile** is the shape of the slope viewed as a cross-section at right angles to the hillside. For analysis it is divided into **slope units**. These are the straight and curved parts. Straight parts are called **rectilinear segments**, curved parts are either **concave** or **convex elements**. The straight parts are characterised by a constant slope angle. The **maximum segment** is the part which is steeper than the slope units above or below it. Below the maximum segment is the concavity, above the **convexity** (Fig. 17).

On simple slopes there is only one sequence of convexity – maximum segment – concavity. More complex slopes have more than one sequence.

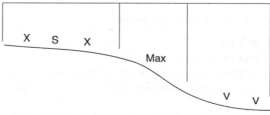

Max	Maximum segment	V Concave elements
X	Convex elements	S Rectilinear segment

Fig. 17 Analysis of slope profile

Slope angles

Slopes may be roughly classified into the following categories.

Description	Angles	General features
Level/almost level	0°–2°	Drainage problems on impermeable rocks
Gentle	2°–5°	Most common slope in many landscapes
Moderate	5°–10°	In humid tropics soil erosion becomes a problem
Moderately steep	10°–18°	Problems for farming and building. In humid tropics, soil erosion could be serious
Steep	18°–30°	Farm machinery cannot be used unless land is terraced. Building is expensive
Very steep	30°–45°	The steepest land to carry a regolith
Precipitous/vertical	> 45°	Free face

SLOPE EVOLUTION

Three models of slope evolution have been developed. None of them is completely appropriate to all slopes. Structural and climatic factors determine to which of the three the retreat in slopes of a particular area most nearly corresponds.

The basic slope model (Fig. 18)

This model is based upon the assumption that the caprock is strong enough to sustain a vertical face at its edge. This might occur, for example, when resistant sandstone or limestone overlies less resistant shale. The diagram shows that the slope has four components:

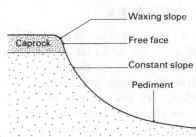

Fig. 18 The basic slope model

❶ The waxing slope is the curve over the edge of the horizontal surface of the hilltop. It was called a waxing slope by Penck because, on a given vertical line, with time, it increases in slope. It is also called the **summital convexity**. The rounding-off of the slope is the result of weathering.

❷ The free face – see definition above.

❸ The constant slope is a slope with a uniform angle that did not alter as the slope developed through time. Many constant slopes only have a very thin veneer (cover) of rock waste.

❹ The pediment is solid rock. It has a concave shape with a decrease in slope angle in the downslope direction.

This model envisages slopes that are retreating.

The nine-unit slope model (Fig. 19)

This is a more complex model which relates slope morphology (form) to the processes of slope formation. The main processes in operation are weathering,

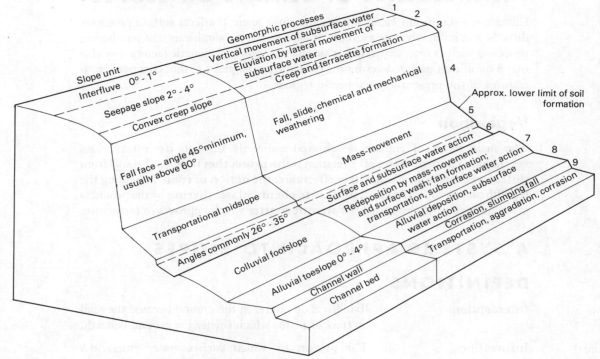

Fig. 19 The nine-unit model

throughflow and mass movements (landslides, slumping, rockfall). Units 1–3 in this model are comparable to the waxing slope and unit 4 is equivalent to the free face. Units 5–7 correspond to the constant slope and the pediment.

The main difference between the models is that the basic slope model is based on semi-arid conditions while the nine-unit model relates to regions with humid, temperate climates. Both models can be used as a static basis for comparison of areas and to identify areas in which similar units may be found. Neither model, however, incorporates the variety of forms that are to be found in different natural environments.

THE INFLUENCE OF STRUCTURE ON SLOPES

Simple slopes composed of one rock type

Lithology influences profile form and angle. The strength, stability and permeability of a rock are important factors in determining slope form. As far as profile is concerned it has been found, for example, that convexities form the greater part of profiles developed on sandstones, about half on limestones and less than half on shales. Maximum slope angles also vary with lithology. For example, maximum slope angle on limestones is usually about 20°, on shales 9°, and on clays 5½°.

The nature of the regolith which is formed is also important. For example, the importance of surface wash as a slope-forming process depends on the permeability of the regolith. Surface wash is more effective on less permeable regoliths such as clay.

Compound slopes

Compound slopes are slopes composed of more than one rock type. Where beds of different degrees of resistance outcrop on a slope there is likely to be a number of convexity—maximum segment—concavity sequences. The maximum segment then corresponds to the most resistant bed.

THE INFLUENCE OF CLIMATE ON SLOPES

Climate is a significant factor influencing slope form. It affects surface processes directly and indirectly. For example, it determines the significance of weathering processes such as frost shattering or surface run-off. Past climatic factors may also play a significant part in determining the nature of slopes, e.g. the relict periglacial features of the present day temperate regions.

Vegetation

The main effect of climate is achieved indirectly through its influence on vegetation. The main effect of vegetation is **the protection it gives the soil** from surface wash and rainsplash. Other effects are: **the action of roots** in holding the regolith on the slope, **the contribution to chemical weathering** by the products of organic acids and **the supply of organic matter** which improves soil structure.

A SYSTEMS APPROACH TO SLOPES

DEFINITIONS

Interception	Raindrops do not reach the ground because they fall on trees or plants which shelter the ground beneath.
Infiltration	The process by which surface water enters the ground vertically through pores in the soil.

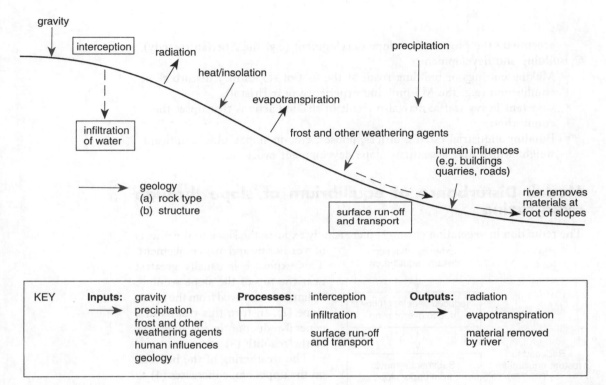

Fig. 20 A systems approach to slopes

Surface run-off	Excess water flows away over the surface of the ground because all the rain cannot be absorbed, e.g. in a thunderstorm.
Radiation	Heat received from the sun warms the surface of the ground which then heats the air next to it by conduction.
Evapotranspiration	Two components:

- evaporation, the physical process by which moisture is lost into the atmosphere from the soil and water surfaces. This is caused by the sun's heat and the movement of air.
- transpiration, the biological process by which water is lost from a plant through its leaves.

THE EFFECTS OF HUMAN ACTIVITIES ON SLOPES

❶ Changes in vegetation cover due to farming activities:
  - Grazing of animals and ploughing remove protective vegetation cover and loosens soil.
  - Cessation of farming activities, e.g. through economic depression (American Mid-west), or by regulations (EC), reduces the effects.
❷ Changes in vegetation cover due to forestry:
  - Deforestation increases the rate of slope movement. Afforestation decreases slope movement.
❸ Mining and quarrying:
  - Quarrying at the foot of a slope may upset slope equilibrium.
  - Mining may make ground liable to subsidence (e.g. Notts coalfield).
  - Dumping waste on hill tops adds weight to the slopes and may

accentuate the processes of slope development (e.g. the Aberfan tragedy).

❹ Building and development:
- Making cuttings or building roads at the foot of slopes may disturb slope equilibrium (e.g. the M5 building experience near Bristol).
- Constant heavy traffic may also result in shaking actions that upset the equilibrium.
- Building industrial estates, offices, houses, etc. on slopes adds significant weight which may accentuate slope development processes.

Model: Disturbance of equilibrium of slope through overgrazing

The reduction in vegetation cover (1) increasingly exposes the slope to the effects of weathering and mass movement. This exposure is usually greatest near the top of the slope so more sediment is removed from the upper slope (2). In turn this results in a general reduction in the thickness of the regolith (3).

The weathering of the bedrock on the upper slope increases (4) so that the rate at which the upper slope is lowered accelerates (5).

As the upper slope is lowered, the overall steepness of the slope is reduced (6).

The reduction in steepness leads to a lessening of the mass movement of material down the slope. So regolith gradually accumulates progressively up the slope. This in turn counteracts the changes that were caused by the reduction in vegetation cover (1).

Thus the slope system becomes stabilised again and vegetation cover may be restored (6).

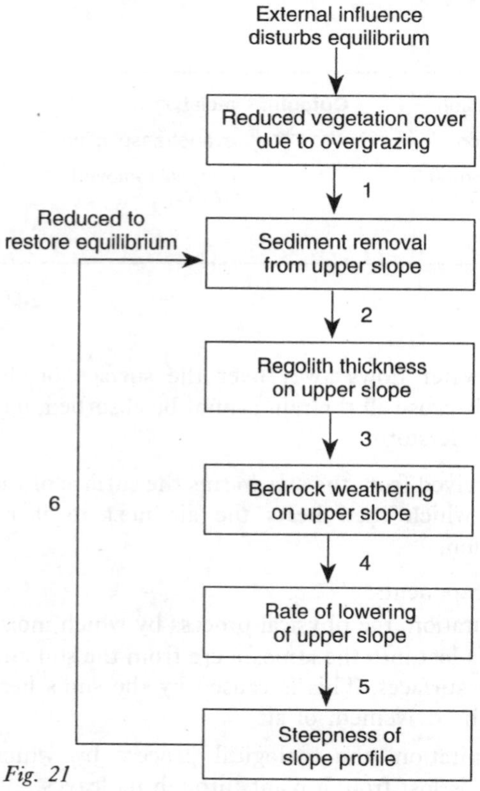

External influence disturbs equilibrium

Reduced vegetation cover due to overgrazing

1

Reduced to restore equilibrium

Sediment removal from upper slope

2

Regolith thickness on upper slope

3

6

Bedrock weathering on upper slope

4

Rate of lowering of upper slope

5

Steepness of slope profile

Fig. 21

2.3 RIVERS AND RIVER VALLEYS

DEFINITIONS

Hydraulic action   The mechanical work of flowing water in which loose fragments may be prised away from the bedrock.

Corrosion   As the result of chemical action, material is dissolved and removed in solution. Limestone is one of the rocks which will dissolve in this way.

Abrasion   The erosion of the stream channel by material suspended in, or moved along by a stream. In the process the river's load is also abraded leading to the

	rounding of pebbles and fragmentation of material.
Cavitation	The shock waves propagated by the collapse of bubbles in turbulent water which hammer any adjacent rock surfaces.
Bed load	That part of a stream's load which is moved along the bed of the stream by sliding, rolling and saltation (hopping). It contrasts with the suspended load which can constitute about three-quarters of a stream's total load.
Stream velocity	The speed of the flowing water. The velocity depends on the slope of the bed, the shape of the channel and the volume of water involved (discharge rate).
Interception	The capture of raindrops by the leaves, branches and stems of plants, preventing some of it reaching the ground.

A STREAM'S ENERGY

The energy possessed by a stream will vary with the gradient and volume of water. There are a number of ways in which the stream loses energy:

- Energy is lost as a result of friction between the river and the sides and bottom of the channel. The most efficient shape for a stream channel is semi-circular. Bends increase friction and dissipate energy as heat into the atmosphere.
- The water in a stream with an uneven bed will be turbulent and lose energy as a result of shearing between turbulent currents.
- Energy is lost transporting material. Less energy is lost transporting material in suspension than in moving material along the river bed. When a stream has insufficient energy to transport its load it starts to **deposit** it. During a flood the enormous increase in the discharge results in greatly increased velocities and load. The additional energy can be used for extensive erosion.

THE LOAD CARRIED BY A STREAM

The amount of material carried by a stream will depend on its potential energy and also on the amount of material delivered to it down the valley slopes. This will depend on such things as the steepness and resistance of the rocks in the river basin to erosion, the nature of the vegetation on the valley slopes (since roots and vegetation can check movement downhill), and also on the amount of weathering to which the rocks are subject.

There is a distinct relationship between velocity of the water in the river channel and the particle sizes which can be eroded, transported and deposited. These relationships are shown in Fig. 22. The top line on the graph shows the lowest speeds at which particles of a given size which are loose on the channel bed will be moved. The section of the graph showing particles transported indicates the speeds at which particles of different sizes will be carried. Particles do not require such high velocities to be transported as they do to be set in motion. In general, the larger the particles the greater the velocity required to transport them. However, once the velocity falls below a certain point the particles are deposited. The velocity at which particles are deposited is higher for the larger and heavier particles than for fine clays and silts which almost float in the water (Fig. 23).

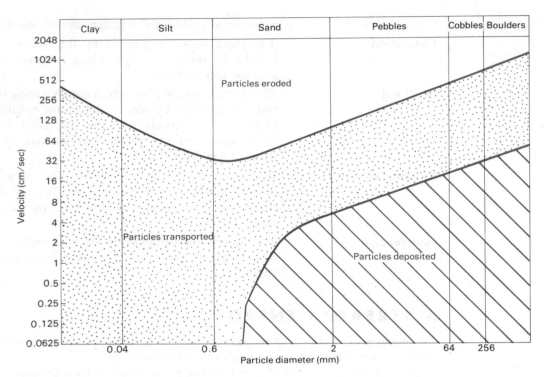

Fig. 22 The relationship between velocity and particle size

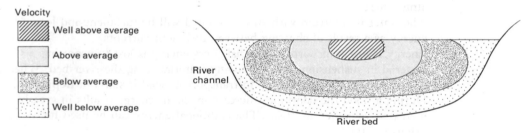

Fig. 23 Velocity distribution in a river channel

THE LONG AND CROSS PROFILES

The description of the long profile of a stream as a concave curve steeper in the headward section and flattening towards the stream mouth is an oversimplification. It is rarely found in practice. This concept is based on the Davisian idea of a graded profile which is set at variance with research findings involving the measurements of stream processes.

Stream channels in general do develop and produce a state of apparent equilibrium (quasi equilibrium) between the channel characteristics and the movement of water and material through them.

It has been pointed out that there are eight interrelated variables involved in determining changes in river slope and channel form throughout the long profile of a river. These variables are **discharge, channel width, water depth, water velocity, amount of sediment load, load particle size, roughness of the channel bed and the slope (gradient) of the channel**. The significance of each of these in the long profile of a stream is shown on Fig. 24. Changes in one of these variables, for example an increase in the sediment load, may be compensated for by adjustment of one or more of the other variables such as an alteration in the depth of the stream and width of the channel.

The cross profile of a river valley includes the shape of the valley as a whole, the valley floor and the river channel. Slopes on the valley sides will be steep if a stream is actively downcutting or the rocks are resistant. Floodplains and meanders occur where the stream is tending to erode laterally rather than downwards.

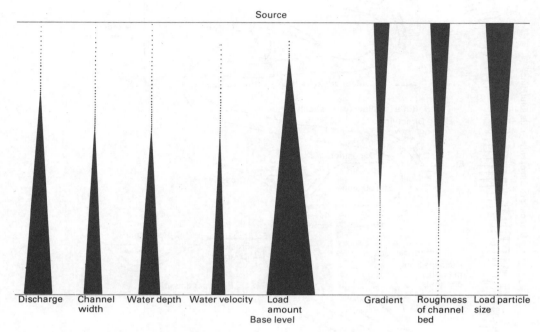

Fig. 24 Variations in stream channel characteristics from the upper reaches to the mouth

Over a period of time, migrating meander belts will widen the floodplain, leaving a low cliff or bluff-line bordering the meander belt. During floods, deposition can occur on the sides of the channel to form levées. In the river channel, dropped sediment can form shoals which cause the channel to braid. If the channel splits many times a network of distributaries develops.

Cross profiles of valleys can be asymmetrical. This may be caused by the structure of the rocks which may dip or contain faults. The stream tends to migrate down the dip (uniclinal shifting) taking the line of least resistance. Asymmetry also occurs where the structure and lithology do not exercise any control. Several theories have been put forward which relate asymmetry in these circumstances to periglacial processes. One group of theories is based on the possibility of periglacial processes steepening the valley slope while the other group assumes that frost action combined with solifluction would lead to a decline in the slope angle.

MEANDERS

The exact reasons why meanders develop in river channels which are straight are not fully understood. Once the current starts to swing it is most likely that meanders will occur. Meandering does not develop in sands where the shape of the channel changes with the amount of discharge.

The characteristic features of a meander belt are shown in Fig. 25. As the diagram shows, in a meander bend the channel cross-section is asymmetrical with erosion on the outer section of the bend and deposition on the inside of the bend.

Migration of meanders downstream 'planes off' higher land adjacent to the river leaving the low cliffs or bluffs. During the migration, point bar accretion occurs on the convex bank where reduced velocity results in deposition. As the meander shifts it leaves cut-offs, swales and scars where the previous point bars occurred.

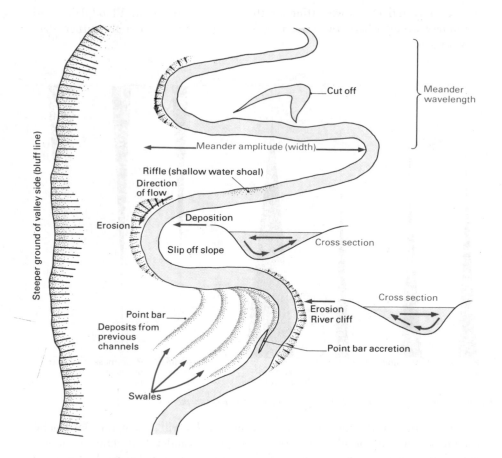

Fig. 25 Features of a meander belt

RIVER RÉGIMES

The régime of a river is the pattern of the rate of discharge over a period of time. A number of factors determine the rate of discharge. They can be summed up as geology and soils, climatic conditions and miscellaneous.

- **Geology and soils** The amount of precipitation which finds its way into a river depends on such things as the gradients, permeability of the rocks, soils and plant cover in the catchment basin.
- **Climatic conditions** The precipitation and its incidence throughout the year constitutes an important factor when linked with the annual temperature range and the evaporation rate. The nature of the precipitation, whether it falls as snow, torrential rain or as light showers, is also significant.
- **Miscellaneous** Streams with many tributaries may have a different régime from streams with few. Tributaries coming from different climatic regions give rivers like the Nile distinctive régimes. Large areas of swamp land or mountain bogs in the catchment basin may even out rates of discharge by acting as reservoirs. A river rising at a high altitude may receive snow-melt when precipitation is low.

EQUILIBRIUM (GRADE)

In most river valleys there are bands of resistant rock which erode more slowly than the other rocks and will appear as 'bumps' on the concave profile. The river will slowly wear away these obstructions and the long profile above the resistant rock outcrops will tend to become smooth as the temporary check resulting from the resistant rock is removed.

Eventually the resistant rock band itself will be smoothed and the profile will form a curve from source to mouth. When this profile has been achieved the stream's total energy is just sufficient to transport its load. The stream is said to be **graded** and to have a **profile of equilibrium**. Any changes such as uplift, flooding, or diversion of some of the water, will upset the equilibrium and the stream will slowly adjust its profile until it is once more graded.

A definition of a graded stream has been put forward by J H Mackin.

> A graded stream is one which, over a period of years, slope is delicately adjusted to provide, with available discharge and with prevailing channel characteristics, just the velocity required for the transportation of the load supplied from the drainage basin.

This definition probably places too much emphasis on channel slope and it is now recognised that rivers which are graded will not have identical long profiles. The shape of the curve will depend on such things as the lithological changes in the valley, the amount of material available for the river to carry and the number and size of the tributaries.

Fig. 26 shows a model of the hydrological cycle. Use the definitions that follow to help you to understand the model.

DEFINITIONS

Evapotranspiration	Made up of two components – evaporation and transpiration. (Transpiration is the biological process by which water is lost from a plant through its leaves.)
Interception storage	Raindrops fall on leaves and tree trunks which shelter the ground beneath. This is called interception storage.
Stemflow/throughfall	Throughfall is the flow of water that has been intercepted down the trunk of a tree. Stemflow is when bushes or grass beneath the tree produce a secondary interception and water then flows down the stems.
Surface storage	If rainfall is very heavy the ground may not be able to absorb it all so there is surface storage.
Overland flow	Surface run-off water.
Channel storage	Water that flows away in the river and is then lost to the system.
Infiltration	The process by which surface water enters the ground vertically through pores in the soil.
Aeration zone storage	Water in the porous soils or rocks through which it is infiltrating.
Percolation	As water moves through soils and rock layers it may reach more compact layers and its rate of movement slows down. The slow movement through these compact layers is called percolation.
Groundwater storage	The process of percolation produces groundwater storage.
Groundwater flow	The water table marks the upper surface of the groundwater zone of saturation. Water which is transferred laterally in the water table is known as groundwater flow.

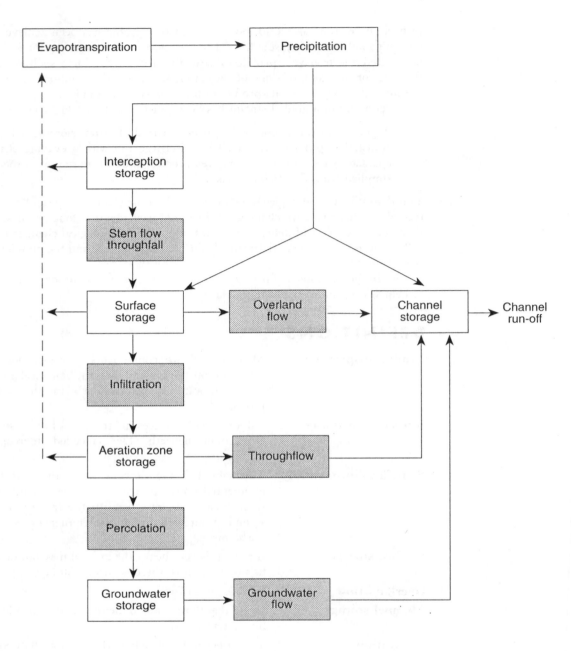

Movement of water

Fig. 26 A model of the hydrological cycle

A STORM HYDROGRAPH

A hydrograph shows the variation in the level, velocity, or discharge of a body of water, such as a stream, over a period of time. You are most likely to meet the storm hydrograph which shows the effects of a period of heavy rainfall on the discharge of a river. The base flow is the amount of water in a stream channel which is derived from groundwater sources. It is a relatively slow and steady transfer of water from within the ground and over a short period is not greatly affected by heavy rainfall. As Fig. 27 shows, base flow rises only slowly and some time after the rain has fallen. The amount of base flow in a river channel depends on seasonal variations in precipitation, evapotranspiration and vegetation.

The hydrograph also shows that there is a lag time between the precipitation

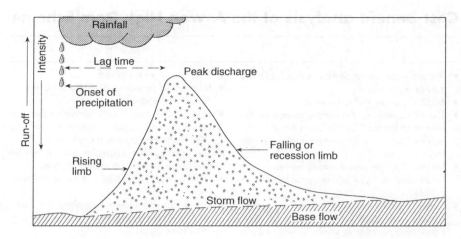

Fig. 27 Components of a hydrograph

and the peak discharge into the river. This lag time is affected by the local geological structure, degree of slope, vegetation cover, amount and intensity of rainfall, extent of soil cover, nature of underlaying rock (permeable or impermeable) and evapotranspiration rate which will vary according to temperatures and humidity. Human activities may also affect the form of the storm hydrograph. Activities causing soil erosion, deforestation or the development of settlements are indirect ways in which the hydrograph will be changed. More direct ways are the building of dams and the diversion of feeder streams.

REGULATION OF RIVER FLOW

Case Study: the River Nile

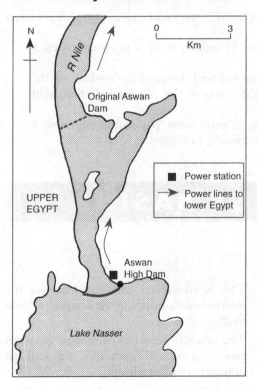

Fig. 28 The Aswan High Dam Scheme

Controlling the flow of the Nile has long been seen as the way to use the river economically and efficiently for the people of the Sudan and Egypt. Early in this century a dam was constructed at Aswan to store water for perennial irrigation in Egypt. Other storage reservoirs were built in Sudan on the Blue Nile and on the White Nile. After the Second World War the Owen Falls Dam was built on the White Nile to generate electricity for Eastern Uganda and to control the flow of the White Nile. In 1960 Egypt began work on the Aswan High Dam which controls river flow into lower Egypt and has effectively stopped flooding by the Nile. Behind the High Dam, completed in 1971, water collected to form Lake Nasser which was planned to produce a range of economic benefits for Egypt.

Cost-benefit analysis of the Aswan High Dam Scheme

Costs	Benefits
• Ancient temples (such as Abu Simbel) had to be moved at great cost.	• Nile floods are controlled.
• 60,000 people had to be relocated.	• Lake Nasser provides sufficient water to irrigate 800,000 hectares.
• The silt carried into the Mediterranean by the Nile provided food for fish: since the dam was built the Eastern Mediterranean sardine industry has collapsed.	• Hydroelectric power is generated at the lake which increased Egypt's electrical output by 300% when the dam was completed.
• Silt from flooding was a natural fertiliser for the Nile Valley. Artificial fertilisers now have to be bought.	• The lake supplies employment for fishermen and a much needed source of protein.
• Controlled flow means that irrigation ditches contain water all year. Formerly the cold winter killed parasite-carrying snails, worms, etc. in dried out irrigation ditches. The spread of irrigation has led to the spread of bilharzia and malaria.	• It gave Egypt high political status in the Arab world.
• The capacity of Lake Nasser is affected by the accumulation of sediments brought down from the highlands by the Nile.	• Crops can be grown throughout the year, instead of only during the six months following the summer flood.
• The Nile delta is retreating because of loss of sediment. Summer resort villages are beginning to disappear.	
• In the past, salt in the soil was washed out during the floods. Today, it rises to the surface where it forms a crust, making the fields infertile.	
• Increasing use of fertilisers and pesticides pollutes the Nile and kills the fish.	

Social effects of the Aswan Dam

The High Dam has been a significant factor in the social changes which have taken place in Egypt.

❶ Rapid increase in population, from 19 million in 1950 to an estimated 54 million in 1990.

❷ Greater use of farm machinery has reduced the need for workers on the land. Cheap electricity has brought power to the villages and stimulated industrial growth.

❸ Despite higher standards of living in rural areas, population migration to the towns – especially Cairo – is creating problems.

2.4 DRAINAGE BASINS

DEFINITIONS

Drainage geometry	This is concerned with the forms of the internal relationships of the drainage system itself.
Descriptive studies of drainage	The classification of drainage patterns according to their appearance, e.g. trellised drainage, radial drainage.
Drainage morphometry	The gathering of accurate data of the features of stream networks and drainage basins, e.g. stream order. The purpose is to compare the properties of individual basins in precise and meaningful ways.

Genetic stream classification   Classification of streams and drainage patterns according to the way in which they were initiated and evolved, e.g. consequent and subsequent streams.

DRAINAGE SYSTEMS

Descriptive studies of drainage

Although drainage systems make many varied patterns it is possible to group many of them by means of a descriptive classification (Fig. 29) e.g:

Parallel or sub-parallel drainage develops on uniformly dipping rocks.

Dendritic (tree-like) drainage is associated with horizontal or very gently dipping strata and low relief. Structural control is very limited so streams are free to form many branches.

Trellised drainage often develops on eroded folded rocks. The main streams run along the fold axes and the tributaries flow down resistant ridges of rock. In areas of Jura folding, for example, the main streams either follow synclines or valleys formed by erosion of anticlines. In areas where cuestas are well developed, dip-slope streams may flow across alternating outcrops of unresistant and resistant rocks. The weak strata are eroded to form strike vales and tributary streams flow over the resistant beds.

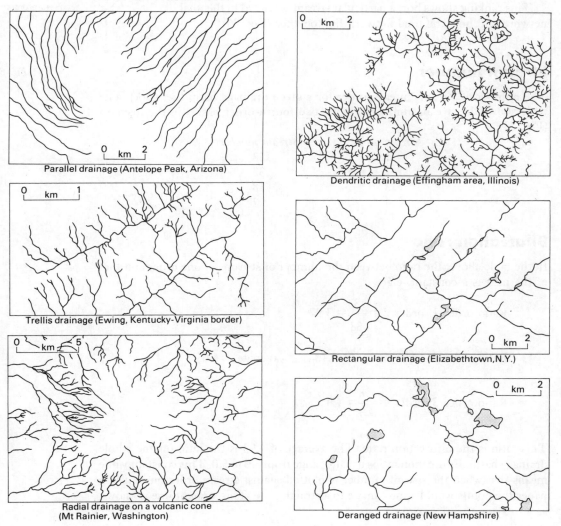

Parallel drainage (Antelope Peak, Arizona)

Dendritic drainage (Effingham area, Illinois)

Trellis drainage (Ewing, Kentucky-Virginia border)

Rectangular drainage (Elizabethtown, N.Y.)

Radial drainage on a volcanic cone
(Mt Rainier, Washington)

Deranged drainage (New Hampshire)

Fig. 29 A descriptive classification of drainage systems

Rectangular drainage is a very angular pattern based on geological controls, usually well-defined lines of weakness such as joints or faults.

Radial drainage Streams flow out from a high point or what was once a high point. This pattern is usually associated with domes such as volcanic cones or laccoliths.

Deranged drainage This is an 'immature' pattern where the drainage network has not had time to organise itself properly to create an integrated system. This is often found on a landscape which has been blanketed by glacial deposits.

DRAINAGE MORPHOMETRY (network geometry)

Many of the indices used in this approach are in the form of ratios or numbers. This makes it possible to make comparisons irrespective of scale.

Stream order

This is the basic concept of network geometry and is the means whereby streams are located in a ranked hierarchy. A headwater stream with no tributaries belongs to the **first-order** (the lowest order). When two first-order streams unite they form a **second-order** stream. Two second-order streams join to form a **third-order** and so on.

This ranking shows how a particular stream is related to the total network and how the total network fits together (Fig. 30).

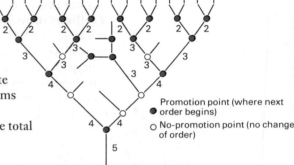

Promotion point (where next
● order begins)

○ No-promotion point (no change of order)

Fig. 30 Stream order

Stream number

The number of streams in each order for a given drainage basin (network). The table shows the stream numbers for the two fourth-order basins in the diagram (Fig. 31).

Stream order	Stream number
1	133
2	33
3	8
4	2

Bifurcation ratio

In the table above, the ratio between the number of streams of one order and that of the next is a constant, e.g:

$$\text{Ratio order 1: order 2} = \frac{133}{33} = 3.97$$

$$\text{Ratio order 2: order 3} = \frac{33}{8} = 4.13 \qquad \text{average} = 4.03$$

$$\text{Ratio order 3: order 4} = \frac{8}{2} = 4.0$$

This ratio is the bifurcation ratio. The average of 4.03 is the ratio for the whole drainage basin. Bifurcation ratios usually range from 3.0 to 5.0. This constant value means that when the stream number is plotted against stream order on semi-log paper the points would approximate to a straight line. This straight line is known as an **exponential curve.**

Stream length

Average length of stream in each order, e.g. the total length of all the first-order streams divided by the number of first-order streams. In the figure the stream length for first-order streams is 0.36 km. Again there is a systematic relationship between stream length and stream order and once more it is represented by the exponential curve.

Drainage density

Total channel length divided by the total area of the basin. This is a measure of the texture of the drainage net, i.e. the dissection of the land surface. In the South Downs the drainage density is 2.8 miles of dry channel (valley) per square mile of basin area. In the badlands of Arizona the network is very fine and density is 200 to 900 miles per square mile.

Basin area or area of catchment

In a drainage network the mean basin areas of the order occur in a roughly geometric sequence.

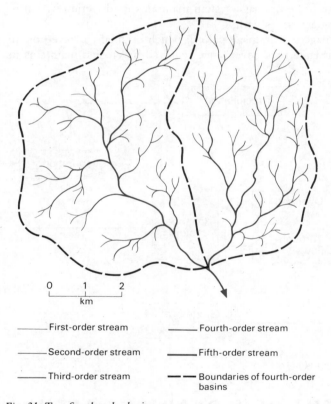

0   1   2
km

———— First-order stream   ———— Fourth-order stream

———— Second-order stream   ———— Fifth-order stream

———— Third-order stream   — — Boundaries of fourth-order basins

Fig. 31 Two fourth-order basins

DRAINAGE BASINS IN RELATION TO STRUCTURE

The initiation and evolution of any drainage system are determined by (a) the nature of the surface on which the stream flows, and (b) the geological structure of the land over which it flows.

In the first instance the drainage pattern develops in response to the nature of the surface. For example, a gently tilting surface will encourage parallel drainage. In a heavily folded area consequent streams develop along synclines.

Genetic stream classification

Consequent streams are streams whose courses are determined by the initial slope of the land. Longitudinal consequents develop in folded areas in the axis of the depression; lateral consequents develop down the sides of the depression.
Subsequent streams are developed by headward erosion along lines of weak structure. Most follow the outcrops of weak strata.
Resequent streams are also called secondary consequents. They flow in the same direction as consequents but belong to a later generation.
Obsequent streams flow in an opposite direction to the consequent streams.

The adaptation of streams to structure

Differential erosion results in the selective lowering of the ground surface on weak rocks and weak structures. Resistant rocks form areas of high relief. This differential erosion involves differential growth of stream systems with especially large streams or those following lines of weak structure developing as master streams.

These processes may result in:
- the inversion of relief;
- river capture
- antecedent drainage – the drainage system maintains its direction by cutting through folds rising across its path;
- superimposed drainage – a drainage pattern which originally evolved on an overlying unconformable rock cover since removed by erosion maintains its direction.

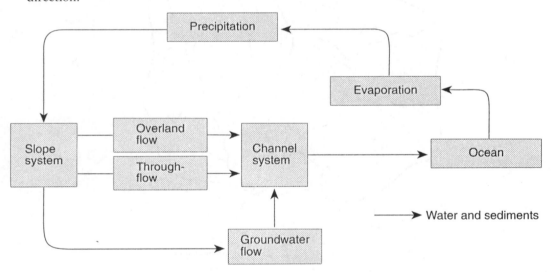

Fig. 32 A systems model of a drainage basin

MANAGEMENT OF A DRAINAGE BASIN

Case Study: River Ouse, Sussex

Background

The River Ouse is the second largest river in Sussex. It is 62 km long and has an overall catchment area of 664 km². It rises in the High Weald and enters the English Channel at the ferry port of Newhaven. It flows mainly over the gently undulating land of the Vale of Sussex and through the chalk escarpment of the South Downs.

Management issues

The main management issues are: water supply; water quality; sewage disposal; conservation of wildlife and flood control.

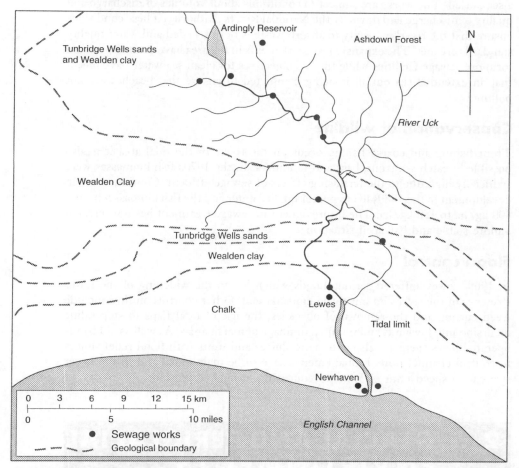

Fig. 33 River Ouse drainage basin

Water supply

The Ouse is the main source of water for the Mid Sussex Water Co. Ardingly Reservoir on the northern edges of the basin has a capacity of 1050 million gallons (4773 million litres). Its main function is to store water when it is plentiful so that it can be distributed in periods of shortage. The basin contains a number of major commuter towns – Haywards Heath, Lewes and Uckfield. These towns are surrounded by rapidly expanding commuter villages in which water usage per family is high. Since the annual precipitation in south-east England is relatively low and there are few suitable sites for major reservoirs, the balance between supply and demand is a delicate one with restrictions on the use of water a regular feature of summer months.

Water quality

This may be measured by Environmental Quality Objectives. For most of the basin the objective is 1B – high-grade water for game and high-grade fish. Some stretches of water from which domestic water supply is obtained have the highest 1A objective – high-quality drinking water. The Ouse basin is a rich agricultural area in which arable crops are grown using modern fertilisers. Seepage of minerals into the water supply is therefore a potential hazard. The thriving towns have also attracted new industrial estates from which waste materials have to be removed safely if ground and surface water is not to be polluted.

Sewage disposal

Fig. 33 shows that a number of sewage works have been constructed on the main river and its tributaries. At the coast, sewage has traditionally been disposed of by a sea outfall. The works are subject to conditions about volumes of discharge and quality of discharge laid down by the National Rivers Authority. These conditions ensure that the river's capacity to absorb waste is not exceeded and water quality standards are met. The expansions of settlements in the area have created pressure for more sewage facilities while the EC objectives for clean sea water have meant that an extended sea outfall is being completed to ensure that beaches are not polluted.

Conservation of wildlife

Trout fishing and coarse fishing occur on the river. In the tidal area it is also possible to catch sea trout, bass and flounders. In the 1970s fish biomasses were artificially high due to the fertilising effects of sewage effluent. Continued urban development in the 1980s led to poorer quality water and the fish biomass fell from 400 kg/ha to 150 kg/ha. The improvement in sewage treatment has now created a more stable and balanced situation.

Flood control

In 1960 Lewes suffered serious floods which led to the widening of the lower stretches of the river and improved embankment. Other controls on flow include weed cutting and the removal of obstacles, the use of tidal flaps to stop saline incursion into lowlands and pumped drainage of marsh areas. As well as old hand-operated locks there are also automatic sluices and weirs with flood relief sluices to control channel flow. Embankments have to be maintained and in the lower stretches a speed limit of 5 knots reduces the danger of erosion.

2.5 GLACIAL AND PERIGLACIAL ENVIRONMENTS

DEFINITIONS

Nivation	A complex process of weathering which deepens hollows by freeze-thaw action and removes material by solifluction (movement of soil and rock fragments down slopes).
Ablation	The melting and evaporation of a glacier.
Abrasion	The wearing away of soil and rocks by ice, wind or water.
Corrasion	This takes place when material carried by ice, water or wind wears away underlying rocks.

THE BACKGROUND

To appreciate what happened during the Ice Ages and understand how this period helped to shape some of our present-day landforms it is necessary to identify the general concepts which underpin the physical details relating to glaciation.

- During the Pleistocene glaciations, temperature conditions fluctuated. The ice retreated in the interglacial periods and then readvanced, tending to destroy earlier landforms of glacial origin.

- Continental ice sheets moved south across North America, northern Europe and parts of Asia. Northern ocean areas were frozen and there was a world-wide lowering of sea level.
- Glaciers also formed on higher ground. Their remnants can be seen today in such ranges as the Rockies and Alps.
- Areas beyond the edge of the ice sheets were subject to frost action. There was an extensive zone of permafrost (ground permanently below freezing point) which has shrunk since the Ice Ages but still covers 26% of the earth's surface.
- Water expands when it freezes. This makes it a formidable destructive force.
- The erosive impact of glaciation is evident in changes to existing landforms, although the process of erosion by ice is not fully understood.
- Meltwater is also an erosive force, as well as being responsible for deposition in sub-glacial channels and the formation of outwash plains.
- The melting of the ice sheets at the end of the Ice Ages resulted in uplift of some of the land as the weight of the ice was removed (isostatic uplift). This uplift is a slow process which still continues. Meltwater has increased the height of sea level, leading to the drowning of the original coastline in some areas.

FEATURES OF MOUNTAIN AND LOWLAND GLACIATION

Knowledge is also required of the distinctive features of both mountain and lowland glaciation, some of which you may have studied for GCSE. The main features are:

- **Mountain glaciation** Cirques (corries), arêtes, pyramidal peaks, trough (U-shaped) valleys, truncated spurs, hanging valleys, ribbon lakes, roches moutonnées, and moraine deposits.
- **Lowland glaciation** Moraine deposits, gravel veneered terraces, outwash plains, underfit (often referred to as **misfit**) streams, erratics, drumlins, till plains, lacustrine deposits, varves, kames, eskers, urstromtäler and kettle holes. Whenever possible you should be able to name examples or precise locations where these features can be seen. The examiner will not consider that locating a moraine in East Anglia is sufficiently precise. You will be expected to give a more exact reference, for example, the Holt-Cromer moraine in north-east Norfolk.

CIRQUES

The 'armchair' shape of the cirque caused by the lengthening, widening and deepening of the hollow which contains a glacier has been the subject of debate. It was thought that frost-shattering at the base of the bergschrund was the cause, but not all cirques have this crevasse. The shape of the cirque probably reflects a number of processes which have been summarised in Fig. 34.

The essential factors which help to produce a cirque are:

❶ Sufficient snowfall to build up the cirque glacier but not so much that the whole area is covered with an ice-cap. Complete coverage by ice would check freeze-thaw weathering of the headwall.

❷ Easily shattered bedrock which is strong enough to maintain the steep headwall and sides required to give the cirque its shape.

❸ Daily seasonal flushings of meltwater which can freeze on the backwall, prising away rock.

❹ Pressure variations which result in melting and refreezing. Water melted under a heavy weight of ice could refreeze when weight is reduced and then prise away rock.

⑤ Pressure release cracking in bedrock which makes the cracks required for freeze-thaw activity.

⑥ Abrasion by loose rock in the lower part of the cirque and the build up of material at the cirque lip.

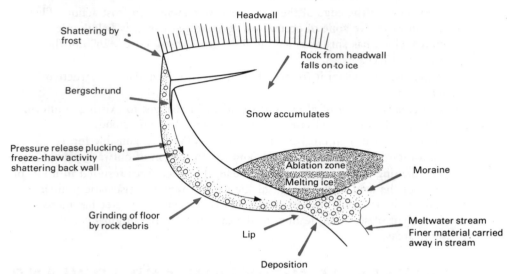

Fig. 34 Cross-section of a cirque glacier

TROUGH VALLEYS

There is still conjecture about how the trough valley becomes over-deepened and the longitudinal profile of the valley becomes stepped. See Fig. 35.

One theory for stepped valleys advanced by Demorest and Streiff-Becker was that the maximum velocity of the glacier is at its base where the pressure of overlying ice is greatest. Less pressure and therefore less erosion takes place where the ice is thinner, so erosion over an uneven surface would produce hollows and steps.

It is now considered that valley steps may be due to different causes in different locations. In some places jointed bedrock may have been plucked and removed to make an irregular surface. Tributary glaciers may have increased erosion, or a narrowing of the valley may have had the same effect. Irregularities in the original valley floor may also have been accentuated by ice action. This action includes (3), (4) and (5) under **Cirques** above, which are collectively known as sapping (Fig. 35).

The depth of trough valleys may have been caused by a number of the factors mentioned above combining to scour an existing valley.

DRUMLINS

These are typically composed of drift, but there are also pure rock drumlins and some which are veneers of drift over rocks. The processes by which drumlins were formed are not fully understood. Irregularly distributed patches of till in the ice may have been deposited when the ice retreated. Drumlins are found in highland regions, often in swarms, where the glaciers would have some velocity and this may account for their egg-like shape, which could have been caused by pressure.

PERIGLACIAL ENVIRONMENTS

DEFINITIONS

Periglacial   The term was originally applied to regions bordering

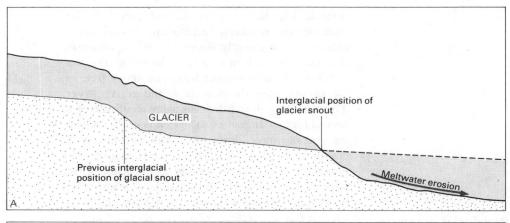

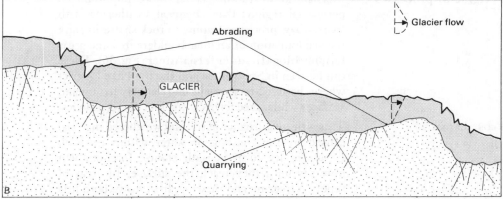

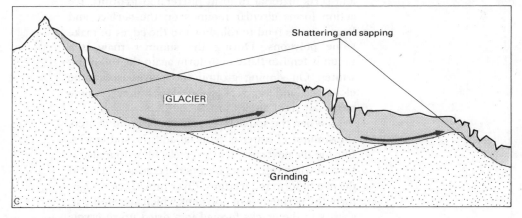

Fig. 35 Possible methods of valley step formation

on ice-sheets where frost and snow are important elements in fashioning the landscape. It is now used more widely to include any area with a cold climate such as mountains in temperate latitudes, or areas which were on the edge of ice sheets in the past, as was southern England during the Quaternary ice age. Freezing and thawing are the dominant processes and the most extensive area with periglacial conditions today lies in the Arctic regions of the Commonwealth of Independent States, Canada and Alaska.

Permafrost Permanently frozen ground found in periglacial regions. Permafrost covers nearly a quarter of the earth's land surface. Continuous permafrost occurs mainly within the Arctic Circle where the summer is too short and too cold for the top layer of the ground to melt. Discontinuous permafrost occurs further south in the northern hemisphere. It consists of islands of permanently frozen ground separated by less cold ground near rivers, lakes or the sea.

Where summer temperatures rise above freezing the surface layer thaws to form the **active layer**. This can vary in depth from a few centimetres to several metres. It is often saturated because meltwater cannot move downwards and is unlikely to evaporate in the low summer temperatures. The ground is consequently poorly drained and forms large areas of wetland. The active layer is important for the production of a variety of periglacial landforms.

Periglacial processes

Mechanical weathering is far more important in periglacial regions than chemical weathering with freeze-thaw processes leading to rock shattering and the accumulation of angular boulders in some areas forming **blockfields** or **felsenmeer** (Fig. 36). These can be seen in Snowdonia and the the Lake District where shattered rocks occur on relatively flat upland surfaces while scree forms at the foot of steep slopes.

Frost heave

This is the disturbance of soil and weathered material caused by the freezing of water within the soil. Layers of ice form beneath stones, forcing them upwards until they reach the surface. In areas of repeated freezing and thawing, frost heave both lifts and sorts material to form **patterned ground**. Ice action forms circular mounds on the surface and larger stones tend to roll down to the edges to make stone polygons. During the summer thaw, the mounds tend to flatten but form again the following winter. On sloping ground the polygons become elongated and on very steep slopes they become stripes at right angles to the contours.

When the active layer refreezes in cold winters the amount of water is reduced and the soil cracks. During the next summer the cracks fill with meltwater and when refreezing occurs the cracks widen and deepen to form **ice wedges**. Over time these wedges form the perimeters of polygons which are similar in shapes to the cracks formed in a dried up reservoir or lake.

Pingos

These are dome-shaped isolated hills with a core of ice. They can reach a height of 50 m and expansion cracks near the summit can allow heat to penetrate during the summer causing melting of the ice core to form a sunken top. Partially decayed pingos can have craters and crater lakes in the top.

Meltwater

During the summer thaw, the soil of the active layer becomes saturated with meltwater from the snow above and the ice within the layer. The ground below remains frozen so the meltwater cannot drain away. The soil flows downhill in a process known as **solifluction**. Valleys and hollows are infilled by the sands and clays and solifluction terraces in river valleys. During the Quaternary period southern England experienced periglacial conditions. Solifluction material flowed down the chalk slopes to form **coombe** deposits in the valleys and on the lower ground. **Dry valleys** in the chalk were formed in periglacial conditions when meltwater rivers flowed over the frozen chalk, cutting V-shaped valleys.

Cold winds blowing over fine silts in earlier glacial conditions picked up the light material and carried it long distances to deposit it as **loess** or **limon** as it is known in France. In north-west China the loess is over 300 m deep and forms the yellow soils of the region.

PROBLEMS OF PERIGLACIAL ENVIRONMENTS

Centrally heated buildings warm the ground underneath causing subsidence to occur when the permafrost layer begins to thaw. Oil pipelines, sewerage and water pipes placed in the active zone may be fractured as the ground moves. Houses are built on concrete stilts which penetrate into the permafrost layer. Cold air can blow under the house and snow does not pile up against the house in a blizzard. Houses are triple glazed and have double walls which are insulated. Roads and air strips are built on gravel pads and are drained so that ice cannot develop and the frost level is maintained.

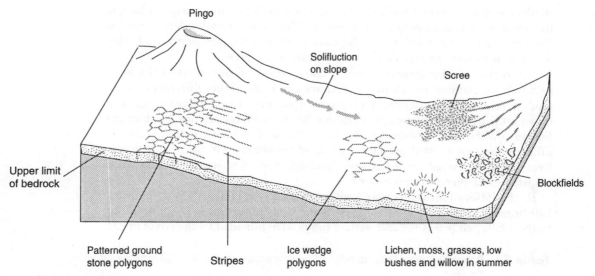

Fig. 36 Periglacial landforms

PROBLEMS OF MAKING A LIVING IN A COLD ENVIRONMENT

Case Study: Arctic Canada

The area north of the tree line in Canada is 11 times the size of the United Kingdom. Distances are vast, e.g. the distance from eastern Baffin Island to Alaska is 3500 km. Less than 0.25% of Canada's population live in this region. About 50,000 people live in Northwest Territories, one-third of them north of the tree line. This is the home of the 18,500-large Inuit population. Most Inuit live in small scattered coastal villages. The villages vary in size from 300–900 people with the average at 400–500.

The traditional Inuit way of life was closely related to environmental conditions and the economy was based on self-sufficiency. This careful balance was destroyed by the introduction of outside influences – whaling by the British and Americans; the killing of traditional food sources (caribou and musk ox) along the coasts by

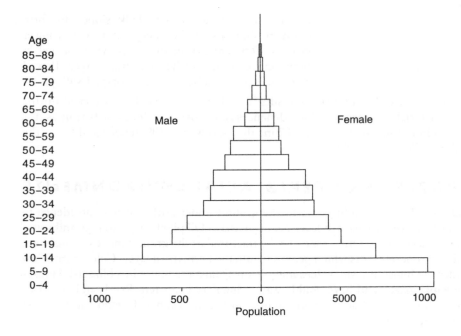

Fig. 37 Typical population pyramid of Inuit people in the Northwest Territories of Canada

whalers who also needed food; the introduction of Western diseases (influenza, the common cold, smallpox) and alcoholism. This led to a massive decrease in the Inuit population. The whalers were followed by fur traders, then miners and today by those who want to exploit oil and minerals in the area.

Before the arrival of these outside influences the Inuits' chief need was for food, materials for clothing and shelter at all times of the year. Since different types of food were available at different places on a seasonal basis, efficient forms of transport had to be developed. The relationship between the seasons, hunting and fishing and transport is shown in Table 5. The need to hunt particular game in different seasons created an annual cycle of movement for each Inuit group. Everything depended on successful hunting, very few items such as jade, soapstone and flint were exchanged.

By the 1900s all the Inuits were trading pelts with the Hudson's Bay Company. Life began to revolve around trading posts and many groups ceased to be nomadic. In the 1950s pelt prices fell and welfare funds were provided by the government.

Table 5 *Pattern of economic activity of Inuit people in N. W. Greenland in the past*

	Winter and spring	Summer	Autumn
Environmental conditions	sea ice	open water	variable, stormy sea
Transport	dog sledge	kayak or umiak	foot or kayak
Main sources of food, skin, etc	seal, fish	seal, fish whale	musk ox, caribou, seal

Nomadic groups moved into settled homes – prefab houses with yards cluttered with snowmobiles, sleds, traps and drying fish. Few have running water – a water truck provides water supplies regularly.

In the north some work is now available on strategic air bases, in mining and exploration camps and as tourism develops. Life is still very harsh. This is reflected in the population pyramid which illustrates the small proportion of both men and women who live beyond the age of 50 (Fig. 37). The life expectancy of the Inuit is significantly lower then that of the non-Inuit population of the region. The harshness of the life is accentuated by the much higher cost of living compared with Canada's southern cities such as Montreal. This is a major disadvantage as attempts are made to diversify the economy (Fig. 38).

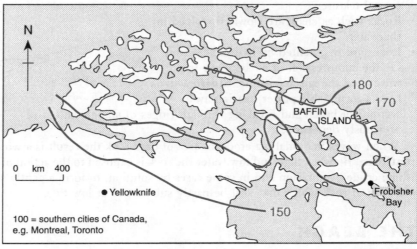

Fig. 38 The cost of living differential in the Northwest Territories

(after Sugden)

2.6 COASTAL ENVIRONMENTS

DEFINITIONS

Longshore drift	Waves usually approach a beach at an angle and material carried by the waves is moved obliquely up the beach. Depending on whether the waves are constructive or destructive the material is deposited or moves down the slope of the beach to be pushed up at an angle by the next wave movement determined by the dominant wind.
Swash	The rush of water up the beach from a breaking wave.
Backwash	The flow of water down the beach after the swash has reached its highest point.
Fetch	The oceanic distance over which the wind blows and generates waves. If the fetch is large and the time during which the wind has been blowing is long, for example from Cape Cod to Cornwall, the waves are likely to be large also. Waves in the North Sea are the product of a limited fetch, and however strongly the wind blows, the waves will have a limited height.

WAVES

Waves are formed by the transfer of energy from air to water by wind blowing across the surface of the sea. Waves can travel long distances so the waves that break on a beach may not be the result of local winds. **Dominant waves** are those which affect the coast most in terms of erosion and deposition. Waves breaking on a beach carry material up the beach and may deposit it, building up the beach in a **constructive** process. Waves can also be **destructive** (Fig. 39). They are responsible for **marine erosion** in the following ways:

- The swash and backwash of large waves cause abrasion of material carried by the waves, as well as erosion of cliffs and other coastal features.
- Rocks such as chalk are slowly dissolved in the water.
- Rocks are fragmented by hydraulic action i.e. the compression of air between the waves and the surface it hits. **Storm waves** have a formidable power, tearing away sections of beach and breaking through ridges of shingle and sand previously deposited.

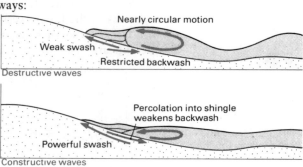

Fig. 39 Waves

When waves in a tidal sea erode an area of hard rock the result is a **wave-cut platform**. Between high and low water the rock is exposed to the action of waves which erode by abrasion and in some cases by solution, to form a gently sloping platform of rock which may still be partly submerged at low tide.

THE BEACH

A beach normally consists of unconsolidated materials such as sand, mud or shingle. The nature of the beach depends on the origin of the material which has been deposited on it. **Longshore drift** may deposit material a considerable distance from the original source.

A shingle beach is more mobile than a sand beach. During storms a ridge of shingle is formed above the normal spring tide level. Smaller ridges may exist, marking the level reached by the high tides of the spring and autumn equinoxes. Further down, the foreshore ridges may mark the last spring and neap tides (Fig. 40). **Sand and mud beaches** are much flatter than shingle because most of the swash sand returns down the beach with the backwash. These beaches do not have tidal ridges except occasionally when a small ridge appears along the spring high-water line. Only rarely is a **storm beach** to be seen.

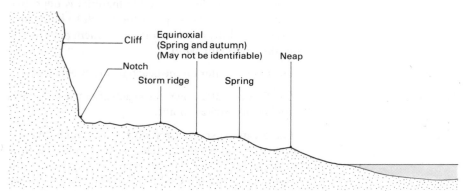

Fig. 40 Profile of a shingle beach at the time of neap

Beach types result from both the supply of rock debris and climatic conditions. Many rocks break down to sand or mud quickly, others, like flint pebbles, are long-lasting. The climatic factor is more significant than the nature of the rock in determining beach types. In the tropics the most important sediment is mud. Pebbles are most common in high latitudes due to the storm waves of these regions. Where coral flourishes the beach is likely to be composed of coral sand with a high calcium carbonate content.

Where there are dominant on-shore winds the dry sand may be blown inland to form a ridge of **dunes**. Apart from the formation of sand dunes, all the beach ridges described in this section are the result of short-term processes such as a storm or a spring tide.

CONSTRUCTIVE ACTION BY THE SEA

A number of coastal features are evidence of the deposition of material which has been transported by longshore drift or by currents. The features caused by long-term processes are offshore bars, spits and tombolos. Features formed by short-term processes are beach cusps and sand bars.

Features formed by long-term processes

The life-cycle of an **offshore bar** is shown in Fig. 41. The development of the bar leads to a lagoon on the inland side which gradually fills in. In time the bar is pushed inland and the marsh is gradually eroded leaving the remnants of the bar as coastal dunes. Much of the material from which the bar is formed is eroded

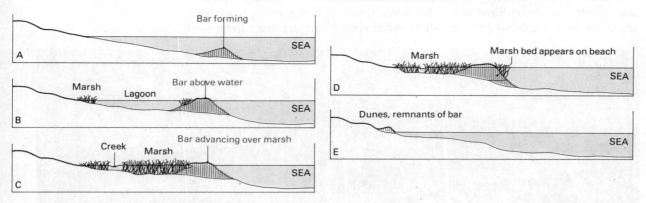

Fig. 41 Life-cycle of an offshore bar

from the sea floor and is not supplied by longshore drift. The most fully developed offshore bar in Britain is Scolt Head Island on the north Norfolk coast. **Spits** are built up with material mainly from longshore drift and extend from the coastline (Fig. 43). There are two kinds of spits, those that leave the coast at a marked angle and those that follow the coastline. Some spits growing from the mainland may connect with islands to form a shingle bar between the island and the mainland known as a **tombolo**, e.g. Chesil Beach in Dorset. A complex area which has resulted from deposition is the cuspate foreland at Dungeness.

Features formed by short-term processes

Beach cusps are small, seaward facing peninsulas of shingle on the beach linked by curving bays. Their origins are not fully understood (see Fig. 42). **Sand bars** (not to be confused with offshore bars), are the result of the concentration of sand in ridges at the point where a wave breaks. They occur in tideless seas like the Mediterranean.

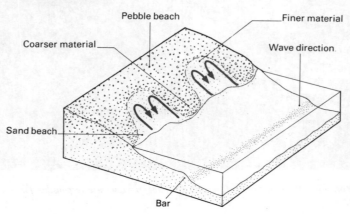

Fig. 42 Beach cusps

CHANGES IN SEA LEVEL

Many parts of the earth's surface are unstable and movement takes place which may raise or lower the land relative to sea level. For example, during the Ice Ages the increase and decrease in the area under ice occurred a number of times as the ice-cap spread and retreated. This resulted in changes in the sea level. These are known as **eustatic changes** because they were widespread and therefore found in many parts of the world. Movements in relative sea level may also occur as a result of warping or faulting of part of the continental crust, or due to an increase or decrease in weight when an ice-sheet is formed or melts. This type of movement which affects the crustal balance is termed **isostatic**.

Any movement where the land rises relative to the sea is described as a **negative movement of sea level**. When the land sinks relative to the sea it is described as a **positive movement of sea level**. Positive movements of sea level result in some of the land being 'drowned'. The most obvious signs of positive movement along the coast are drowned river valleys called **rias**. There are many to be seen

Fig. 43 Spurn Head, Yorkshire. What is this feature called? What processes are responsible for its development?

around the peninsulas of south-west Ireland, Cornwall, Brittany and north-west Spain.

Low-lying areas along the coastline such as the Fens were also covered by the sea when the level rose and layers of marine silt were deposited. Inland, swampy vegetation gradually built up a layer of peat. Small islands remained above this poorly drained area.

When hills and valleys lying parallel to the coastline were invaded by the sea, as for example along the longitudinal coast of Yugoslavia, long, narrow islands separated by inlets were formed.

Negative movements of sea level produce a number of distinctive landforms. Along coasts raised beaches and marine terraces are formed, in river valleys terraces, incised meanders and nick points can be found.

Raised beaches consist of platforms of rock with or without beach deposits. If the land form occurs above approximately 50 m it is called a marine terrace and beach deposits are rarely found. There are many raised beaches in western Scotland resulting from isostatic uplift.

Marine terraces occur at different heights. They have bench-like shapes and are backed by steep slopes. Identification of marine terraces is not always easy since other landforms which look like marine terraces can result from a warping (bending) of the strata.

SEA CLIFF EROSION

Cliffs are subject to both marine and sub-aerial weathering.

Marine erosion

This is caused by waves and salt crystallisation (the formation of salt crystals in cracks and pores causing the breaking off of mineral particles). Its effects depend on the nature of the rock forming the cliffs. Hard rocks with little jointing erode slowly. Most rapid erosion takes place in uncemented rock such as sands and clays of the Eocene and Pleistocene periods.

Sub-aerial weathering

This process depends on the nature of the rock – whether there are joints and bedding planes, whether the rock can be dissolved easily, its hardness and mineral composition and whether the beds consist of different rock types. The main processes involved are:
- **Mechanical weathering** This consists of freeze-thaw action by water trapped in the rock.
- **Chemical weathering** There are a number of processes involved. These include **hydration** in which certain minerals absorb water and expand; **oxidation**, especially of clays when they dry out; **hydrolysis**, for example when felspar in igneous rocks break down to form clay minerals; and **carbonation** in which rocks such as chalk and limestone decompose as a result of the action of acid in rainwater on calcium.
- **Organic weathering** This is the action of plants and animals living on the cliffs. Visual evidence is the rabbit burrows which riddle many cliff tops but more destructive action results from the increase in the carbon dioxide content of the soil and reaction between organisms and the minerals in the rocks.

The nature of cliff profiles depends on the **composition of the cliffs** and on the **balance** between the marine and sub-aerial processes at work. The **dip of the strata** is also important. Blocks cannot break off easily from beds which are vertical, horizontal or dip inland, so cliffs with such strata arrangements tend to be nearly vertical.

Sub-aerial processes are most effective on cliffs formed of drift material. Excessive rainfall or snow melt causes the cliffs to slump onto the beach to be washed away by waves and currents. Marine processes erode notches in the base of hard cliffs and exploit weaknesses in the rock, eventually causing sections to collapse.

COASTAL MANAGEMENT

Coastal management is a complex and difficult process. The coast is subject to many natural forces and changes and is also subject to human intervention.

We know that coastal land is subject to rapid changes. A sudden cliff collapse will have immediate effect on the land above and the shore below. In the Middle Ages, Rye in Sussex was a port located on a cliff immediately above the sea. The shoreline shifted as a result of violent storms whose effects were then reinforced by longshore drift. Today Rye is five km from the sea. Less resistant walls are quickly eroded by the sea – the Holderness area of East Yorkshire is being eroded at approximately two metres a year.

Fig. 44 shows ways in which man attempts to regularise erosion and coastal deposition. There are three main elements:

❶ **Beach control** The most common evidence of this around our coast is the

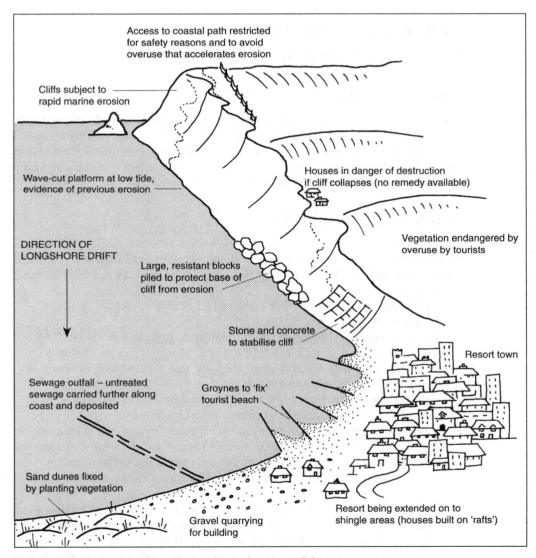

Fig. 44 Coastal management: regulation of coastal erosion and deposition

groynes which were constructed in many seaside resorts to retain beach material which would otherwise be carried away by longshore drift. Although material is retained by the groynes, coastal areas further along the coast are then deprived of drift materials and may be eroded more quickly as a result.

❷ **Cliff stabilisation** may be achieved through a number of protective measures, including the construction of walls resistant to wave power to protect sections of a cliff which are liable to collapse. Large blocks may also be dumped at the foot of a cliff so that the cliff base is not subjected to the full erosive force of the waves. Tourists may also contribute to erosion by overusing paths and eroding the vegetation alongside so that the surface is more exposed to erosion. In some areas expensive sea walls and breakwaters are constructed to check wave power before it reaches the cliff.

❸ **Dune stabilisation** is usually achieved by planting species such as marram grass, which checks the surface movement of sand and begins the process of establishing a protective vegetation cover.

Coastal management also involves problems of pollution. Key causes of shoreline pollution are:

❶ Accidental spillages or illegal dumpings of cargoes that damage the environment, e.g. oil spillage; escape of poisonous chemicals as the result of a shipwreck.

❷ Pollution as a result of inefficient waste disposal systems, especially old-fashioned sewage disposal systems which empty into the sea.

❸ Excavation of shingle and gravel for the construction industry can also cause pollution as a result of constant use of diesel- and petrol-fuelled machinery and lorries.

The sea is also capable of depositing vast quantities of materials that may cause environmental problems and hazards. The most common feature is the silting up of river mouths and harbours: the silt has to be removed to maintain channel flow and economic activities. Barrier beaches are common along the east coast of the USA. These beaches are believed to be formed as offshore bars of sand which move inland until a line of smooth sand dunes are separated from the mainland by a lagoon. In some locations, such as Miami, resorts have been built on these beaches. Storm waves can create considerable damage to low-lying settlements on these barrier beaches.

There is evidence to suggest that beach building as a result of the deposition of sand is becoming less common and that 70% of the world's sandy beaches are now reducing in size. This is because nearby rivers have been dammed and sediment no longer reaches the sea. For example, the Nile delta is declining as a result of the building of the Aswan High Dam.

FACTORS AFFECTING THE SITING OF A MARINA

Case study: Brighton

Reasons for building a marina

- **Demand** Yachting and sailing have grown tremendously in popularity. Moorings for boats have become increasingly both hard to find and expensive to build. A marina is therefore a sound commercial investment.
- **Commercial potential** A comprehensively planned marina provides a range of potentially profitable enterprises and sources of income. Services needed by sailors or services they find attractive include: ships' chandlers; pubs and restaurants; secure car parks; supermarket; on-shore accommodation; taxi-ranks, etc.
- **Residential potential** Land made available for housing within the marina

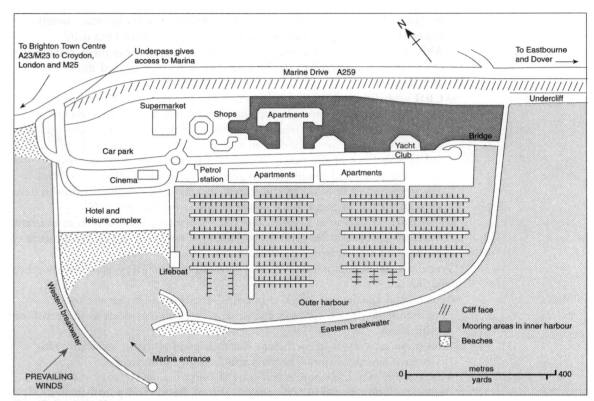

Fig. 45 Brighton Marina

development occupies a prime coastal site and can command high prices and rents.

Reasons for location at Brighton

- The greatest demand for moorings and marinas exists along the south coast.
- There is little competition as the nearest major sailing centre is Chichester harbour, 48 km to the west.
- Brighton attracts high-income residents and visitors who could afford to use the prestigious new development.
- Brighton hotels and shops are an attractive bonus for those using the marina.
- The coastal road and the A23 provide easy access to the south-east region and London.
- It is a good base for sailing to France.
- Local businessmen were prepared to speculate in the scheme.
- There was physical space available away from the main tourist beach.

Issues raised by the scheme

The granting of planning permission for the marina was strongly opposed on the following grounds:
- It was an environmental eyesore on the foreshore.
- Brighton residents with expensive seafront flats and houses objected to their sea view being ruined.
- The cost of building access roads would have to be partly met by residents.
- The coastal road would become even more congested and traffic would increase on the A23.
- Users of the marina would bring very little additional income to the town.
- It was a speculative venture which the town did not need.

2.7 ARID ENVIRONMENTS

DEFINITIONS

Exfoliation The peeling off of thin layers of rock from a surface. It is caused by the heating of the surface during the day and cooling at night. The resulting alternate expansion and contraction leads to the weakening of a thin rock layer which may be further weakened by the freezing of dew trapped in it.

Deflation Removal by the wind of fine products of weathering such as sand. The lightest material is blown away as dust and heavier material is blown along the surface. Some desert hollows are mainly formed by deflation.

Saltation The movement of particles by a series of jumps. This can happen in a stream when the current moves small stones or in desert landscapes where wind moves the sand.

THE NATURE OF PRESENT-DAY WEATHERING

- **Mechanical or insolation weathering** includes **exfoliation**, **block disintegration** – the breakdown of well-jointed rocks into boulders, **granular disintegration** – resulting from the varying capacity of the rock minerals for absorbing heat, and **salt crystallisation** leading to expansion.
- **Chemical weathering** leads to rock disintegration which occurs even in the presence of very small quantities of moisture.

PRESENT-DAY WIND EROSION AND DEPOSITION

Erosion

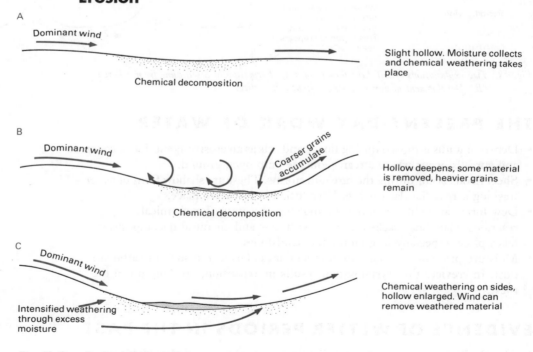

Fig. 46 Growth of a deflation hollow

The material carried by the wind is responsible for the etching of **yardangs** and for **deflation hollows** (Fig. 46), leaving a stone-strewn plain known as **hamada** from which smaller material has been removed.

Deposition

A number of depositional forms are derived from the wind. They are **sand ripples, ridges, barchans** (Fig. 47) and **seif dunes** (Fig. 48).

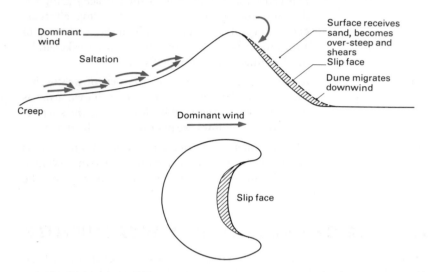

Fig. 47 Formation of a barchan

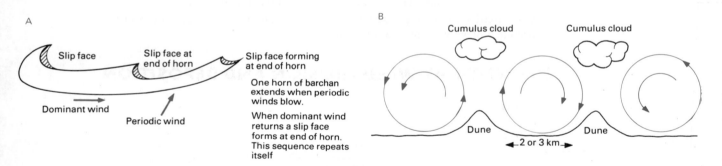

Fig. 48   Two explanations of seif dune formation (A) Formation of a seif dune from a barchan (B) Development of dunes by longitudinal roll vortices

THE PRESENT-DAY WORK OF WATER

- Debris in wadis is moved during floods and acts as an erosive agent. Fans, cones and spreads occur where streams emerge onto open ground.
- Sheet floods occur during the rare rain storms. These are shallow films of water washing across the flat surface. Very little erosion takes place.
- Dew forms at night providing the moisture necessary for chemical reactions. Hair-line cracks are filled with dew and chemical decomposition takes place, especially in granites and sandstones.
- Moisture promotes crystallisation in sodium chloride and sodium carbonate dust. In crevices the crystallisation results in expansion, breaking down the rock.

EVIDENCE OF WETTER PERIODS IN THE PAST

During the Pleistocene period and earlier there were pluvial periods which account for many desert landforms today. The evidence for these wetter periods is:

❶ Extensive valley systems in the Tibesti and Hoggar Massifs of the Sahara with valleys radiating outwards. These could not have been carved by the present limited rainfall.

❷ Archaeological evidence indicating that the central Sahara between the Tassili Plateau and the Hoggar Massif was occupied by palaeolithic people who hunted antelope, gazelle, rhino and elephant – all animals which live in a savanna environment.

❸ Pollen analysis in the Tibesti which proves that oak and cedar forests once flourished there.

❹ Lake Chad was once larger than it is now; shorelines exist more then 50 m above the present lake surface.

❺ Desert varnish (a layer of iron and manganese oxides drawn to the rock surface by evaporation) has been formed. This varnish can only form in alternate wet and dry conditions.

❻ Plateaux such as the Gilf Kebir in the Libyan desert have been dissected by stream action.

❼ The duricrusts of some desert surfaces could only have been formed during past wetter periods. Duricrust is a hardened layer formed on or near the surface. In hot climates with wet and dry seasons, salt solutions are drawn up by capillary action and after evaporation are deposited as hard nodules. The climatic conditions required – periods of high temperatures interspersed with periods of heavier rainfall than the present-day climate provides – indicate a different climatic régime in the past.

THE FORMATION OF EROSIONAL PLAINS

L C King has proposed a pediplanation cycle to explain the development of almost level plains which are to be found in many desert regions. Steep-sided hills called **inselbergs** rise from these plains and King's theory (1967) is based on the parallel retreat of slopes following river incision of the original surface (Fig. 49). This theory does not fully explain the vast areas of near flatness in semi-arid regions and further research is required.

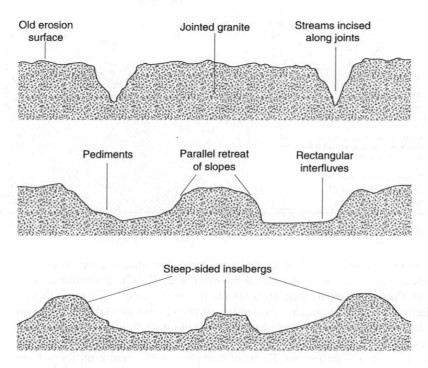

Fig. 49 Development of an inselberg landscape

INSELBERGS

As Fig. 50 shows, there are two forms of inselberg. Their shape and the formation of the pediment are not fully understood. Beyond the pediment is the **bahada** made up of rock material from the inselberg. Further from the inselberg, finer material may fill structural basins. After rainstorms, temporary lakes may exist and their sites are marked by flat plains called **playas** which are covered by salt after the lake water has evaporated.

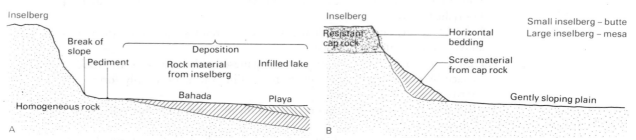

Fig. 50 Two forms of inselberg

DESERTIFICATION

Desertification is the spread of desert conditions beyond the present regions. The process is partly the result of global environmental changes. It is also due to human activities as summarised in the diagram. Deserts are enlarging at the rate of 3% every 25 years. The area in which desertification was first noted as a major environmental problem was in the Sahel which suffered severe drought and famines in the 1970s. In the Sahel it is very difficult to distinguish between the effects of a shift of climatic zones and the effects of the ways in which the people are using the land.

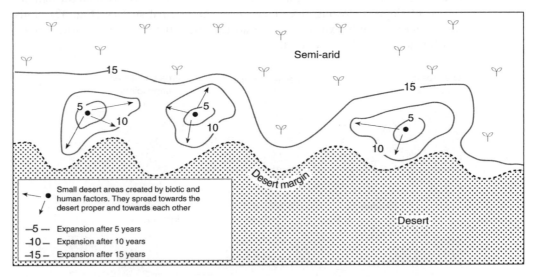

Fig. 51 The process of desertification

The process by which small, degraded areas created by human activities expand outwards and towards the desert area is shown in Fig. 51. The development and growth of these small areas ultimately results in the advance of the main desert.

Desertification results in the destruction of the environmental balance upon which the indigenous peoples have based their economies (Fig. 52). Herders and crop farmers are no longer able to produce food and goods for exchange upon which their communities depend. To avoid starvation, whole communities migrate

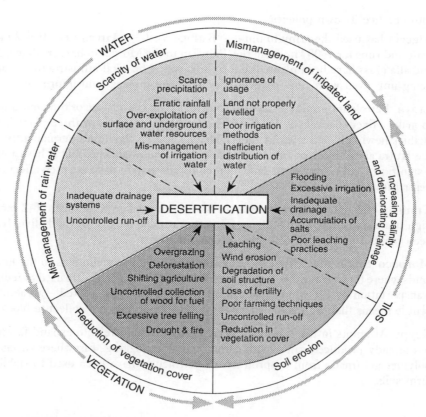

Fig. 52 The causes of desertification

as refugees to neighbouring lands which do not have the infrastructure or resources to provide adequate help. International aid agencies find that transportation and distribution networks in the neighbouring areas are often incapable of providing facilities needed to meet the basic needs of the refugees.

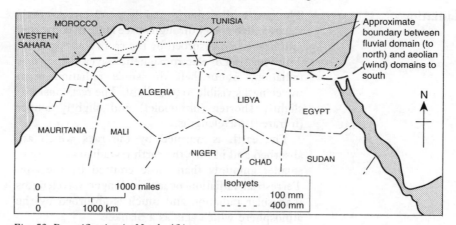

Fig. 53 Desertification in North Africa

TACKLING DESERTIFICATION

Case study: North Africa

The region of desertification in North Africa is found between the isohyets of 100 mm and 400 mm (Fig. 53). In this region, groundwater is being exploited to irrigate barley and wheat crops and to water herds of sheep and goats. Salt water is entering the aquifers from which fresh water is drawn and the contamination reduces the supply of good quality water. Each independent community is putting into practice its own policies:

Algeria has used the army to build a 'Barrage Vert' – a Green Belt. It is 20 km wide and runs for 1500 km, from the Tunisian to the Moroccan border. Pine trees and alfa grass have been planted to form this belt. The rural infrastructure is also being improved with rural roads modernised and grazing land improved.

Libya Petroleum products have been sprinkled on the surface of the sand dunes to make a fixed black layer that holds the sand dunes for two or three years. This enables newly planted trees to get established and fix the dunes permanently. In the Kufra area a modern irrigation system has been established but it has caused a significant fall of the water table and could ultimately have counter-effects on desertification.

Tunisia Old but effective techniques have been used in S. Tunisia. 1–2 metre high stone dams have been built across waterways. Palm trees, figs and olives have been planted on the soil collected behind the dams.

Morocco Storm water from the Atlas mountains carries sediments to the lower lands where they form active sand dunes. Fences of palm-fronds are used to reduce transportation by the wind. The camber of roads has been altered – an aerofoil profile means that sand is blown across the road and does not collect to block it.

Egypt Attempts in the Western Desert to use artesian wells to expand farming has already produced salt accumulation and waterlogging. Elsewhere sheets of polymer gel (made from by-products of petroleum) have been used to stabilise farm soils.

2.8 ATMOSPHERIC SYSTEMS

DEFINITIONS

Radiation

The sun emits energy mainly as electromagnetic waves which travel through space and are converted into heat when absorbed by the earth's atmosphere. This emission of electromagnetic waves is known as radiation. About half the sun's radiation is in wavelengths visible to us as light. The rest consist of slightly shorter (ultraviolet) and slightly longer (infrared) wavelengths.

The earth is warmed by the rays which are absorbed and in turn the earth re-radiates energy in smaller amounts than those emitted by the sun. Terrestrial radiation occurs in longer wavelengths than solar radiation and much is absorbed by the atmosphere which acts as a blanket.

Heat passes from the earth to the atmosphere by turbulence and by latent heat transfer, that is, evaporation at the earth's surface resulting in the absorption of latent heat and condensation in clouds with the release of this heat into the atmosphere.

Conduction

Heating by contact, for example, heating of the lower layers of air by direct contact with the earth.

Convection

The upward movement of a liquid or gas, such as air, which has been heated. It expands, the density is reduced causing it to rise, carrying its heat with it.

It is replaced in the lower layers by cooler fluid or gas.

Advection	The transfer of heat by horizontal movement of air, e.g. movement of tropical air from low to higher latitudes.
Anabatic wind	A local wind caused by the heating of slopes during the day resulting in warm air rising up the slope.
Katabatic wind	This is the reverse effect, occurring when the hill slope is cooling. It cools the air close to it which becomes more dense and sinks down the valley slope.
Air mass	A widespread section of the atmosphere whose temperature and humidity characteristics are similar horizontally at all levels above the earth's surface. When air rests over an extensive uniform surface for long periods it acquires the temperature and humidity characteristics of that surface. These characteristics will be gradually distributed vertically through the air mass. Those parts of the earth where air masses occur and acquire such characteristics are called **source regions**.
Relative humidity	The actual moisture content in a given volume of air, expressed as a percentage of that contained in the same volume of saturated air at the same temperature. It can be calculated using the formula:

$$\frac{\text{relative humidity}}{100} = \frac{\text{absolute humidity}}{\substack{\text{saturation content at} \\ \text{the same temperature}}}$$

Dew point	The temperature to which air must be cooled to become saturated by the water vapour it holds, i.e. the relative humidity is 100%.
Environmental lapse rate (ELR)	The actual temperature decrease with height such as an observer might record ascending in a balloon. The actual lapse rate will depend on local air temperature conditions.
Dry adiabatic lapse rate (DALR)	The rate at which rising unsaturated air cools, or subsiding unsaturated air warms. It is at the rate of 3°C per 300 metres.
Saturated adiabatic lapse rate (SALR)	The rate of decrease in temperature in ascending saturated air, or of increase in descending saturated air. Rising, moist air will cool as it rises, but the cooling will be less than 3°C for each 300 metres.
Temperature inversion	Normally air temperatures decrease as height increases, but sometimes the lower layers of air are cooler than those at higher altitudes. This reversal of the normal pattern is often produced by rapid cooling of the earth's surface (Fig. 54).

WATER VAPOUR IN THE ATMOSPHERE

Water may be present in the atmosphere as an invisible vapour, as water droplets or as ice. The source of water vapour includes the oceans and large areas of forest. There is a maximum amount of water vapour that a given quantity of air can hold at a certain temperature. The process by which invisible water vapour is condensed and returns to the earth's surface as precipitation is as follows. The atmosphere contains a multitude of condensation nuclei, such as dust and sea salt. Condensation occurs around these nuclei as air is cooled. Cooling may result from:

- radiation;
- movement up a slope;
- convection;
- advection (warm air crossing a cold surface);
- mixing of air, e.g. at a frontal boundary.

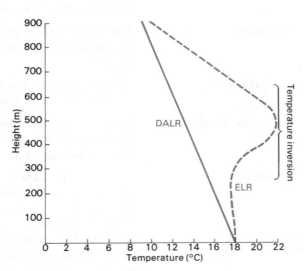

Fig. 54 Inversion: air is warmer above the Earth's surface with an increase in the difference between the DALR and the ELR

STABILITY AND INSTABILITY

Air is stable when, if forced to rise, it tends to return to its original position. This will happen when the air is cooler than the surrounding air. If, as the air rises, the temperature of the surrounding air falls more slowly than the temperature of the rising air, the rising air will be cooler and denser than its surroundings and tend to sink back (Figs. 55 and 56).

If, on the other hand, the temperature of the environmental air falls rapidly with

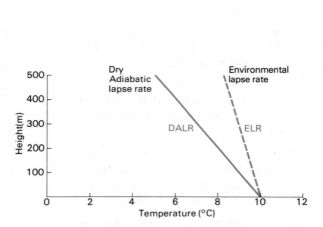

Fig. 55 Stable conditions: uplifted air (DALR) cooler than surrounding air (ELR)

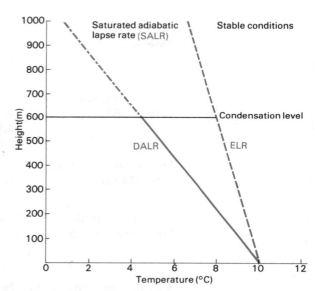

Fig. 56 Stable conditions: uplifted air above condensation level cooling slowly at SALR

height faster than the dry adiabatic lapse rate, the rising parcel of air will become warmer as it rises and its speed of uplift will increase. Such air is unstable (see Figs. 57 and 58).

Conditional instability occurs when moist air is forced upwards and is at first cooler than its surroundings. At some point condensation will occur and heat will be released into the rising air. It will then cool less rapidly, eventually becoming warmer than its surroundings and therefore unstable as it continues to rise (Fig. 58).

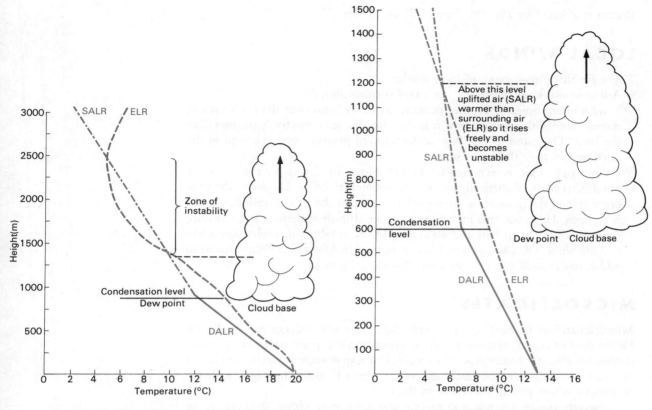

Fig. 57   *Instability: ELR varies with height giving a zone of instability*

Fig. 58   *Conditional instability: above 1200 m SALR air is warmer and less dense*

CLOUDS

Cloud formation is associated with lapse rates. Clouds occur at the height at which dew point is reached and condensation takes place. In turbulent conditions layers of air are mixed so that water vapour is fairly evenly distributed throughout the air mass. Adiabatic changes in the rising and falling air produce conditions in which clouds form. **Turbulent cloud** is usually low and of the layer type. **Orographic cloud** forms when air, which has been heated from below, is forced to ascend to the level of its dew point. Under stable conditions **fair weather cumulus** will form. Under unstable conditions thunderstorms associated with **cumulonimbus clouds** of great vertical extent are possible.

Cloud will form when warm, moist air is forced to move above colder air. Condensation will occur under these **frontal** conditions.

Clouds can be classified according to the height at which they occur.

AIR MASSES

Air masses cover many hundreds of kilometres. They originate from source regions such as the sub-tropical high pressure zones, polar and continental regions, from which they migrate and affect the climate of areas over which they pass. Two air masses with different characteristics may meet. They do not mix easily and tend to have sloping boundaries called **fronts** between them.

Air masses are classified according to their source regions and according to the paths they take after leaving the source region. They are called Arctic, Polar and Tropical and depending whether they pass over maritime or continental regions are described as:

Am	Arctic maritime	*Pc*	Polar continental
Ac	Arctic continental	*Tm*	Tropical maritime
Pm	Polar maritime	*Tc*	Tropical continental

Britain is affected by *Pm*, *Pc*, *Tm* and *Tc* air masses.

LOCAL WINDS

There are three main types of local winds:
❶ Anabatic and katabatic winds. (see **Definitions** above).
❷ Land and sea breezes. During daytime air flows from over the cooler sea to warmer land with a reverse flow at night when the sea is relatively warmer than the land. The cause of this flow is the reduced pressure over the land in the daytime and over the sea at night.
❸ Föhn wind. This is experienced in the Alps. Air forced to rise over the mountains cools adiabatically and condensation may occur. On descending the other side of the mountains the air will warm up at the SALR until dew point is reached. However, this may be at a higher altitude if there is less moisture present. Then the air will heat up at the DALR, resulting in a relatively warm and dry wind. The chinook which is experienced in Alberta is a Föhn-type wind which has crossed the Rockies from British Columbia.

MICROCLIMATES

Microclimatology is the study of climatic differences which occur in a small area. Differences of aspect, slope, soil colour, vegetation and plant cover can produce distinctive climatic conditions. Man-made landscapes such as streets, buildings and reservoirs all produce local contrasts in climate when compared with the conditions which prevail elsewhere in the region.

Although people cannot control climate they can, either deliberately or accidentally, affect microclimates by such actions as removing or changing the vegetation pattern, urban development and water control.

ATMOSPHERIC SYSTEMS: THE INFLUENCE OF CITIES

The development of great cities and the urbanisation of many landscapes has had an impact upon the operation of the hydrological cycle and increased pollution. These effects include:
❶ **Land surface effects** (a) Natural vegetation has been removed which immediately accelerates run-off. Erosion also accelerates while the ground is bare. (b) Impermeable concrete and metalled surfaces are created which:
  • restrict infiltration
  • create greater flood potential
  • increase the accumulation of sediments
❷ **Underground effects** Underground drainage may be interrupted as poorly drained areas are filled with waste materials which are compacted and built upon.
❸ **Sewage disposal** The cheapest possible methods are often used and on coasts this means that raw or partly treated sewage may be dumped in the sea, causing water pollution and creating health hazards. On the edges of the cities septic tank sewage systems may seep into underground water systems and pollute the water supply.
❹ **Industrial waste disposal** Ammonia, acids, oils and other dangerous substances may be dumped in the sea or leak from environmentally 'safe' disposal sites on land. Seepage into groundwater will affect the quality of the water supply. Uncontrolled dumping pollutes the coastal waters.
These effects can be placed approximately in a developmental framework with some being more significant in one phase of urban development than in another.

Table 6

Urban growth and development	Land-use changes	Hydrological effects
Low-scale development	Vegetation removed Wells and septic tanks sunk	Decrease in transpiration Increased sedimentation of river or streams Water table drops
Increasing growth and development	Many construction sites Large-scale building Roads laid down	Erosion and sedimentation increase Less water infiltrates ground Flooding is more likely Quality of water decreases Water table continues to fall
High-scale development	Public utilities installed Water brought from distant areas Environmental concern grows	Seepage of sewage and industrial pollutants into groundwater storage Controls established on water supply and quality Demand begins to exceed supply

Urban heat islands

As large cities grow, elements of the atmosphere are affected. This in turn means that conurbations and large cities develop their own microclimates. Cities generate more dust, and condensation nuclei change the moisture and chemical composition of the air and generate heat.

Under calm conditions, temperatures recorded in the city centres tend to be higher than those in the suburbs and surrounding areas. Typically, the heat island has a temperature of about 8°C higher than surrounding areas.

Causes of the heat island

Tall buildings, vertical surfaces, paved streets and road systems, and large car parking areas increase solar radiation.

The concentration of waste material emitted from industry and vehicles dramatically increases the amount of dust and condensation nuclei in the atmosphere which tend to act as an insulating blanket, holding heat within the city.

Characteristic features of the heat island microclimate

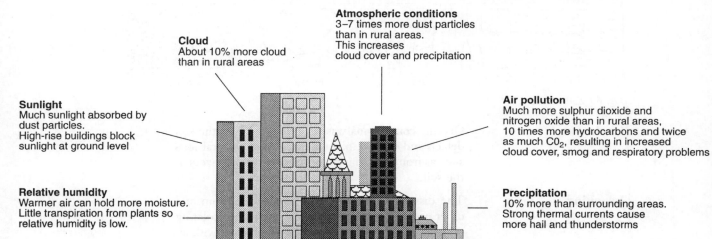

Cloud
About 10% more cloud than in rural areas

Atmospheric conditions
3–7 times more dust particles than in rural areas.
This increases cloud cover and precipitation

Sunlight
Much sunlight absorbed by dust particles.
High-rise buildings block sunlight at ground level

Air pollution
Much more sulphur dioxide and nitrogen oxide than in rural areas, 10 times more hydrocarbons and twice as much CO_2, resulting in increased cloud cover, smog and respiratory problems

Relative humidity
Warmer air can hold more moisture. Little transpiration from plants so relative humidity is low.

Precipitation
10% more than surrounding areas.
Strong thermal currents cause more hail and thunderstorms

Fig. 59 Urban heat island

Compared with rural areas, urban heat islands have:
- higher annual mean temperatures;
- higher winter minimum temperatures;
- less sunlight;
- more clouds;
- more fog;
- more precipitation;
- less snow;
- more days of heavy rainfall;
- less wind;
- fewer extreme gusts of wind.

So a city centre has greater need for air conditioning in the summer than in the winter. In addition its trees come into leaf sooner and its parks flower earlier than they do in the countryside nearby.

2.9 SOILS

DEFINITIONS

Regolith
The layer of weathered rock fragments which covers most of the earth's land area. It varies in thickness from place to place and the surface layers are called soil.

Texture
This is determined by the percentages of sand, silt and clay which are present. Soils with a large proportion of clay are plastic, sticky and cohesive. Sandy soils are the opposite and feel gritty when rubbed between the fingers.

Structure
This is very important to the soil's fertility since the structure affects aeration and workability. There are five types: structureless, platy structures, prismatic structures, blocky structures and crumb structures. All these result from the nature of the organic matter and the properties of the soil (Fig. 60).

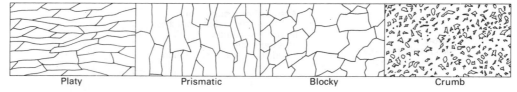

| Platy | Prismatic | Blocky | Crumb |

Fig. 60 Soil structures

Chelation
Organic compounds washed down through the soil detach and remove plant nutrient and mineral ions such as iron and aluminium from the upper layers of the soil.

Leaching
The dissolving and washing down of calcium and other bases through the soil as a result of percolating rain water. Bases are substances which react with an acid to form a salt and water. Some bases dissolve in water and are then called alkalis, e.g. the hydroxides of sodium, calcium and potassium.

Eluviation	The process of washing down material such as organic matter or minerals through the soil.
Illuviation	The deposition in a soil horizon of minerals, humus and other materials.
Soil profile	A section through the soil showing the different layers or horizons. The horizons are usually lettered from A to D with A as the upper horizon and D as the bedrock.
Soil catena	The relationship of soil types to the local topography. The changes depend mainly on changes in gradient, hydrological conditions and vegetation.
Zonal soils	Soils occurring over wide areas on well-drained land which have been there long enough for the climate and organisms to have expressed their full influence, e.g. chestnut soils.
Azonal soils	Immature soils without well-developed soil characteristics e.g. alluvial soils or lithosols (those at high altitudes on resistant parent material).
Intrazonal soils	Soils affected by some local conditions not involving climate or vegetation, such as poor drainage, e.g. gleyed soils or those where parent material exerts a strong influence such as calcimorphic soils (soils which exhibit distinct features as a result of the parent rock being limestone).

CONSTITUENTS OF SOILS

There are four soil constituents. They are:

❶ **Mineral matter** This is derived from weathering of the parent material and consists of particles of different sizes such as clay, silt and sand.

❷ **Organic matter** This is formed by the decomposition and assimilation of plant tissues and animal matter. Decomposed organic matter is called humus.

❸ **Air** This is usually saturated with water vapour and rich in carbon dioxide.

❹ **Water** This can be acid, neutral or alkaline and is held as a thin film around particles. It is the medium by which plants are supplied with nutrients.

SOIL-FORMING FACTORS

There is a complex interrelationship between the following factors:

- **Parent material** The nature of the parent material will have a marked effect on young soils. Its influence will become less as soil becomes older.

- **Climate** This is of major importance in soil formation. Rainfall, temperature and their seasonal and diurnal variations affect soil.

- **Type and amount of organic life** Although vegetation is usually dependent on climate, it can act as an independent variable, as the supply of organic material can be altered and interrupted if the vegetation is changed. Also organisms such as bacteria and earthworms have a marked effect on soil formation by helping the breakdown and incorporation of organic material.

- **Relief** Altitude can affect climate, aspect can influence solar warming and slope angle can affect run-off and soil erosion.

- **Time** Soils form over a period of time at different rates and gradually develop features of maturity.

SOIL-FORMING PROCESSES

- **Podsolisation** This occurs in the cool, humid regions where leaching is dominant. Sesquioxides (oxides of aluminium and iron) and clay minerals are removed from the upper soil horizons.

  This produces the true podsol, particularly in association with heath or coniferous forest. Podsolic or leached soils also occur under a range of vegetation types including deciduous forest and pasture land.
- **Calcification** This is characteristic of dry regions in continental interiors where leaching is slight and there is considerable evaporation.
- **Ferrallitisation** The accumulation in the humid tropics of sesquioxides in the B horizon.
- **Salinisation** This takes place in arid areas where drainage is impeded and salt accumulates, usually by upward leaching from a saline groundwater supply.
- **Gleying** The reduction of iron compounds by microorganisms in waterlogged soils.

  Many of these soil forming processes are associated with **eluviation, illuviation, leaching** and **chelation**.

SOME ASPECTS OF SOIL CHEMISTRY

The main products of chemical weathering in the soil are insoluble clay minerals. These are very small particles carrying a negative charge of electricity on their surface. These particles are dispersed evenly, forming a colloidal state. Associated with the clay particles is humus. The two form a clay-humus particle which is negatively charged.

Also present in the soil in solution are electrically charged ions – atoms which have lost an electron (cation) or a proton (anion). The positively charged ions (cations) include calcium, sodium and potassium. The negatively charged ions (anions) include soluble silica and bicarbonate.

The negatively charged clay-humus particles attract the positively charged ions (cations) which attach themselves loosely to the clay-humus particles. They are then said to be adsorbed, i.e. loosely captured and capable of being exchanged for others.

The amount of negative charge varies for different types of clay-humus particles and this affects the total amount of exchangeable ions. This amount is known as the cation exchange capacity of the soil. The interchange of ions takes place, for example, after a heavy rainfall. The rain washes away (leaches) cations of minerals such as potassium, calcium and magnesium and replaces them with hydrogen ions, increasing the concentration of hydrogen ions on the clay-humus particles and making the soil more acid.

In time the soil water acquires more calcium and other cations as a result of mineral weathering and plant decay and more ion exchanges take place. However, where rainfall amounts are consistently high the hydrogen ions predominate and the soil remains acid. Where the climate is drier and less leaching takes place there is an accumulation of calcium and magnesium ions, for example in chernozem soils.

HUMAN INFLUENCE ON SOILS

The main ways in which soils are modified by man are by: altering the plant succession through grazing, etc., removing the natural plant cover and replacing it with crops, timber, etc., and by ploughing and draining, which changes the soil structure and the arrangements of the horizons.

SOIL FERTILITY

Soil fertility is dependent on the following factors:

- **The physical properties of the soil** These are its depth, texture, structure, stoniness and drainage. A fertile soil should have a deep and well-aerated rooting zone.
- **The availability of organic matter (humus)** This increases the chance of creating a fertile soil by improving the structure and increasing the moisture-holding capacity of sandy soils.
- **Suitable conditions for organic decomposition and the incorporation of organic matter in the soil** These vary according to the amount and type of litter available, the nature of the soil and the climate. The richest soil forms where there is plenty of plant litter, aeration and drainage are good and the soil is neutral or alkaline and soil fauna such as earthworms mix the plant material with the soil minerals. Under these conditions the organic matter breaks down completely and the humus is evenly distributed in the upper part of the soil. This type of organic distribution is called mull.

  Less fertile soils are called moder and mor.
- **The appropriate chemicals must be present in the soil** Some 16 chemical elements are known to be essential to cultivated plants, though some are only required in trace amounts. Calcium is one such element – improving the structure of the soil.
- **The degree of soil acidity or alkalinity** is also important as several nutrients become less available to plants at the extremes of pH values. (The concentration of hydrogen ions in solution is indicated by the pH scale. Neutral soils have a pH value of 7: higher values are alkaline, lower ones are acid.)

SOIL PROFILES

Coniferous forest zone

Pine needles and other litter from coniferous forests form an acid humus (mor). Litter accumulates during the cold winters and the spring thaw removes plant nutrients, iron and aluminium from the upper soil layers which therefore have a bleached colourless layer of silica. Lower down, the iron and aluminium accumulate to form a darker illuvial horizon which may give rise to an impervious layer known as hardpan. This soil is known as a podsol (Fig. 61).

Prairie grassland

In this area the main organic matter is grass and its roots. Precipitation is light and there is an accumulation of humus and base chemicals near the surface. This produces a black earth or chernozem soil with a crumb structure (Fig. 62). In dry seasons, when precipitation is less than evaporation, capillary water rises and a calcic horizon of calcium carbonate forms.

Deciduous woodland

Leaf fall accumulates in the autumn and decays into a less acidic humus known as mull. Precipitation is greater than evaporation so there is still marked leaching but the minerals are not broken down chemically. The soil is called a brown earth. It is fairly uniform in colour, lacking the distinct horizons of the podsol. This is due to the greater number of organisms which turn over the soil (Fig. 63).

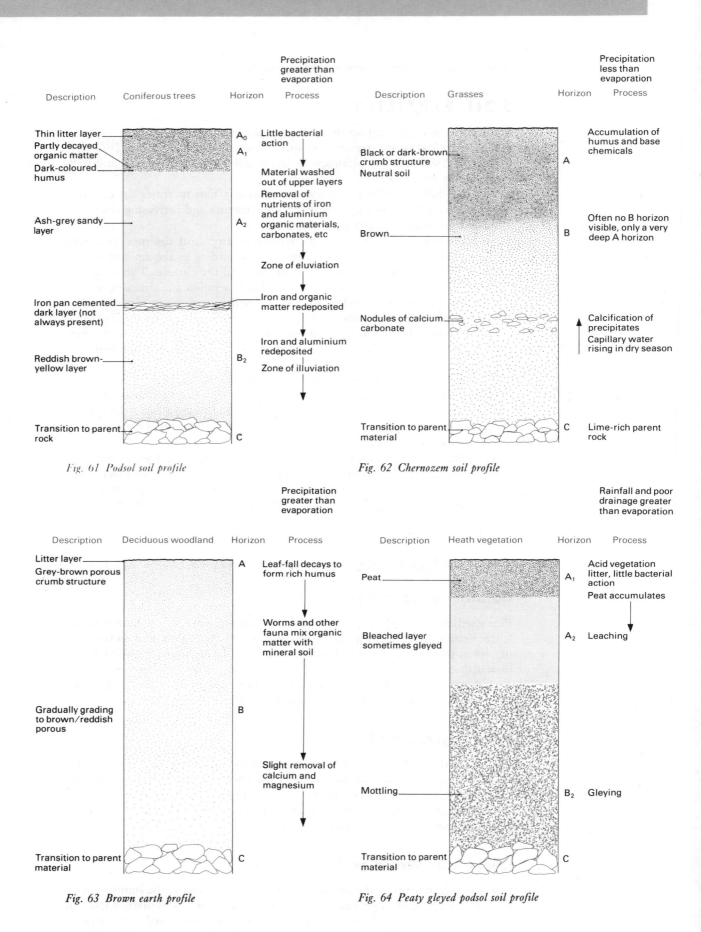

Fig. 61 Podsol soil profile

Fig. 62 Chernozem soil profile

Fig. 63 Brown earth profile

Fig. 64 Peaty gleyed podsol soil profile

Heathland soils

In upland areas, rainfall totals are high, drainage is often poor and the natural vegetation is heathland. In these areas a peaty gleyed podsol develops. The vegetation provides an acid litter, there is still bacterial action and peat accumulates. Heavy rain leaches the soil to form a bleached layer and a mottled B horizon, sometimes with an iron pan development (Fig. 64).

Tropical soils

High temperatures and rainfall speed up rock and mineral weathering in the tropics. The leaf fall and its rapid decay keeps bases in rapid circulation. Leaching is heavy but, rather than silica, iron and aluminium oxides remain to give the soil its characteristic red or yellowish colour. Such soils tend to be infertile due to the lack of humus content and lasting bases. Where there is a marked dry season many of the soils develop lateritic crusts which may be as much as 10 metres thick and which are rich in iron.

WORLD SOILS

Fig. 65 gives a diagrammatic representation of the major soil profiles to be found between the Pole and the Equator in the northern hemisphere. It also shows soil-forming processes associated with the soil types. The diagram indicates that there are no natural boundaries between the different groups and that sub-groups also exist.

There are two major groups of soils: those with calcium carbonate present, called **pedocals**, and those with aluminium and iron present, but no calcium carbonate, called **pedalfers**.

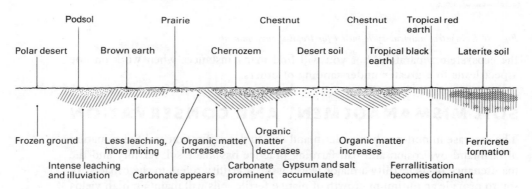

Fig. 65 *Profile relationships of zonal soils in a transverse from Pole to Equator*

SOIL AS A SYSTEM

Soil can be considered as a kind of working organisation, a system through which there is a flow of materials and energy. A soil system can thus be considered as a series of inputs and outputs of energy and matter within which a recycling of nutrients occurs. A model of this nutrient recycling process can be designed consisting of:

- **a biomass store** – plants and organisms living near or above the surface;
- **litter** – organic material which decays to make humus;
- **soil** – derived from parent rock, deposition and weathering.

Fig. 66 is an example of an ecosystem nutrient-cycle model designed for different tropical environments.

Soil studies are closely interrelated with aspects of biogeography, climate, geology and physical geography. It is convenient to study different elements of

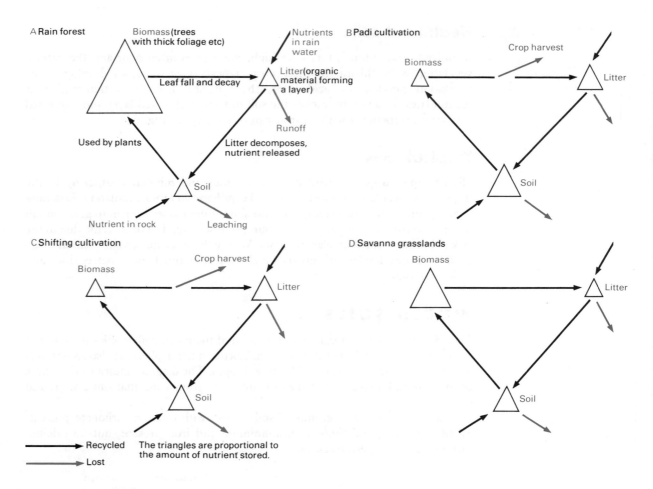

Fig. 66 Ecostystem nutrient-cycle model for tropical environments

the ecosystem separately, but you will find many instances when work on one aspect leads to a greater understanding of others.

SOIL MISMANAGEMENT AND CONSERVATION

The increase in non-productive farmland due to desertification and the ruination of farmland by erosion and bad farming practice has made soil fertility and the maintenance of its fertility a major world issue. Fertility refers to the capacity of soil to provide an optimum growth of plants: fertile soils will maintain high yields and infertile low yields. The capacity to produce low or high yields depends upon such variables as structure, texture, acidity and nutrient content as well as climate, relief and farming practices. If fertility is to be conserved the two key factors are the supply of water and of nitrogen. In order to grow, plants need to have a supply of nutrients and trace elements. As vegetation dies and decomposes in unexploited areas the nutrients it has taken up are returned to the soil. In farming, when a crop is harvested less organic matter is left to decompose. More nutrients are taken out of the soil than are replaced naturally. Other nutrients may also be leaked from the soil. In order to maintain yields, fertilisers have to be added.

Modern farming techniques, although very cost effective, may damage the soil, e.g.

❶ Soil structure may be altered as a result of intensive ploughing.

❷ Soil compaction occurs where animals concentrate in large numbers at food and water supply points. Plough pan compaction may also occur at the level in the soil reached by the base of the plough.

❸ Erosion may be caused by deforestation and the removal of hedgerows.

❹ Waterlogging may occur on heavy soils by land being used for large numbers of animals.

⑤ Wilting point may be reached in regions using modern irrigation techniques as salts accumulate in the soil. Yields are then reduced.

In many parts of the world the agricultural system depends upon the careful balance of climatic, relief, farming practice and other forms of human intervention. Where imbalances develop, major problems of soil conservation arise. Table 7 summarises some of the problems, their causes and the solutions which are being introduced.

Table 7 *Soil conservation*

Problems	Possible solutions
Erosions due to removal of vegetation	Add vegetation by: • Afforestation. Trees intercept rainfall, reduce surface run-off, their roots hold soil in place • Planting cover crops which reduce surface run-off and rainsplash
Evapotranspiration exceeds precipitation	Dry farming methods may be used. The soil is covered with a mulch. This reduces the loss of moisture and checks erosion
Reduction of nutrients in soil	Grow leguminous crops. They fix atmospheric nitrogen in the soil and so improve soil quality
Bad farming practice	Educate farmers to enable them to use better techniques Change farming practice, e.g. • Rotation of crops to replace harmful monoculture • Diversify farming to avoid effects of overgrazing
Shortage of water	More dams or weirs to trap water for use and to help rebuild groundwater reserves. Dams will also trap silt and provide more farmland
Excess of water	Dams to control floods Field drainage to improve waterlogged soils Sand and lime added to clay soils to improve structure and drainage (expensive)
Farming steep slopes	Contour ploughing Terracing of the steepest slopes. Slows down run-off and gives water time to infiltrate the ground
Wind erosion of soils	Plant shelter belts, rows of poplars or other quick-growing tall trees
Continuous irrigation causes salinisation	Water has to be flushed through the system regularly

2.10 ECOSYSTEMS

DEFINITIONS

System

A system is a structured set of objects (i.e. components), or a structured set of attributes, or a structured set of objects and attributes combined together.

Set of objects

means that a system has boundaries which separate it from other systems. **Structured** means that the system has internal order, that is, the components are

Attributes   arranged and interconnected in some kind of pattern. are the characteristics of the system and include appearance and behaviour. These attributes can be measured.

Ecosystem   An ecosystem is a system in which both the living organisms and their environment form components (elements) of the system. These elements are linked together by flows and are separated from outside elements by a boundary, e.g. a pond or forest is an ecosystem.

Food chains   Within the biological part of the ecosystem there are food chains in which one living organism is dependent on another. The levels in the food chain may be seen as forming a pyramid with each step of the pyramid called a trophic level (Fig. 68).

Ecological community   An assemblage (grouping) of particular species of plants and animals which are linked by the flow of energy, the cycling of nutrients and the regulation of population within a particular physical and chemical environment.

Biomes   Major terrestial ecosystems of the world. They may also be called provinces, biochores or regions (see Fig. 70).

Biomass   The total content of the organic matter. The higher the trophic level in a food chain, the less the biomass. The proportion between the biomass at a given trophic level and that at the next higher trophic level is called the **biomass ratio**. Biomass ratios vary within an ecosystem and from one ecosystem to another. The biomass is usually measured as dry weight per unit area of organism.

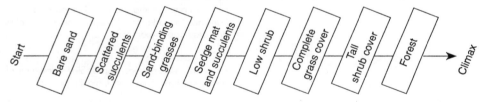

Fig. 67

Ecological succession   Bare ground is soon colonised by plants where growth is possible. Subsequently there is a series of sequential replacements as one set of dominant plants is replaced by another. This process of sequential replacement is known as **succession** (Fig. 67).

Ecological niche   Within an ecosystem the place that a particular species occupies in the total system is called its **ecological niche**. The number of niches in a given ecosystem is a measure of how complex the system is. In polar regions there are few niches in the ecosystem, in the humid tropical areas the number of niches is enormous.

Trophic level   See Fig. 68

Climax community   Like other systems, ecosystems move towards a state of stability. Each species alters its own environment and that of its associates over time. Factors such as competition and parasitism lead to vegetative change over time. Dominant species emerge and plant succession occurs whereby the dominants become larger and more complex. In Fig. 67 you can see the succession of plants in a coastal area of Australia with a humid sub-tropical climate. The end product of the process of succession (in the diagram, forest) is known as the **climate climax vegetation**. Unless climate or geological conditions change significantly this vegetation will persist. The nature of the climax is determined chiefly by the physical environment – the climate, rocks and soils. Forest is the usual climax in those places on land where there is sufficient light and where temperatures are not too extreme. In drier regions the climax is grassland. The normal climax may however be **arrested** by flooding, fires and human interference.

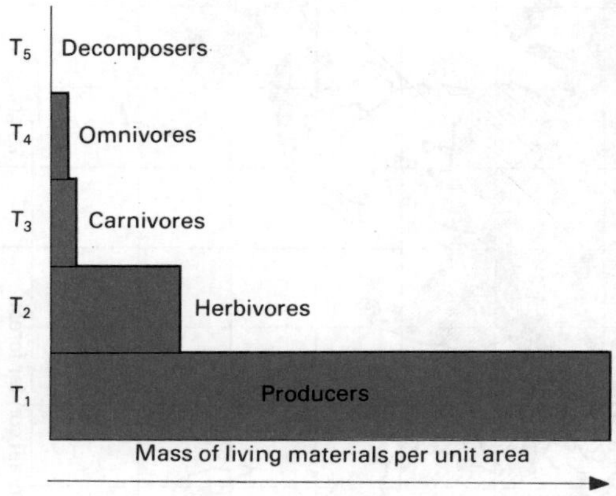

T_5	Decomposers
T_4	Omnivores
T_3	Carnivores
T_2	Herbivores
T_1	Producers

Mass of living materials per unit area →

Fig. 68 Trophic levels

ECOSYSTEMS

An ecosystem includes both organisms and their environments. So a forest ecosystem includes all the living organisms of the forest (plant and animal), the soil in which most of the plants live, the moisture taken in by the plants and animals as well as the special microclimate which a forest establishes itself.

Ecosystems are therefore very complex. There may be many components (e.g. the different species in a forest). The linkages between the components may be very intricate. So we isolate aspects of the ecosystem in order to study them, e.g. the food web.

Although there is a great variety of ecosystems in existence, all of them are characterised by general structural and functional attributes. Ecological relationships exist between **abiotic** (non-living) environmental substances, e.g. water, carbon dioxide, and **biotic** components i.e. plants, microbes, animals.

Ecological relationships are fundamentally energy-orientated

The basic source of energy for any ecosystem is radiant energy (sunlight). This energy is converted by **producers** (Fig. 69) by the process of photosynthesis into a chemical form by the production of carbohydrates. The producers are such chlorophyll-bearing plants as grass and trees and phytoplankton in the oceans as well as bacteria which oxidise inorganic compounds, important in creating the

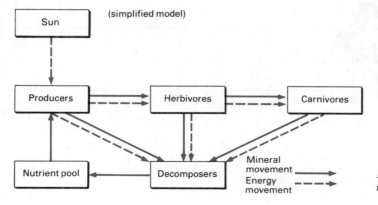

Fig. 69 Energy and mineral movement in ecosystems

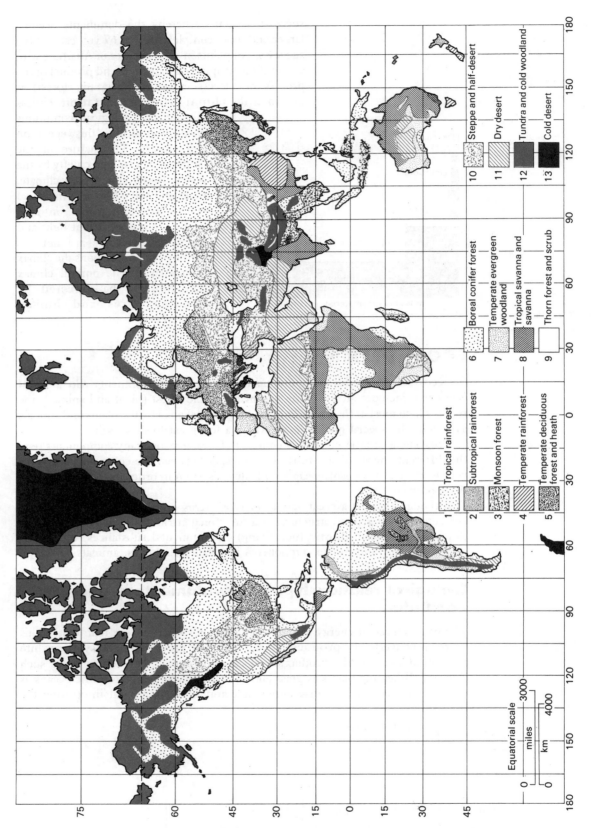

Fig. 70 *World distribution of biome types*

movement of nutrients through the system.

One of the principal features of the ecosystem is a one-way flow of energy (see diagram). The energy moves to **primary consumers** such as herbivores that derive energy directly from the plants (producers). Carnivores are **secondary consumers** which obtain their energy indirectly from the producers by way of the herbivores. Both groups of consumers are called **heterotrophic** (other feeding) because they get nutrition by feeding on other organisms.

A third group of heterotrophs are the **decomposers** – mainly bacteria and fungi. Through the action of enzymes the decomposers mineralise organic matter and make it available for re-use by producers.

From the diagram you can see that the movement of energy within an ecosystem is non-cyclic and undirectional. The movement of nutrients, however, is cyclical.

The processes of energy flow and mineral cycling are fundamental to the ecosystem. These processes occur through the vehicle of living organisms – animals, plants, etc. Since each species has unique attributes, no two ecosystems are exactly alike. In analysing different ecosystems we are essentially concerned with the **interdependence** of life forms, with the relationship of particular life forms to the whole system, and with ecosystem stability.

The dynamics of population

This term refers to the flows of energy and matter in the form of organisms, and the capacity of a species to alter its own environment and that of its associates together with the ability to adjust to its habitat. The number of individuals of a species is partially determined by the difference between birth rate and death rate. Low percentage death rates will produce high populations (see Unit 3.1). Migration also plays a part in the control of animal population. Populations do not expand indefinitely; the rate of growth levels off at a level called the **carrying capacity of the habitat**. This capacity is the product of a number of factors which are usually grouped as factors of **environmental resistance**. The process is known as **population self-regulation**.

A steady state

Like other systems therefore the ecosystem moves towards a condition of stability – the steady state. It is the result of the dynamic interaction of all the forces operating within the system. This does not mean that the number of species within the system becomes constant. Instead there is a dynamic state of fluctuation around a mean. The steady state is characterised by the evolution of the climax community.

ECOLOGICAL COMMUNITIES

The significant properties of ecosystems are energy flow, nutrient cycling and population self-regulation. These processes do not occur in isolation. They operate in particular environments in relation to particular assemblages of different species populations. These assemblages are known as ecological communities.

At both a micro (small scale) and macro (large scale) level it is possible to recognise zones or belts which are characterised by particular assemblages. For example, there is on one scale the world latitudinal zoning into biomes and on the other the summer zoning of plants from the shoreline into a lake, characterised by terrestial plants (e.g. elm trees) then sub-aquatic plants (e.g. willow trees) to reeds, water-lilies and finally totally submerged plants.

BIOMES

Biomes are arranged latitudinally. The same biome is found within the same general latitudes in different continents (Fig. 69) e.g. the tundra stretches across northern North America, northern Europe and northern Asia.

In the mountainous areas of the world the distribution of biomes relates to altitude rather than latitude. The particular biome found at a particular altitude depends however upon latitude. In the northern hemisphere, for example, a given zone is found at progressively lower altitudes in mountainous regions as one moves northwards.

The latitudinal distribution of biomes reflects the prime influence of climate in determining the pattern. Temperature is largely dependent on the incidence of solar radiation. This is directly related to latitude. Wind patterns are similarly associated with latitude (remember the wind and pressure belts of the world diagram you learned for GCSE) and this strongly influences patterns of precipitation. Climatic factors are therefore vital. Soil is also an important regulatory factor in determining the distribution of biomes though the soil is itself partly the production of climatic conditions.

CASE STUDY: A HEATHLAND ECOSYSTEM

Heathland is characterised by an absence of trees: tall bushes and shrubs are also scarce and the main ground cover is heather or its close relatives. This provides the dominant layer below which there may be a variety of other creeping plants – grass, sedges, ferns and a ground stratum of lichens.

Location

Heathland is found where cool, humid conditions prevail – in the uplands and central and eastern areas of Britain, for example. Westwards, heath gives way to peat bog because of the heavier rainfall. Heath usually develops on arid soils – podsols from which minerals have been leached from the upper profile to give a white or ash-coloured band.

Dominance of heather

The heather exerts a strong influence on the environment in which all other plants

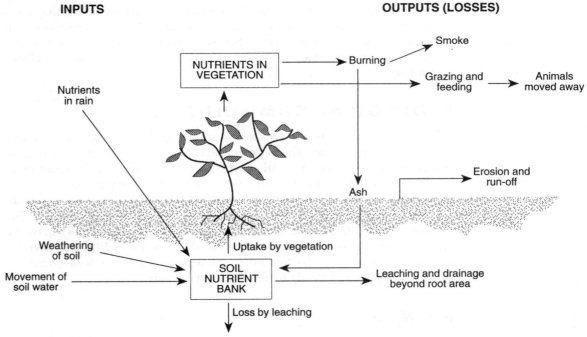

Fig. 71 Nutrient fund in heathland vegetation

of the community have to live. As the heather plant goes through its life cycle the density of shade it casts is a major factor in influencing the growth of the plants. Heather itself has a degree of tolerance towards restriction of water supply and is able to thrive on acid soils which are poor in nutrient minerals. The heath in turn provides food and support for other elements of the community. Large numbers of invertebrates are associated with heathland vegetation. All are influenced by the microenvironment in different ways. They respond to changes in food supply and environmental conditions which occur as the heather's life cycle proceeds. For example, the heather beetle and caterpillars of some moths are most common when the heather is making its canopy and biomass is at a maximum. Litter-inhabiting organisms such as mites increase in numbers as the quality of litter increases. Shade and shelter provided by the mature heather favours millipedes. The greater light and variability of humidity that occur as the heather degenerates attract ants and certain beetles. So as the growth phases of the heather occur, the food supply and habitat beneath the heather changes, producing parallel changes in the population of small animals.

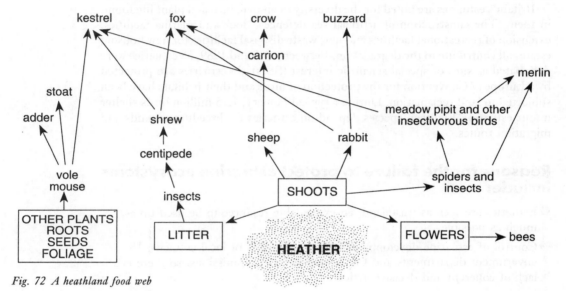

Fig. 72 A heathland food web

Burning of heathland

This has been a traditional way of managing heathland. There are two purposes:
- to regenerate the heather;
- to provide fresh young shoots for grazing animals, especially sheep.

Burning destroys most of the above-ground vegetation. 70–80% of the nitrogen disappears in the smoke. The remainder and other nutrients are deposited as ash. Burning best takes place before the heather is 15 years old. Productivity of young shoots is then at its peak and heather is less successful at generating itself after 15 years. Burning stops the heather getting too tall and reduces the litter accumulation.

Plants with underground organs which perennate survive the fire and produce new growths from below. Others are able to establish large populations of seedlings quickly. Trees and shrubs may disappear but heather, bell heather, blueberry and bracken quickly re-establish themselves. Grasses and sedges are largely unaffected.

Disadvantages of burning:

- Trees and tall shrubs may be destroyed.
- Animal life may be endangered.
- If the vegetation does not regenerate quickly nutrients may be leached from base soil.

- Burning on steep slopes encourages soil erosion.
- Burning disfigures the landscape for a while.

The economic value of heathland

Heathland provides grazing for sheep and grouse. In some areas the heathland has been replaced by forestry and by planted grasses to improve the farm economy. Today heathland is seen as a major countryside amenity. Private heathlands provide an income from grouse shooting.

CASE STUDY: AN ESTUARINE HABITAT

Half the coastline of England and Wales is made up of estuarine habitats. 85% of these mudflats, the salt marshes and the sand dunes that surround them have been damaged by human activities. Major land reclamation schemes have degraded 45 estuaries of which 26 are internationally important wildlife sites.

Britain's estuaries are noted for the diversity of animal, bird and plant life found in them. The construction of artificial sea defences, dock and marina facilities, extension of recreational facilities and new waste disposal facilities for new housing estates all contribute to the degradation. Between 1988 and 1989, 58 estuaries were designated as sites of special scientific interest (SSIs). 36 estuaries are protected by a European Convention for the protection of birds and their habitats have been subjected to land reclamation. During a typical January, 1.75 million birds shelter in our estuaries. Eighteen species depend on estuaries for breeding grounds and migration routes.

Reasons for the failure to protect estuarine ecosystems include:

❶ Estuaries are seen as wasteland, an expendable resource to be used up as much as possible.

❷ Control of estuarine development falls to a number of local councils, 18 government departments and the Crown Estate Commissions, so there is a lack of coherent and decisive action.

❸ There is no national policy for estuaries which would guide development.

The Orwell Estuary

The Orwell Estuary (Fig. 73) is of international importance ecologically. It provides a habitat for birds such as the redshank, dunlin, ringed plover, black-tailed gannet and Brent goose. It is bordered by stretches of sea lavender and unspoiled salt marshes. At its mouth there are mussel beds.

Threats to the Orwell habitats

These come from:

❶ The expanding water sports industry: many marinas have been built and facilities for 3000 leisure craft are planned at Felixstowe;

❷ Sewage and waste disposal for Ipswich;

❸ Oil pollution from the docks at Ipswich;

❹ The proposal to make further extensions to Felixstowe docks;

❺ Dredging of the river channel to ease navigation.

Unless development is controlled, rare wildlife and plants will be destroyed. The Suffolk waterline will be less picturesque and its wildlife less diverse than it is at present.

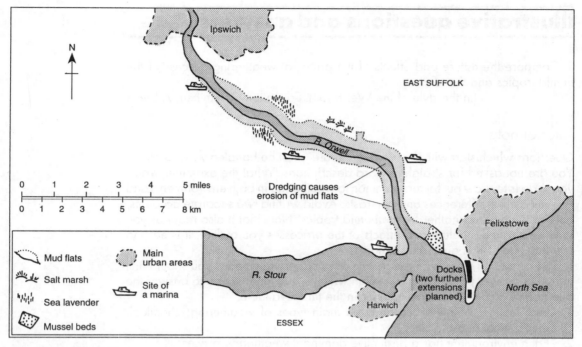

Fig. 73 The Orwell Estuary

Chapter roundup

A very important aspect of Physical Geography which can be easily ignored is the interrelationship between parts of the physical environment and that between people and their physical surroundings. When you are reading one of these units keep at the back of your mind the connections between it and other units in this chapter. For example, Unit 2.9 has close connections with Unit 2.10 and with 2.1. Similarly, Unit 2.2, Unit 2.7 and Unit 2.1 are interrelated.

You should appreciate that the physical environment exercises an influence on many human activities, and that people can modify, regulate and transform the environment either deliberately or accidentally.

Some chief examiners report a lack of fundamental knowledge about the basic principles of Physical Geography. Because a full understanding of the working of physical processes is lacking, questions are poorly answered. Do not concentrate on Human Geography at the expense of Physical. Most papers are planned so that you must answer questions on both aspects and you cannot afford to put all your examination eggs in one basket.

There is also considerable scope to select a physical theme for your Individual Study. A field study of a local ecosystem, such as a marsh or a piece of heathland, would give you the opportunity to use a range of skills, including making quadrats and transects, soil sampling, drawing soil profiles and using correlation techniques. There are numerous opportunities in many localities to study mass movement on a slope, longshore drift or river channel geometry.

When you are studying Physical Geography, or carrying out field work, remember that, where possible, the emphasis should be on a systems approach, describing and explaining the linkages between one set of features and another.

Illustrative questions and answers

1 Compare the nature and effects of the principal weathering process of the humid tropics and the tundra.

(in the style of the Welsh Joint Education Committee, A Level)

Tutorial note

Questions which start with the word 'compare' must be handled very carefully. You are not asked for straightforward descriptions. What the examiner wants you to do is to draw out factors common to weathering in both environments and to point out the differences and contrasts. Avoid writing two separate accounts, one for the tundra another for the humid tropics. Note that it also requires you to write about the nature and effects of the processes you outline. It is easy to overlook the effects and so lose marks.

This question requires an essay-style answer and that means you should first make an answer plan. Here is a plan which would enable you to answer the question in a comprehensive manner in the time available:

1   Introduction, pointing out the three main types of weathering: chemical, mechanical and organic.
2   Each environment has a distinctive dominant weathering process.
3   In both environments weathering occurs at two levels.
4   In both environments organic weathering occurs.
5   In both environments effectiveness of weathering depends on the nature of underlying rocks.
6   The effects differ considerably.

Suggested answer

The principal weathering processes are mechanical weathering and chemical weathering. Organic weathering involves both mechanical and chemical weathering. Both major weathering processes are present in different intensities in the two environments. In the tundra regions, mechanical weathering is predominant but recent research has established that chemical weathering is more important than was previously believed. Carbon dioxide is more soluble at low temperatures so in the tundra summer meltwater can absorb the gas, making weak carbonic acid which encourages chemical rotting. By contrast, in humid tropical environments chemical weathering predominates. This is the result of high rainfall and high temperatures. High rainfall encourages solution, hydration, hydrolysis and carbonation. High temperatures accelerate these processes.

In tundra regions mechanical weathering takes place at the surface of the ground where bare rocks are reduced by ice-wedging, while above the permafrost layer there is freeze-thaw action to break up the rocks. In the humid tropics weathering occurs on the surface on bare rock and also below the surface above the basal weathering front (etchplain). This feature of weathering occurring at two levels is common to both climatic regions.

One thing that is not common is the time span during which weathering can take place. In tundra regions the time span is limited by the number of days when the temperature does not rise above freezing point. This will vary according to location for example, coastal areas with longer springs and autumns and heavier precipitation are the most intensely weathered areas. In the humid tropics, weathering is a continuing process throughout the year.

In both environments organic weathering occurs. This serves to complement the dominant weathering process. In the humid tropics rapid root growth forces the mechanical splitting of some rocks along fractures and joints. In the tundra where there is less vegetation cover, organic weathering is not as significant. Flat, water-logged areas encourage the growth of peaty masses which produce organic acids which, in turn, stimulate chemical weathering.

In both environments the effectiveness of the weathering processes varies with the nature of the rock. Well-jointed soluble limestones are very susceptible to weathering. Other rocks such as granite may be fairly resistant to mechanical weathering but break down chemically in humid conditions.

In both regions the effects of the weathering processes are evident on the landscape. The weathering processes expose fresh surfaces of bare rock which, in turn, are attacked by the weathering agents. The weathering debris in the tundra regions, since it is mainly mechanically derived, is angular and used by moving ice to erode the land. The weathering debris in the humid tropics becomes part of the bedload of rivers and can form large depositions downstream, or, in its finest form, as rock powder, spread layers of silt over the land when flooding occurs. Artificial lakes can be filled quickly with these deposits and dams destroyed or silted up by the quantity of weathered material.

Because the rotten rock may extend to considerable depths in the humid tropics, it is often easy to cut new roads. On the other hand it is difficult to quarry sound rock for building purposes. In the tundra the freeze-thaw process affects building. Foundations must be formed at a deeper level than the freeze-thaw zone and this means sinking concrete piles deep into the permafrost to support large buildings. Without deep foundations the buildings would collapse when the ground thaws. The transfer of materials in both regions produces landslides and solifluction but the long period with temperatures below freezing point in the tundra means that these processes only occur for a limited period.

2   Fig. 74 shows a temperate grassland ecosystem. Column A depicts human activities, column B the main compartments of the ecosystem and column C shows changes to the ecosystem resulting from human activities.

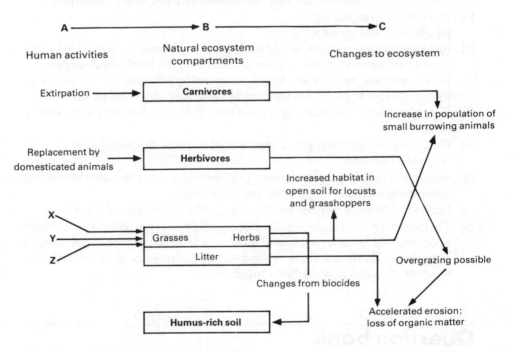

Fig. 74 A temperate grassland ecosystem

(a) Explain the term 'extirpation' in column A.
(b) Using information on the diagram, list two consequences of the introduction of domestic animals.
(c) Explain each of the two consequences.

(d) Give three possible human processes, X, Y and Z (column A), which might affect the grasses and herbs compartment.

(e) Which of the three processes, X, Y or Z, would lead to an increase in the population of small burrowing animals?

(f) Give reasons for your answer to (e).

(g) Name three major areas of temperate grassland.

(h) Explain the meaning of the statement, 'Grassland ecosystems have a much smaller biomass than forest ecosystems.'

(in the style of the University of London School Examinations Board, A Level)

Tutorial note

In contrast to the last question which required an essay-style answer, this question consists of short, structured sections which require short, structured answers. Many examination boards give you a booklet in which to write your answers and sufficient ruled lines after each section on which to write your answer. The chief examiners expect only the space provided to be used and if you run over onto blank paper you will break the rubric. The University of London rubric says, 'your answers should be clearly and concisely expressed and must be confined to the lined spaces provided. Supplementary answer sheets may not be used unless you have made substantial deletions in your answers.' Examiners strictly follow this rubric so that double-lining or work in the margins does not obtain you any further credit. Allowance is, however, made for candidates who cross out work and re-write it in another available space and for candidates who have exceptionally large handwriting.

Suggested answer

(a) The term extirpation means that the carnivores were totally destroyed.

(b) (i) Possible overgrazing.
(ii) Accelerated erosion.

(c) (i) Domesticated animals would be kept for profit and poor land management could result in grazing more animals than the land could support.
(ii) Accelerated erosion will follow overgrazing because the turf mat is no longer present to check the removal of surface soil by wind or water.

(d) X – ploughing; Y – planting grass seed; Z – using herbicides to destroy weeds.

(e) Ploughing and planting grass seed would increase the population of small burrowing animals.

(f) Increase in locust and grasshopper populations as food for some burrowing carnivores. Increase in grass for small herbivores.

(g) Prairies of North America; Veldt of South Africa; Pampas of Argentina.

(h) The biomass is the weight or volume of organic matter per unit area. In a forest ecosystem the biomass is about eight or nine times as great as in a grassland ecosystem. There are more limited nutrient reservoirs in grassland and turnover of nutrients is relatively rapid.

Question bank

1 (Time allowed: 45 minutes)

(a) Explain briefly the differences between mechanical (physical) weathering and chemical weathering, using **one** example of each type of weathering to illustrate your answer.   (4)

Study Figure 75.
(b) Explain why:
(i) the areas of intense chemical weathering usually have a deep mantle of weathered material;
(ii) the tectonically active areas often have thin, or non-existent, weathered mantles. (7)
(c) Describe the types of weathering which are typical of tropical arid areas and discuss the environmental conditions which foster **each** of these types of weathering in tropical arid areas. (9)
(d) Explain how weathering has contributed to the development of landforms in tropical arid areas. (5)

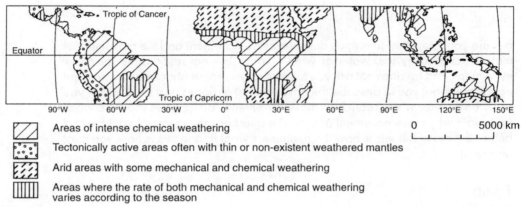

Fig. 75

Areas of intense chemical weathering

Tectonically active areas often with thin or non-existent weathered mantles

Arid areas with some mechanical and chemical weathering

Areas where the rate of both mechanical and chemical weathering varies according to the season

(Joint Matriculation Board, A Level, June 1989)

Pitfalls

Be certain you know what weathering means: do not confuse it with erosion or mass movement. When considering the depth of the mantles in (b) (i) and (ii) do not ignore soil which is part of the weathered mantle. In (b) (ii) do not exaggerate the movement of plates: mass-movement on steep slopes caused by tectonic activity is also important. The most difficult part of the question is (d) and it is inaccurate to stress freeze-thaw weathering in tropical arid environments because temperatures below freezing point only occur in highland regions. More important is chemical weathering causing hydration and exfoliation.

Points

(a) Give clear definitions of each weathering process and one example of each, identifying the area from which the example has been taken, e.g. thermal expansion in the tropics resulting in exfoliation.

(b) Intense chemical weathering takes place in areas with high temperatures and heavy rainfall. List the specific processes and explain how the process goes on throughout the year and is helped by the vegetation cover.
Tectonically active areas are constantly changing so the time factor in the weathering processes is very important. On steep slopes, mass-movement takes place.

(c) The major processes of exfoliation and salt weathering involve a combination of both chemical and mechanical weathering. Recent research has shown that chemical weathering is far more important than had previously been believed. The environmental conditions are not uniform. The coastal regions (Atacama and Namib) experience fogs, providing moisture. Even Death Valley in the interior of California gets 17 days of rain a year and dew frequently forms. Explain temperatures, diurnal ranges, and the resulting temperature extremes.

(d) Landforms such as sand dunes and mushroom rock pedestals are the result of erosion, not weathering. However, the particles causing the erosion were partly formed by weathering. Rock scree in deserts is the result of weathering and rounded domes such as Ayers Rock in Australia, owe their shapes to pressure release and other factors.

2 (Time allowed: 45 mins)

(a) Describe the slope features which result from mass-movement. (10)
(b) Analyse the factors which encourage such movement. (15)

(The Associated Examining Board, A Level, June 1988)

Pitfalls

Be sure you know the difference between mass-movement and the movement of material caused by ice, water or wind – which are not responsible for mass-movement. Part (a) does not ask you to write all you know about mass-movement nor does it want you to describe the development of slopes. Instead it wants you to list the features which result from mass-movement. Part (b) gives you the chance to explain why mass-movement occurs. The question may appear to put the cart before the horse but this is how the examiners want it, and this is how you must answer it.

Points

Describe each slope feature with the aid of an annotated diagram, where possible, and the name of an example or area where it can be seen, e.g. slumping – below cliffs, Walton-on-Naze, Essex.

In part (b) remember types of mass-movements can be classified according to their speed of movement and the amount of water required to assist the movement. Use the following classification for your answer, giving examples and explanatory diagrams where possible: slow movements; more rapid movements; rapid movements; very rapid movements.

3 (Time allowed: 45 minutes)

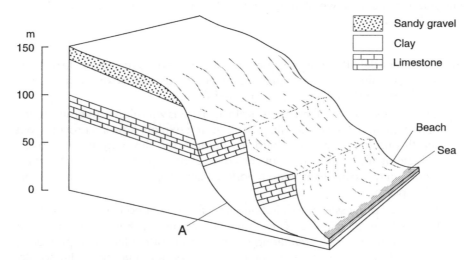

Fig. 76 A section through cliffs

Fig. 76 shows a section through the cliffs on a part of the south coast of England.
(a) What is the name given to (i) this type of slope failure, (ii) the junction at A? (4)

(b) Describe the processes which may lead to this form of slope failure. (8)

(c) Suggest how denudation may further modify the features shown. (7)

(d) In what ways does this form of slope failure cause problems in coastal environments? (6)

(in the style of the Associated Examining Board, A Level)

Pitfalls

This question tests your knowledge of the causes for slope failure of this kind and then asks for its significance as a problem in coastal environments.

There are two important features in the question which you must appreciate. The first is the use of the word 'denudation' in part (c). Denudation means the weathering away of the earth's surface and includes the processes of weathering, mass-movement, erosion and transportation. Consequently you must not confine this part of your answer to erosion which would exclude weathering.

The second feature is the fact that this is a sea cliff, so marine processes will also be active, as well as sub-aerial processes.

Points

The diagram shows a form of rotational slip or slide. The clue is the preponderance of clay, a weak rock between the limestone strata. This sliding takes place along a slip surface.

A number of processes may contribute to rotational slipping. These include gravity, the nature of the rock material and the hydrological conditions which allow for a concentration of sun-surface water. The formation of the rock materials is highly significant, a permeable surface capping, weak, impermeable clays and limestone which can store water.

The presence of the sea may result in the undermining of the soft clays at the base of the cliff but this is unlikely to cause a landslip on the scale shown in the diagram.

In part (b) describe the processes at work emphasising the role of water.

In part (c) the agents of erosion will denude the slope. Remember that the limestone is the most resistant rock present so small cuestas will form where each outcrop occurs. These outcrops will slowly retreat and further rotational sliding may occur. The capping of sandy gravel is likely to be partly removed by being washed down the slope. Marine processes will weaken the lower strata, remove material and steepen the slope, producing conditions favourable to further mass-movement.

Part (d) is concerned with the results of cliff failure on nearby human activities such as roads, housing and other features of the built environment. There are also the problems of erosion of the coastline by the sea and the deposition elsewhere of the eroded material.

4 (Time allowed: 45 mins)

(a) Define the following hydrological characteristics:
    (i)   interception (2)
    (ii)   evaporation (2)
    (iii) infiltration (2)

(b) Discuss the significance of the above hydrological characteristics to the production of:
    (i)   surface run-off in a drainage basin; (5)
    (ii)   throughflow in a drainage basin. (5)

(c) Explain, illustrating your answer with specific examples, how human activity may modify the hydrological characteristics listed in (a) and (b). (9)

(University of Oxford Delegacy of Local Examinations, A Level, June 1990)

Pitfalls

When writing down the definitions in part (a) you must give a clear explanation which is also succinct. The key words in (c) are 'illustrating your answer with specific examples'. Marks are easily lost for ignoring examples.

Points

Keep your answers to part (a) fairly short, for example, 'Interception – The capture of drops of rain by the leaves, branches and stems of plants. The amount of interception that takes place depends on the character of the vegetation and the duration and intensity of the rainfall.'

In (b) you may find that a diagram helps you with your explanations.

In part (c) do not forget to give examples. Deforestation may be one of the human activities you quote to show evidence of modification of the hydrological characteristics. An example would be the hills of Assam and Nepal, with an acceleration of flooding in Bangladesh.

5 (Time allowed: 25 mins)

Study Fig. 77 which shows a highland region after glaciation.

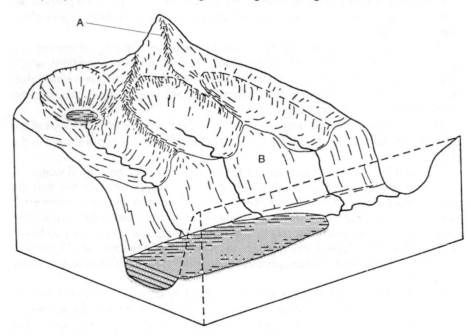

Fig 77 A highland region after glaciation

(a) (i) Name the features marked: A and B   (1)
(ii) Explain, with the aid of diagrams, how each feature you have named in (a) (i) has been formed.   (10)
(b) Describe the distinguishing features of a corrie.   (6)
(c) Explain why some parts of a glaciated valley are often more deeply eroded by ice than other parts of the valley.   (8)

(University of London School Examinations Board, A Level, June 1991)

Pitfalls

The examiner's report states that many candidates had little idea on the formation of the features and that the diagrams were often better than the text. As usual, some candidates failed to read the question with sufficient care with the result that in (b) they gave accounts of formation rather than a description of features. Some explanations were too vague and did not fully answer the question as a result.

Points

Feature A is an arête, while feature B is a truncated spur.

An arête is formed when two adjacent cirques erode backwards or sidewards towards each other. The headwalls of the cirques eventually meet leaving a knife-like ridge between them. Explain the shattering, sapping and grinding which causes this erosion.

A truncated spur is formed when morainic material being carried in the main valley glacier removes the tips of pre-glacial interlocking spurs, leaving steep, cliff-like truncated spurs.

In (b) the distinguishing features of a corrie should be described in sentences and also shown on an accompanying diagram. They should include the steep backwall, rock basin and bergschrund.

(c) This can be tackled from the microscale of striations and differential erosion caused by variations in the rock structure of the valley, to the macroscale of differing ice advances.

6 (Time allowed: 15 mins)

Study the cross-section of an idealised beach of shingle and sand.

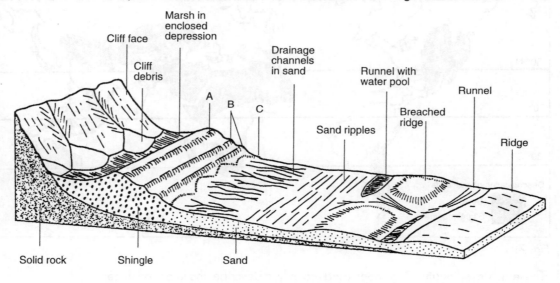

After Collard. R. (1988). *The Physical Geography of Landscape*, Unwin Hyman

Fig. 78 A cross-section of an idealised beach of shingle and sand

(a) Name the features labelled A, B and C on the cross-section. (3)
(b) (i) What physical conditions give rise to the feature labelled A? (2)
     (ii) What conditions give rise to the feature labelled B? (2)
(c) Outline **two** ways in which the supply of material to the beach may be altered. (4)
(d) For one named example, explain why and how the amount of material on a beach has been artificially maintained. (4)

(The Associated Examining Board, A Level, June 1991)

Pitfalls

Be careful when you identify the features in (a), you must know the correct terms otherwise you will not receive marks. For example, it is no good saying that A is a shingle ridge – it must be identified as the storm beach. The features are not formed by longshore drift but by wave actions. In (d) you must give details in your case study, identifying the place, give specific information about the methods used and the reasons.

Points

In part (a) A is storm beach; B shows berms, marking the limits of successively lower tides; C is the residue from the last high tide.

A is formed by wave action during a storm. The energy in the wave carries shingle high up the beach and deposits it.

B is formed by wave action during the spring high tide and subsequent tides which are not as high.

Supply of material to the beach may be altered by human action – the construction of groynes; sea defences, dredging and by physical processes such as a cliff-fall.

Choose an example you know well and name it. Seaside resorts often have to take drastic measures to retain their beach material and you may know of such action at a resort you have visited recently. Describe what changes have taken place and why they were necessary to stop the beach from disappearing.

7 (Time allowed: 25 mins)

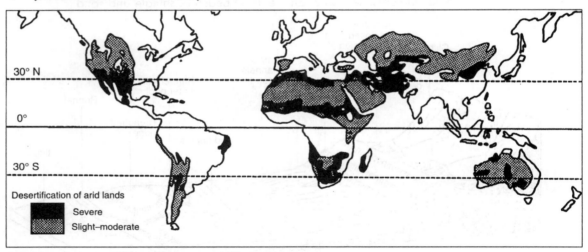

Fig. 79

The term 'desertification' has been used recently to describe 'the impoverishment of arid and semi-arid areas by the combined impact of man's activities and drought. These changes can be measured by reduced productivity of desirable plants, alterations in the flora and fauna, accelerated soil deterioration, and increased hazards for human occupancy.' (H E Dregne).

(a) Examine reference map Fig. 79.
    (i) Briefly describe the world distribution of areas of severe desertification
    (ii) Explain how desertification develops.   (10)
(b) Outline the physical, social and economic consequences of desertification in an area you have studied.   (10)
(c) With reference to specific examples, discuss the attempts being made to reduce the harmful effects of desertification.   (10)

(Scottish Certificate of Education, Higher Grade, Specimen question paper for Geography in and after 1991)

Pitfalls

Look carefully at the map because desertification in its most severe form does not take place in arid areas but in semi-arid areas which, in most cases, are on the margins of true deserts. It can occur on the margins of cold deserts, as in northern China, as well as hot deserts, as in north Africa. Desertification is not caused by one set of factors – you should know of short-term and long-term factors.

Note the key words in (b) 'physical, social and economic', and in (c) 'specific examples'.

Points

(a) When answering you should mention that main areas of severe desertification are within the tropics and marginal to arid areas such as the Sahara desert. Exceptions are the areas in north China and the southern states of the Commonwealth of Independent States. An area in north-east Brazil is not adjacent to an arid area.

(b) Desertification is caused by deforestation, overgrazing, farming leading to soil erosion and lower amounts of incoming radiation being deflected (the albedo or reflection coefficient). Deforestation and overgrazing increase the albedo, reducing the possibility of cloud formation and rainfall. The inter-tropical convergence zone (ITCZ) may also be a contributory cause. Some people believe it has failed to migrate as far as normal in recent years, being replaced by the easterly jet stream which consists of subsiding, dry air.

(c) The effects of desertification are extensive. They include famine, conflict (over land and water), migration, reductions in the standard of living and disease. Take one example you have studied such as the Sahel and give specific information about conditions there and what is being done to alleviate the problem.

8 (Time allowed: 45 mins)

(a) Define the term *air mass*. (3)

(b) Describe and explain the basis of air mass classification. (4)

(c) Choose any **two** of the major types of air masses which affect the British Isles. For **each** of the air masses that you have chosen, state its name and give a reasoned account of the weather associated with its occurrence. In your answer you should refer to diurnal, seasonal and regional variations which may be evident. (15)

(Joint Matriculation Board, A level, June 1990)

Pitfalls

To obtain full marks in (a) you must give some idea of the size of an air mass or describe the horizontal element of uniformity. Do not just describe it as 'a parcel of air'.

In part (a) it is not sufficient to describe an air mass as 'warm' or 'hot' without specifying temperatures or time of year.

When describing the weather of a particular air mass, relate it to the stability or instability of the air mass. Air masses do not occur throughout the year and you must relate weather conditions produced by an air mass to a season when it occurs. For example, Pc air rarely occurs over Britain in summer.

Points

An air mass is a mass of air with similar properties of temperature and moisture covering a large area of the earth's surface.

(b) requires a detailed explanation of how an air mass assumes the temperature and properties of the region where it is formed. When air masses move from their source regions they are modified by the surface over which they pass. Give the five major air mass types which influence British weather and briefly describe their characteristics.

In (c) elaborate on the two air masses you have chosen and give clear accounts of the weather associated with each, mentioning temperatures, precipitation, diurnal, seasonal and regional differences.

9 (Time allowed: 18 mins)

(a) Study reference map Fig. 80.
     Describe the soil-forming processes which lead to the formation of **either** podsols **or** brown forest soils.   (5)

(b) Explain why temperate deciduous forest landscapes have been subjected to much greater change, as a result of human activity, than coniferous forest landscapes.   (5)

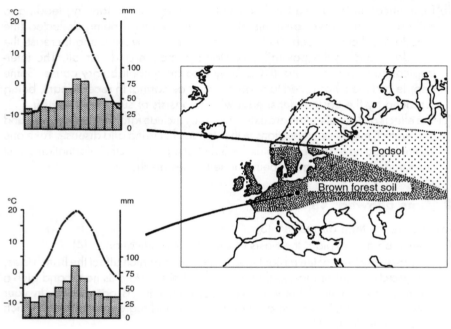

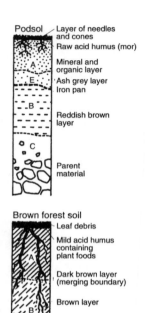

Fig. 80

(Scottish Examination Board, Higher Grade, May 1991)

Pitfalls

Do not spend all your time when answering (a) describing just one or two soil-forming processes. Remember that there are five main factors involved in soil formation and they are closely interconnected and interdependent. They are: parent material, climate, topography, organisms and time. Follow the rubric and write about either podsol or brown forest soils formation.

In part (b) do not fall into the trap of saying that deciduous trees are of greater value to humans, or that they are easier than coniferous trees to cut down. The clues to the answer are to be found on the temperature charts in the diagram, knowledge of the soils and the effects of the tree cover on those soils.

Points

In (a) make your choice carefully and describe the climate, the influence of that climate on vegetation cover, earthworms, bacteria, and the soil-forming processes. Then describe the influence on the soil of the vegetation cover.

In (b), mention that human activities which make the greatest changes to vegetation cover are initially connected with farming. Explain why brown forest soils contain the nutrients plants need in much larger quantities than are to be found in podsols. Explain how podsol acid humus contains little plant food and the climate limits organisms. As a result, podsols, unlike brown forest soils, are not naturally fertile.

10 (Time allowed: 45 mins)

Ecosystems are subject to human interference. What adaptations do ecosystems make in such circumstances?

(Oxford and Cambridge Schools Examination Board, A Level, June 1991)

Pitfalls

You can easily fall into the trap of reading the first part of the question, writing an answer about various forms of human interference, and then find you cannot give a satisfactory description of the adaptations which ecosystems make to this interference. The key word in the question is 'adaptations' and if this is an area you know little about, it is best to select another question.

Points

Give a brief definition of an ecosystem and point out that human interference can affect the atmosphere (e.g. acid rain), landscape (e.g. soil erosion) and the ecology (e.g. use of fertilisers and pesticides). Humans interfere with ecosystems by directing the energy and material cycles in ecosystems towards themselves. The larger part of your answer must be concerned with the adaptations ecosystems make to specific examples of human interference. For example, cutting down deciduous woodland for the timber can result in the development of a primary succession. After several stages this will result in the return of the climax vegetation. This type of succession will occur in other circumstances such as the burning of heathland and overgrazing by animals. Some specific examples are:

- Destruction of the bison on the North American prairies resulted in the growth of taller grasses because the grazing animals had disappeared.
- The introduction of nitrates from field fertilisers into lakes and rivers will kill some species but promote the growth of others, such as algae.

HUMAN GEOGRAPHY

Units in this chapter

Chapter objectives

When you have studied the units in this chapter you should be able to:

• describe and explain the ways in which population changes;

• understand the different types of population movement and the reasons why they occur;

• appreciate the different types, locations and functions of rural settlement and the factors leading to changes in the functions, character and density of rural settlement;

• understand the concepts of central place theory, hierarchies of settlements and the Christaller model;

• offer explanations for the development of specialised functional zones in urban environments;

• explain, with the aid of models, the nature and causes of urban growth and zoning;

• appreciate the problems related to cities and the attempts to provide solutions to these problems;

• understand the factors influencing agricultural land use and the relevance of Von Thünen's models;

• describe the factors influencing industrial location and Weber's model of industrial location;

• understand the importance and limitations of different types of transport; the concept of a transport network and the factors which influence network patterns;

• appreciate the different ways in which inequalities of economic development can be measured and describe the various strategies for development which have been adopted;

• have an understanding of differing human responses to contrasting opportunities and constraints in different environments.

Relevance of the units

This chapter focuses on the interactions of humans with the environment. It examines the spatial patterns and processes resulting from the decisions made by people about their environment. These are influenced by factors which may vary according to time and place. Human decisions are affected by physical, social, economic, historical and political factors. For example, the decision where to build a factory for producing microchips depends on the physical suitability of the site, the availability of a suitable workforce and the economic advantages of the location, some of which may relate to the historical development of the area. Political and financial factors, such as low interest loans to encourage location in an area of high unemployment, may also help to determine where the factory is built.

Human geography deals with the world around us and studying it will make you more aware of contemporary issues and problems. It will provide you with background information about topical events, be they local, national or international. The relevance of the material in these units becomes self-evident when you read or hear about such topics as inner cities, migration between countries or attempts to reduce poverty in developing countries.

Key ideas and concepts

The theme of interrelationships which we explored in Chapter 2 is continued throughout this chapter. This theme is best understood, where relevant, within a systems approach. Whereas physical geography is mainly concerned with scientific facts, many aspects of human geography can be interpreted in a variety of ways. For example, there are different models to explain economic development and a number of strategies are being used to encourage development. In other words, there are different perspectives about development which you need to understand. You will find that units dealing with topics where different perspectives can be identified contain information at the end of the unit about these perspectives.

There are a number of key concepts which are essential to the understanding of human geography. The concept of urbanisation is very important, partly because of the association with industrialisation and competition for space. Population movement is another key area which may take a number of forms including movement from or to cities, and from periphery to core areas. Economic activities give rise to a number of key concepts including the concepts of optimum location and regional concentration. Many other concepts and key ideas will be found in the units which follow. Remember that some of them, for example, development, are multi-dimensional. This means they can only be fully understood by examining a range of processes, models, strategies and alternative solutions.

3.1 POPULATION GROWTH AND DISTRIBUTION

POPULATION GROWTH

Population growth is the sum of population changes due to natural increase and population changes due to migration. Both these variables may have positive or negative effects upon growth. Natural increase is the difference between the birth rate and the death rate. This may also be positive or negative. For example, if the death rate exceeds the birth rate the total population (ignoring the effects of migration) will fall, so the natural increase then has a negative value.

Fig. 81 shows how rapidly world population has grown since 1750. Before that time the total population was fairly stable but over the last two hundred years the rate of growth has become increasingly rapid.

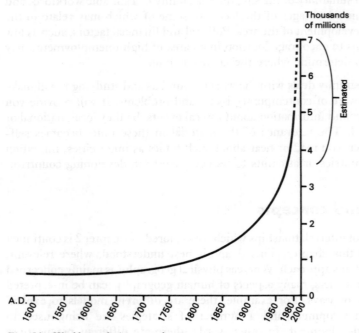

Fig. 81 World population growth

Reasons for this growth include:
1. The creation of modern economic systems as a result of the Agricultural and Industrial Revolutions (see the demographic transition model in Unit 4.3.)
2. The vast increase in medical knowledge has increased the proportion of babies born live (out of the total number of births) and decreased death rates.
3. Modern technology and communications have enabled us to tackle and overcome the worst effects of floods, famine and other natural hazards.

World population is very unevenly distributed. One-fifth of the world's population is in China. The people of China and India together make up one-third of the total population of the world.

There are two main clusters of people in the world – one in the western hemisphere between 40° and 60° north (Europe and North America) and one in the eastern hemisphere between 20° and 40° north.

Three-quarters of the population of the world now live in developing countries and it is in these countries that population growth is the most rapid.

The features of world population distribution do not correlate neatly with physical conditions. Eighty per cent of the world's population occupy 10% of the earth's surface. It is possible to say that most people live in warm, humid, lowland areas (90% of humanity lives at altitudes less than 450 m above sea level). But it is only possible to make very broad generalisations. This is because the environment is a complex of potentialities of which different cultures and societies at different levels of technological advance make changing use.

The distribution of population is the expression of all the factors that affect human societies. These factors may be divided into three broad categories:

❶ **Biological factors** include sex, age, race, morbidity (prevalence and types of diseases);

❷ **Social factors** i.e. place of residence, occupation, socioeconomic class, place of birth, religion, nationality;

❸ **Dynamic factors** i.e. birth rates, death rates, migrations out of and into a given area.

Any explanation of a pattern of distribution has to be historical in nature. It is only through the operation of processes over time and under conditions which prevailed in the past that present day features came into being, e.g. the distribution of people and cities in northern England at present is basically the result of the importance of coal as the raw material which enabled rapid industrialisation in the eighteenth and nineteenth centuries.

Economic factors generally have a more direct effect on distribution patterns than do characteristics of the physical environment. This is partly because the nature of an economy determines the extent to which a group of people controls the physical features of the region in which they live. As resources are exploited, markets develop and technological changes occur, the distribution of population can alter dramatically. For example, prior to industrialisation the distribution of population in Chile reflected the farming opportunities provided by the physical factors of relief and climate. The introduction of mining in the Atacama has resulted in roughly nine times as many people living in one of the driest deserts of the world than live in the cool, temperate highland region of south Chile.

Another reason is that a particular economic system may lead to a distribution of population and densities regardless of variations in the physical landscape. For example, in the USA 70% of the people live in a vast urban area which has little direct relationship to the physical nature of the land occupied.

AGE STRUCTURE OF THE POPULATION

The age structure of a population is the proportion of people who fall into particular age categories. Each category usually spans five years. This data is usually represented by **population pyramids**.

Fig. 82 is two pyramids which show contrasting patterns of population structure found in the world today. The pyramid for the developing country (A) shows a large infant population but as one moves up the pyramid each consecutive age category gets smaller. So only a small proportion of the total population is more than 50 years of age. In contrast, the population pyramid for a country like the United Kingdom (B) is very different. It is not a pyramid in the geometrical sense for each age category is very like the others until the age of about 60.

The shape of the pyramid is important because population growth and life in a society are affected by the proportion of people in different categories. For example if there are many old or many young people in a country the number of workers may be comparatively small i.e. there is a **high dependency rate**. In a society with many young children there will be a need for resources to be used for education, health care, etc. and for consumer goods such as children's clothes, toys and books. Where there are many old people in the population resources are required to provide pensions, nursing homes, etc.

The stabilisation model (the 'S' curve model)

This model assumes that population growth will continue for some time but that then there is an eventual reduction of the growth rate. The graph of such growth shows an 'S' curve which has three main parts. The base represents a period of relatively slow population growth, a steeply inclined portion represents rapid growth and the third portion represents the period in which the rate of population growth declines.

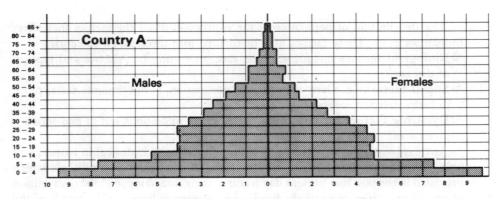

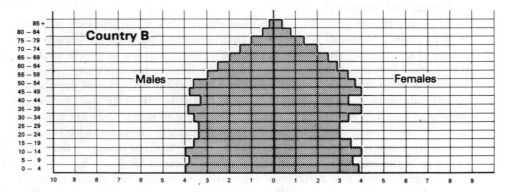

Fig. 82 Population pyramids typical of a developing country and a developed country

The reduction in growth leads to a stabilisation of population at a size which can be supported by the environmental system. Stabilisation is achieved when birth rates and death rates are in equilibrium (balanced).

The rapid growth and rapid decline model (the 'J' curve model)

This model also assumes that the population will continue to grow (see Fig. 83). Instead of stabilising within the capacity of the environment, however, the model envisages the population increasing until it 'overshoots' the environment's capacity to carry the population. This results in a catastrophic decline in population. This is a 'J' curve growth pattern. It is argued that as the world's non-renewable resources are used up, the productive base of agriculture, industry and services will collapse. Food shortages and environmental degradation will lead to a major rise in death rates and a rapid population decline.

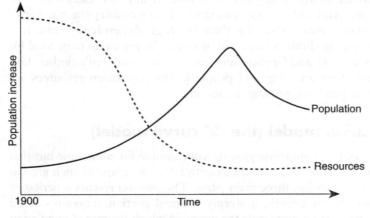

Fig. 83 The rapid growth and rapid decline model

DEPENDENCY RATIOS

The dependency ratio is one way of judging how far a country can be economically active. It takes into account the fact that in any country there is a proportion of the population that is not economically active and that the proportion of active to non-active can vary significantly from one country to another.

- The economically inactive or non-active are in the main the very young and the very old. The categories are those under 15 and those over 65. This is a very rough guide since in many developing countries children earn money as soon as they are able while in Britain they remain at school until they are 16.
- The economically active are those of working age i.e. aged 15–64.

The dependency ratio formula:

$$\frac{\text{Number of children } 0-14 \ + \text{ number of elderly 65 and over}}{\text{those of working age}} \times 100$$

The dependency ratio applied to the UK (population figures in millions).

$$1971 \quad \frac{13.39 + 10.51}{31.62} \times 100 = 75.59$$

$$1981 \quad \frac{11.46 + 11.02}{32.64} \times 100 = 68.87$$

$$1990 \quad \frac{13.16 + 12.02}{32.63} \times 100 = 77.17$$

In 1971, therefore, for every 100 people of working age, 75.59 depended on them. In 1981 the ratio had fallen to 68.87 because the larger elderly population was offset by a fall in the number of children. By 1990 the increase in both the elderly and the number of children had raised the ratio again. The dependency ratio does not take account of those who are unemployed.

In contrast, for Nigeria the ratio is:

$$1990 \quad \frac{49.92 + 4.34}{54.28} \times 100 = 99.96$$

This is typical of a developing country with its non-active group containing a high proportion of young children.

For most developed countries the dependency ratio is usually between 50 and 70; for developing countries it is often over 100.

POPULATION CONTROL

CASE STUDY: CHINA

The population of the world has doubled in the last 37 years and will grow by another billion by the end of the century. The total population of the world is about 5.4 billion. Many countries will experience massive population growth for years to come but some, like China, have implemented strong population controls. As a result, whereas in 1978 it was calculated that the population of China in 2000 AD would be as large as that of the world in 1980, it is now forecast that China's population will level off at a manageable 1.5 billion (1 500 000 000).

Reasons for the population control policy

In 1975 the average family in China had three children. It was calculated that if this family size was maintained the Chinese population could rise to 5 billion during the twenty-first century. So in 1979 it was decided that the ideal family should have one child only which meant that the total population would be kept down to 1200 million by the year 2000.

The policy of one child per family had its greatest effect in the big cities. By 1984, 90% of the babies born in Beijing (Peking) were first children and by 1986 there were 35 million single-child families in China. Eighty-three per cent of the families in the chief cities: Beijing, Shanghai, Tianjin and Guangzhou (Canton) had one child but in the countryside, where the policy was resisted, only 62% of the families had one child.

How the policy was implemented

It was strictly enforcd by the central government through a policy which included:
- incentives for having only one child;
- fines or extra taxes for having two or more children;
- peer group pressure in the villages to discourage bigger families;
- constant propaganda of the virtue of small families;
- forced abortions and sterilisation if necessary.

Why the policy was less successful in the rural areas

- Large families are traditional.
- Farming families find children a valuable source of free labour.
- Male babies are greatly prized, so if a girl was born first the family wants to have another baby in the hope it will be a boy.
- Families are prepared to pay the fines to have a boy child and to have a large family.
- As peasants became more prosperous, the taxes and fines were not so burdensome anyway.

Some compromises were therefore made. Rural families were allowed to have two children but were discouraged from having three. In 1986 a new policy allowed a second child if the first born was a girl. As a result, in 1987 14 million more children were born than the planners had anticipated.

Some dangers in maintaining the one-child policy

❶ The 1-2-4 family: 1 grandchild, 2 parents, 4 grandparents was becoming the common pattern and it was realised that the population would not replace itself. One estimate suggested that in the twenty-first century the population of China could fall back to 370 million.

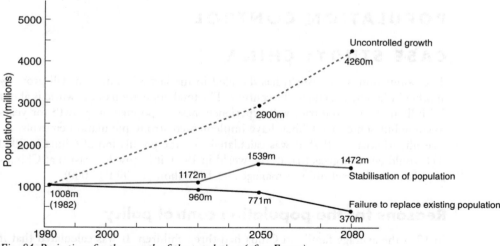

Fig. 84 Projections for the growth of the population (after Fraser)

❷ The population would have an age imbalance: as the present adults grow old there would be relatively fewer young people to become the economically active population.

❸ Enforced control could cause social unrest.

❹ Girl babies are undervalued. Some first-born girls have been killed, sickly ones neglected. If a girl died the family could try again for a boy. Infanticide of girl babies is still being reported from remote regions of China.

Conclusion

Other countries have adopted less strict policies which have been succesful. For example, in Thailand in 1965, the average Thai woman had 6–7 children; now the figure is 2.3. This was achieved through education, health care, establishing reasonable rights for women and making contraception easily available. In educating women to plan their families they have also created a better-educated workforce for the modern industries which the country is developing.

DIFFERENT PERSPECTIVES AND DEMOGRAPHIC TRANSITION

Malthusian perspective and demographic transition perspective model

See Unit 4.3.

Biological perspective

The growth of population of living organisms seems to follow generalised patterns. The population of any species seems unable to grow indefinitely. Population growth is eventually checked by factors such as the depletion of essential resources. For human beings, food supply and the availability of living space are important limiting factors. So the identification of the prevalent growth pattern is important. If human population is not stabilised there may be a catastrophic decline of world population if it overshoots the carrying capacity of the environment. Campaigns to recycle non-renewable resources, to limit pollution, etc. are attempts to maintain the present level of carrying capacity.

Biologists also see **population regulation** in human populations. There appears to be an intrinsic self-regulating mechanism in some species. By this process a natural population size will be reached and maintained unless significant changes take place in the environment. In technologically underdeveloped societies in the past the human population grew very slowly (see the graph on page 148) and many societies were probably stable.

Social perspective

In examining the relationship between population and resources a critical issue which arises is that of population control. In some countries such as India and China, official campaigns have been mounted to encourage people to practise birth control in order to limit population growth. In contrast, in other countries, e.g. the Catholic countries of South America, the Church and governments oppose such measures so population growth is unchecked despite the social and economic problems which could result. Cultural factors can also affect attitudes and policies, e.g. in Nigeria a large family is regarded as a status symbol so people are reluctant to limit family size.

3.2 POPULATION MOVEMENT

DEFINITIONS

Migration cannot be defined simply. It is generally defined as a permanent or semi-permanent movement on the part of an individual or group of people. If this definition is accepted, migration involves two things:
- going to a new place to live;
- staying there for a certain amount of time.

This cannot be a hard and fast definition, e.g. university students satisfy both these conditions but are not regarded as migrants.

There are varied ideas about how long a person must move away from home to become a migrant. As far as international migration is concerned the United Nations defines **permanent** migration as removal from a former place of residence for one year. On the other hand, one in five of the gastarbeiter (guest workers) in Germany lived there for more than seven years but were still regarded as **temporary** migrants.

Within Britain the census definition of migration is movement from one local administrative area to another within one to five years prior to the census.

CLASSIFICATION OF MIGRATIONS

In order to define more clearly and to understand the different types of movement involved in migration, different classifications have been developed.

Scale classification is based upon the distance travelled and the nature of the movements, e.g.

international	(Jamaica to Brixton)
inter-regional	(NE England to the SW peninsula)
inter-urban	(Belfast to London)
rural-urban	(Scottish Highlands to Edinburgh)
intra-urban	(Southall to Barnet)

Movements may also be classified according to the purpose of the movement, e.g.

economic	(to a new job in Canada)
forced	(Ugandan Asians)
leisure/retirement	(New York to the sun belt of the South-West)
religion and culture	(Jews to Israel)

Time classification is based on the length of time spent in a new location. The major subdivisions are into recurrent (repeated) and non-recurrent movements.

Return migration is a movement away from the place of residence followed by a return to the point of origin (e.g. circulatory movements of African migrant workers to S. African mines; British contract workers in the Middle East).

Emigration is a change of habitat with no return. **Nomadism** is a constant change of movement with cyclical paths (Bedouins).

MODELS OF MIGRATION

The 'Laws' of migration (1885)

The earliest model of migration was Ravenstein's 'Laws' of migration which list persistent regularities which characterise the areas of origins, destinations and migrants themselves:

❶ The majority of migrants go only a short distance.

❷ Migration proceeds step by step.

❸ Migrants going long distances generally prefer to go to one of the great centres of commerce or industry.

❹ Each current of migration encourages a compensatory counter-current.

❺ Townspeople are less migratory than people from rural areas.

❻ Females are more migratory than males within the kingdom of their birth, but males more frequently venture beyond.

❼ Most migrants are adults; families rarely migrate out of their countries of birth.

❽ Large towns grow more by migration than by natural increase.

❾ Migration increases in volume as industries and commerce develop and transport improves.

❿ The major direction of migration is from the agricultural areas to the centre of industry and commerce.

⓫ The major causes of migration are economic.

The gravity model

It is a fundamental fact that most migrations take place over relatively short distances. There are relatively few long-range movers. This model is based on the premise that migration is some function of distance:

$$I = fD$$

I = migration interaction

D = distance

Migration occurs according to the degree of attraction of a region or location. The volume of migration depends upon the population of the two localities involved and the distance between them, i.e.

$$M_{ij} = \frac{P_i P_j}{d_{ij}}$$

M_{ij} = migration between i and j

$\left.\begin{array}{l} P_i \\ P_j \end{array}\right\}$ = population of the 2 centres

d_{ij} = distance between them

The weakness of the model is that although the function of distance is an important factor, there are other variables which also influence the movements, e.g. other competing locations may also attract the migrants (intervening opportunities). And some of the greatest migrations recorded have occurred for reasons unrelated to the gravity model.

Intervening opportunities model (Stouffer)

This model attempts to translate the distance factor into social as well as economic terms. Stouffer argued that the number of migrants over a distance was **directly** related to the number of 'opportunities' at that distance and **inversely related** to the number of intervening opportunities which exist:

$$I_{ij} = \frac{(P_i P_j)}{(O_{ij})(C_{ij})}$$

I and P as above

O_{ij} = number of intervening opportunities

C_{ij} = number of competing migrants

This model is more elaborate than the simple gravity model but it is still descriptive. It does not explain the causes of migration nor take into account other significant variables.

151

Multivariate analysis models (e.g. Olsson)

Olsson showed that there were five variables with significant relationship with the function of distance:

❶ the level of income at place of out-migration;

❷ the size of place of in-migration;

❸ the size of place of out-migration;

❹ the level of unemployment at place of out-migration;

❺ the level of unemployment at place of in-migration.

A systems approach to migration

Some writers explain the process of migration in terms of systems theory. A potential migrant receives stimuli from his environment, to which he may or may not respond. There are two sub-systems – the urban control sub-system and the rural sub-system. The urban control sub-system includes factors such as the organisation of employment and the city administration. The rural sub-system includes family, community beliefs and inheritance laws. As movement occurs adjustments take place and the information flows become important. The importance of this model is that it demonstrates that a variety of interrelated factors lead to population movements.

GENERAL FEATURES OF MIGRATION

* **Migration is one of the processes leading to the redistribution of world population.** For example, in the nineteenth century Europe had a net loss of 40 million people through migration.

* **Migration may be viewed as an adjustment to economic inequalities.** The key motivation may be the better job opportunities that may exist in the receiving place. These inequalities may be different regional employment rates within a country (e.g. Northern Ireland compared with south-east England) or international. They may have a 'push' effect (movement from an overpopulated country) or a 'pull' effect (the attraction of Third World cities to the rural poor).

* **There are regularities in the patterns of movement.** At present, on a world scale, rural-urban movement (urbanisation) is dominant, but now the population of inner cities is declining. The movements are **age and sex selective** – it is predominantly young men who migrate. This is partly because, in wage-earning economies, most of the jobs that exist are for male workers and partly because in most societies, men are still the chief wage earners. Another influencing factor is that in many rural societies, the young men have greater independence than the young women, and so are freer to move.

    Traditionally, immigrants take up jobs which are the least attractive to the indigenous population, e.g. in Britain in the 1960s immigrants took shift work in textile mills, jobs on buses and trains, hospital work, etc. These are usually the lower-paid jobs and are concentrated in the cities. A poor migrant who then finds a low-paid job is not able to afford to move his family and rent a home for them until he has worked long enough to save the money needed. This is another reason why, in the first instance, men migrate alone. In some countries the wives stay at home to maintain the traditional way of life and to farm the land, e.g. in Kenya, Kikuyu wives stay in the rural village while their husbands migrate to Nairobi looking for well-paid work.

* **Movement from the less well-off regions is controlled.** Migration may be prohibited by the more advanced regions which do not welcome large-

scale immigration of people of lower socioeconomic status. The USA operates a quota system to control immigration; Australia previously had a 'White Australia' policy; New Zealand and Canada favour skilled workers; our immigration laws limit immigration from the new Commonwealth.

Movement out of conurbations in the UK

Table 8 summarises changes in the populations of the major metropolitan areas of the UK in the last twenty years. The most distinctive feature is that for both ten-year periods shown, every area listed suffered population loss. The losses are

Table 8 *Changes in population 1971–91*

	1971 pop. 000s	1971–81 % change	1981 pop. 000s	1981–91 % change	1991 pop. 000s
Greater London	7,452.3	–10.5	6,696.2	–4.75	6,377.9
Inner London	3,031.9	–17.65	2,496.8	–5.88	2,349.9
Greater Manchester	2,728.8	–4.91	2,594.7	–5.39	2,454.8
Merseyside	1,656.5	–8.66	1,513.1	–9.01	1,376.8
South Yorkshire	1,322.5	–1.57	1,301.8	–4.09	1,248.5
Tyne & Wear	1,211.7	–5.65	1,143.2	–4.92	1,087.0
W Midlands	2,793.3	–5.27	2,646.1	–5.55	2,499.3
W Yorkshire	2,067.6	–1.46	2,037.4	–2.59	1,984.7
Glasgow	982.3	–22.06	765.6	–14.51	654.5

not even, however. Merseyside suffered the greatest proportion decline in England for both periods but the Merseyside losses were by no means as great as the losses experienced by Glasgow. The movement out of the cities in part reflects the decline of the the manufacturing base of the UK, for the largest cities were the centres of traditional industries. The losses also reflect the decline of the inner city areas, e.g. Inner London had significantly greater percentage losses than Greater London as a whole. The figures also reflect the movement of modern industries to green belt sites and to attractive smaller towns. It also includes the suburbanisation of the population as those who can afford to do so, move to the fringes of the cities.

The contrast between the metropolitan areas and the regions that have attracted new industries and immigrants can be seen by comparing the table above with that for two counties in two relatively prosperous regions – Buckinghamshire (SE region) and Cambridgeshire (East Anglia). Comparable percentage changes for the 1971–91 period are:

Table 9

	1971–81 % change	1981–91 % change
Buckinghamshire	+18.84	+9.49
Cambridgeshire	+13.35	+11.80

CAUSES FOR MIGRATION IN A DEVELOPING AND A DEVELOPED REGION

Below are surveys of migrants in very different circumstances. Table 10 summarises the reasons why rural migrants moved into Monteagudo district of Bolivia which is more fertile than surrounding mountain areas. Table 11 summarises the results of a survey in Wisconsin in 1974 when city dwellers were asked what factors had made them move home.

Table 10 *Reasons for migration to Monteagudo*

	%
Poor land	38.89
Livestock diseases	10.19
Lack of pasture	8.50
Large family	3.70
Family already in Monteagudo	4.63
Family problems	13.00
Give children education	8.30
Forced to leave former home	9.26
Other reasons	3.53
	100

(Adapted from White and Woods, 1980)

Table 11 *Reasons for moving home in Wisconsin*

	%
Change in family circumstances	26.8
Wanted cheaper housing	6.5
Wanted different type of house or tenancy	19.5
Wanted change in space and quality	23.6
More convenient location	4.6
Wanted better neighbourhood	9.6
Had to leave	9.4
	100

(After McCarthy, 1976)

Certain elements are common. In both surveys some had been forced to move. Changes in family circumstances were also important to both groups. Whereas the farming population in the developing country was essentially concerned with making a living and providing better opportunities for their children, the American migrants were able to give social and quality of life factors more importance.

Case study: Migration in the USA

Three key types of movements are shown in Fig. 85.

❶ **International migration** from neighbouring territories. Although Canadians move southwards across the border, attracted by milder climates and greater opportunities for work, the major pressure is in the South, especially from Mexico and Central America. Some of the immigration from Mexico is illegal but despite constant efforts to control movement, large numbers of 'wet backs' enter the USA each year. The long USA/Mexican border is difficult to seal without investing considerable resources and since the USA purchases oil and other products from Mexico, it is not disposed to imposing harsh restrictions.

❷ **Movement to the sunbelt** The cities of the South and West are the new magnets for Americans leaving the decaying old industrial regions of the North-East seaboard and the Chicago and Detroit manufacturing region. Some migrate, seasonally attracted by the warm winters, and are known as 'snowbirds'. The move to the sunbelt is an extension of a much older

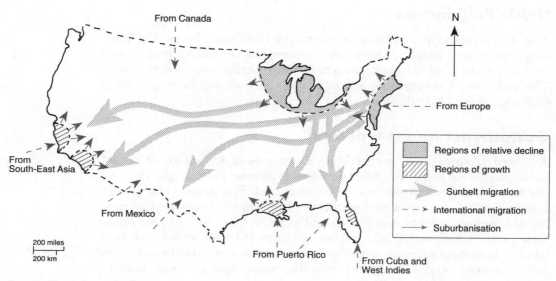

Fig. 85 Migration in the USA

migration pattern of retired people from New York and the North–East to Florida. Between 1980 and 1989 the South and West absorbed 87% of the nation's growth. These regions now contain 55% of the total population (48% in 1970).

❸ **Decentralisation from the large cities** Increasing numbers of Americans choose to live in suburbs and on the fringes of cities. Each major urban region has an outward flow of migrants to more rural areas. The migrants are often the well-educated, well-paid members of communities and the cities they leave behind are impoverished financially and socially as those who can afford costlier services leave. In the older regions the cities decline as the suburbs grow. In the expanding sunbelt the cities grow but the suburbs grow even faster (Table 12).

Table 12   *Changes in population 1970–1980*

	% Total urban areas	% Central areas of cities	% Suburbs
USA as a whole	−6.9	−4.9	+10.0
Declining regions			
North-East	−4.9	−12.3	+1.0
North-Central	+0.3	−14.1	+10.5
Sunbelt regions			
South	+19.8	+2.4	+35.3
West	+17.7	+8.1	+10.0

(after Carr)

GENERAL CONCEPTS

Differential population pressure (Thompson)

This is the idea that migrants tend to move from a place of high economic and social pressure to places with lower pressure, i.e. people tend to follow the line of least resistance. For example, white people went to the White Highlands of Kenya and to Southern Rhodesia (now Zimbabwe) because it was easier to become a member of a social and economic elite than it was in Britain.

'Push/Pull' factors

Migration is conceived of as being the result of two conflicting forces. The 'push' factor encourages people to leave overpopulated and economically depressed regions, e.g. the West Indian migration to England, English migration to Canada. The 'pull' effect is the attraction offered by a new location, e.g. the magnetism of California in the USA; the cities of the Third World.

Gastarbeiter (guest workers)

Advanced countries which are short of labour make use of migrant labour without having to give the immigrants full civic rights as citizens. For example, there are southern Mediterranean workers in Germany and Switzerland. For racialist reasons South Africa has a permit scheme which allows African workers from neighbouring countries to work for a period in South Africa without civic rights. Some workers have stayed in a country for years and have settled with their families. In times of economic depression however work permits can be withdrawn and 'temporary workers' may not have the same right to social benefits, unemployment pay, etc. as citizens.

Immigrant

This is a loosely used word which often has overtones of prejudice or even racial discrimination. For example, although more white people than black or Asian enter Britain in a year the word now is used for people from new Commonwealth countries (India, Pakistan, etc.). Before World War I for a time it was used almost exclusively to describe Jewish people.

DIFFERENT PERSPECTIVES

The demographic perspective

Demographers see migration as a balancing factor in the basic population equation because it provides a dynamic element over and above the factor of natural increase (birth and death rates). The demographer is interested in the effects on the age and sex structure of the sending and receiving areas and in the imbalance of flow between these regions.

The economic perspective

This perspective is symbolised by the gravity, intervening opportunities and multivariate analysis models above. Distance is regarded as a frictional cost with man making purely rational decisions.

The behavioural perspective

This approach is concerned with why moves are made or not made, i.e. with the decision-making of the migrants themselves. Pred for example believes that people move according to the quality of information available to them and the use they are able to make of that information. Migrants respond to social and economic factors with varying degrees of rationality. People are not totally rational in their decisions as 'economic man' would be. They act in a **bounded rational way** according to such factors as the level of information, the stage they have reached in the life-cycle and the opportunities they perceive in the new location.

3.3 RURAL SETTLEMENT

DEFINITIONS

Site
The actual land upon which the settlement is built. The initial site will continue to influence the plan of the settlement even when the settlement has outgrown it. The significance of factors of siting change over time, e.g. factors such as the availability of spring water or a defensive location are no longer key factors to rural settlements in Britain.

Morphology
The form of the settlement, e.g. street villages have a linear form with the houses, farms and other buildings strung along a road. In contrast a green village will originally have had a more compact appearance, with the buildings clustered around a village green.

Nucleated settlements
are those in which farms and other buildings are grouped together as a nucleus from which the village has evolved. Both street villages and green villages are forms of nucleated settlement.

Dispersed settlements
are those in which individual farms are scattered over the cultivable land.

Sequent occupance
Britain has been settled by successive waves of invaders. Each band of new settlers exercised choice in where they would settle and the types of settlement they would establish. Sequent occupance implies that each successive wave of new settlers entered existing settlements and in so doing added to their form and character; thus the landscape was constantly adapted and changed.

Palimpsest
A landscape may be regarded as being made up of a series of layers of different settlement patterns which have in turn been established on top of relics of previous times. For example, Saxon settlements were established in a landscape which already contained relic settlements from Celtic and Roman times with distinctive forms and patterns of distribution. This is an alternative concept to that of sequent occupance.

CLASSIFICATIONS OF SETTLEMENTS

We classify rural settlements in order to understand them and to try to identify the processes by which they have achieved their present forms and distribution.

Physical classification

In GCSE studies you may have labelled villages according to initial site factors e.g. **gap settlement, spring line village, bridging point**, etc. This is a physical classification. Although these labels relate villages to specific physical features they do not help us understand the nature of the settlements as they now are. If you do examine the physical features of sites it is important that you ask what the people who originated the settlements believed to be the chief priorities in choosing a site.

For example, when establishing villages in south-east England the Saxons would have had a shopping list of items which made up an ideal site for a village such as: easy to defend, ready water supply, materials to build houses and barns, grazing land for animals, arable land for crops. At different times and at different places in the south-east the order of priority of these factors would have varied.

Morphological classifications

Villages may also be classified according to their form. The form of the village reflects vital characteristics such as the basic type of farming practised, the people who founded the settlement, the conditions under which it was originally established.

Evolutionary classifications

This approach is concerned with the classification of settlements according to their origins. Residual or relic features are identified in the present landscape and the distribution and forms of these remains are related to the economic and social systems which operated at the time of origin.

Social classification

Villages may be classified in terms of their social make-up, e.g. classification according to the social groups living in the village, classification based upon patterns of land ownership. The concepts of 'open' and 'closed' villages is a way of identifying social characteristics according to social criteria.

THE EVOLUTION OF RURAL SETTLEMENT IN ENGLAND AND WALES

The main phases of rural settlement were:

Celtic settlement

This formed isolated clusters of housing usually located on easily defended sites, e.g. hill tops. They are found mainly in the north and west of Britain and most of the sites still evident have been abandoned.

Roman settlement

Remains of Roman villas are found in lowland Britain e.g. Bignor, W. Sussex and Chedworth, Glos. The villas were largely self-supporting country estates. Many of them had their own small industries such as pottery, cloth making and milling. The estates provided nearby towns with farm produce which could be transported along the new road system.

Saxon settlement

Many street and green villages in England are of Saxon origin. Many Saxon villages still exist, mainly in south and central England. They too were linked by new routeways which followed the grain of the land and cut across the Roman road system.

Scandinavian settlement (Viking, Norse)

These settlements were set up by invaders in the ninth and tenth centuries. They are found in eastern and north-western parts of England and in Ireland. At first they built defensive forts but these evolved into villages and towns such as

Stamford and Gainsborough in Lincolnshire.

Norman settlement

This was a very important period of expanding rural settlement. The growth of population led to the need to cultivate more land. More villages were therefore established. The typical village in cultivable areas was the nucleated village farming large open fields.

Late medieval settlement

This was a negative period when many villages disappeared. The population was decimated by the Black Death (1348). Depopulation led to the desertion of many village sites. There were fewer people to work the land and the badly hit towns needed less food so arable land was converted to pasture and sheep greatly outnumbered people in England.

Since the Middle Ages

The development of trade has at times brought great prosperity to rural areas e.g. the sixteenth century saw the building of 'wool' churches in the Cotswolds and East Anglia. The need for capital to invest in industry has led to the concentration of land ownership into fewer hands. The common lands and open spaces have also been enclosed with a resultant secondary dispersion of people from the original nucleated villages.

FACTORS LEADING TO THE NUCLEATION OF SETTLEMENT

Nucleation is a settlement form which is often related to the ways in which the land is farmed and owned. It is encouraged by:
➊ a cooperative system of working the land (open field)
➋ defence (hill top, inside a meander)
➌ water supply considerations (spring line)
➍ need for dry sites in marshy areas (Fenland)
➎ scarcity of building materials – settlements concentrate where they can be obtained, e.g. near a source of brick clay
➏ planned villages established by the land owner

FACTORS LEADING TO A DISPERSED SETTLEMENT PATTERN

➊ dependence on livestock farming (Scotland)
➋ specialist intensive farming (market gardening)
➌ Celtic influence (Wales)
➍ very low densities of population (W Highlands)
➎ dissolution of large estates (of monasteries during Reformation)
➏ secondary movement away from nucleated villages (as a result of enclosure)
➐ planned dispersal (on to new holdings in Sicily)

OPEN AND CLOSED VILLAGES

This is a basis for classifying villages according to patterns of land ownership.

The closed village

This was a village in which all aspects of life were dominated by the landowner or his squire. The land is usually divided into a few large farms. The farmers were tenant farmers with high social status in the village. Traditionally the farmers employed many workers. The size of the village has been controlled by limiting the number of estate cottages. Farming has totally dominated the economy, there were few village industries and few tradespeople. On the OS map the closed village may be identified by such features as: a large country house, a model estate village, landscaped parkland, a few large farms and plenty of woodland to provide shooting.

The open village

This is a village in which land ownership was shared by a number of landlords. The farms are therefore sometimes not very large. Small landowners often diversified their interests by developing industries and trades. The open village often became the service centre for nearby closed villages. Because there was less social control the population was not restricted. Population densities are therefore higher than in closed villages. On a map, instead of a great house you are likely to find more than one manor. Shops, workshops and small industries may also be indicated. Fields are usually not very large and have irregular shapes. There is no evidence of domination, e.g. estate lodges, parkland, etc.

The suburbanised village

In some rural areas of Britain, particularly the south–east, the character and functions of villages have changed dramatically. This particularly applies to

Table 13

	Original villages	Incomers
Housing	Younger villagers cannot afford houses in village	Elderly incomers can pay cash Younger couples have high incomes and can afford a large mortgage
Transport	Elderly depend on frequent bus services Families need a car	Many do not use buses; a large number of families have two cars Wives drive husbands to and from station daily
Inhabitants	Many elderly who have always lived in village Young adults leave because of lack of work	Elderly retired professionals and middle-aged middle-income adults with grown-up children Relatively few children
Services	Village shops have disappeared Shops have gone up-market and prices are high	Use pubs as restaurants Shop in nearby towns Keep craft shops for tourists
Social Life	Focuses on village school, darts team and Women's Institute	Active in village church and voluntary organisations Village dramatic society revived Started Morris dancing group and other 'imagined' rural activities
Village School	Used by fewer families as number of children declines	Appointed as school governors Children and grandchildren go to nurseries and independent schools in nearby towns
Environment	Dislike some of changes and 'prettification' of High Street Find it an increasingly expensive place to live	Environmentally aware form pressure groups if planning proposals are disliked Keen to improve appearance of village

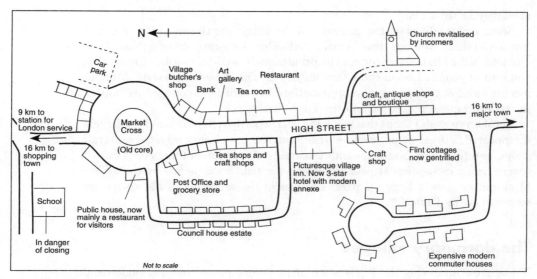

Fig. 86 The suburbanised village

villages located conveniently near large towns and towns with stations on commuter railway lines and which have attractive historical cores. These villages are called suburbanised villages because they display some of the characteristics

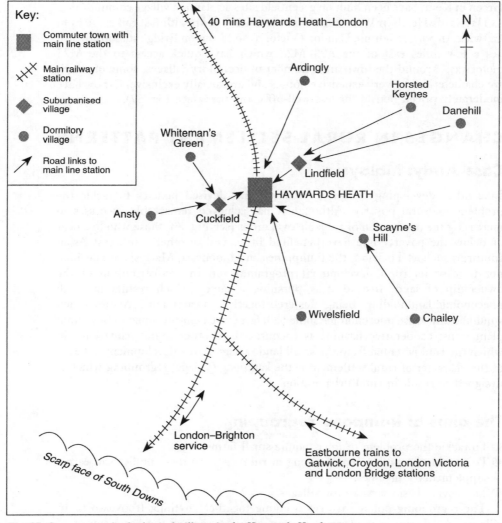

Fig. 87 Commuter and suburbanised villages in the Haywards Heath area

of nearby urban areas.

Some major effects on the structure of the village are shown in Fig. 86. The few agricultural workers that remain and other low-wage earners have been replaced in the High Street cottages by professionals, well-off two-income families and retired people. Low-income families now live on the council estate. Middle-income families and others who cannot afford expensive old cottages are housed in modern houses tucked behind the High Street.

Local services and shops that made the village partly self-sufficient have largely disappeared. Village shops, workshops and cottages have been converted into craft shops, antique shops, boutiques and restaurants. Attraction of tourists has caused severe traffic congestion at peak times and the field once owned by the village blacksmith is now a large car park. Changes in the social life of the village are summarised in Table 13.

The dormitory villages

These grew up during the 1930s when many people moved out of London and large cities to rural environments. This process was made possible by fast and frequent rail services and increased ownership of cars. Dormitory villages share many of the characteristics of the suburban village described above but the dormitory village has expanded and achieved its present character because it has ready access to the city. Some dormitory villages have attractive historic cores; many consist almost entirely of post-1930 housing estates. A few such as New Ash Green in Kent, have been built on greenfield sites as planned village communities.

Haywards Heath in West Sussex is a dormitory town with fast rail services to Gatwick Airport, Brighton, London (Victoria) and London Bridge stations. It also lies a few miles east of the A23/M23 which have quick access to the M25 motorway. Around the town are a number of dormitory villages, some of which are characterised by very expensive houses and are socially exclusive. Others have moderately priced houses for less well-off commuters (see Fig. 87).

CHANGES IN RURAL SETTLEMENT PATTERNS

Case study: Malaysia

Like other developing countries, Malaysia has devised policies to tackle the problems of rural poverty. Although it has achieved remarkable successes in increasing the production of valuable cash crops (see Fig. 88) those who live near or below the poverty line have benefited little. Unlike other south-east Asian countries such as Thailand, the Philippines and Indonesia, Malaysia has decided not to base its rural development programme on the redistribution of the ownership of land. Instead it is pursuing a policy which results in small uneconomic landholdings being clustered together to carry out activities which would be otherwise uneconomic. Some padi farms are being grouped to form mini plantations; cooperative farming is encouraged on other 'mini plantations' in which the land is rented from the small landowners. A key development in terms of the character of rural settlement is the kampong (village) regrouping which is designed to result in rural urbanisation.

The aims of kampong regrouping

❶ To tackle the problem of uneconomic small farms.
❷ To provide jobs other than farming in rural areas so that families can earn supplementary incomes.
❸ To provide basic services for villages.

The regrouping policy involves bringing together anything from two to 15 villages, developing a modern plantation of cash crops as the basic source of

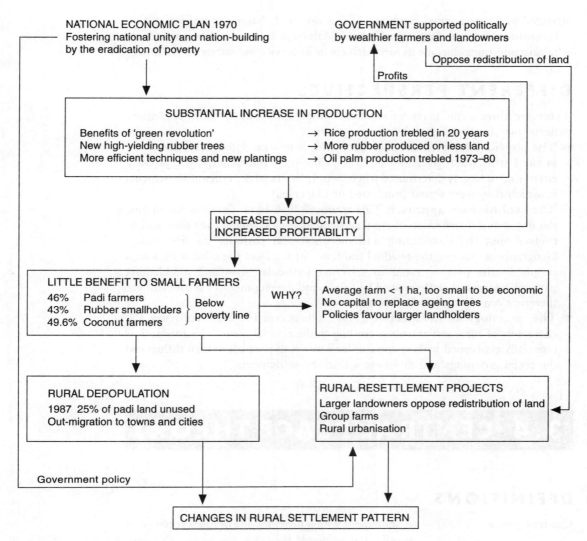

Fig. 88 Dynamics of changes in rural settlement pattern in Malaysia

employment, re-housing villagers in a small township in better housing and with basic services and providing small local industries.

The success of the scheme will depend upon whether new industries can be

Cost-benefit analysis of the scheme

Costs	Benefits
1 Villagers have to pay a mortgage on their new homes	1 Regrouped land holdings are large enough to justify modern farming techniques
2 Those who owned land will continue to work on the land; the landless have lost traditional casual labour jobs that gave them a little money	2 Equipment can be bought that single farmers could not afford
3 The elderly now have little chance of finding paid work	3 More efficient farming of larger units will increase productivity
4 Development costs have to be repaid —smallest landowners find this particularly hard	4 Capital is available to replace old trees with new high-yielding stock on plantations
5 Traditional homes have to be abandoned	5 The 'surplus labour' created can find jobs in new industries
6 It is difficult to attract industries to the new towns	6 The government is able to provide health services, schools, water and electricity as well as low-cost housing in the new towns

attracted to the regrouped kampong. If this does not happen, rural emigration will continue and even larger numbers of Malaysian farmers will be part-timers who earn additional income as lorry drivers or in service industries in the towns.

DIFFERENT PERSPECTIVES

There are three main perspectives from which the study of rural settlement patterns may be approached by the geographer:

❶ **The physical determinist approach** (this is now outdated) It assumed that in rural areas where agriculture is the prime economic activity, the physical environment largely determined where people lived and the types of settlements in which they were found (nucleated or dispersed).

❷ **The evolutionary approach** This approach focuses on the question of how the forms and distribution of rural settlement have changed over time and so evolved into the distribution and morphological patterns we find today. Geographers examine the residual features which reflect the criteria by which people in the past operated in selecting particular sites and establishing particular forms of settlement. The origin and development of settlement are therefore central studies in this approach.

❸ **The sociological perspective** This is concerned with identifying the characters of rural settlements according to their social form. The approach is especially concerned with systems of land ownership which in turn influenced the social groupings and divisions within the settlements.

3.4 CENTRAL PLACE THEORY

DEFINITIONS

Central place	A settlement which provides one or more services for people living outside it.
Central place theory	This is concerned with the principles which determine the number, size and spacing of settlements. It provides a framework by which settlement systems all over the world may be studied.
Hierarchy	Organisation into ranks and orders of towns and cities (urban hierarchy) and functions (hierarchy of functions) is a basic concept in central place theory. In the hierarchy of functions there are lower order and higher order functions. In the United Kingdom whenever a high order function occurs in a central place, the full range of lower order functions is usually present. However, in other countries, such as France and the USA, large out-of-town specialist stores are quite common.
Spatial competition	This is the process which determines which central places will attract new functions and how the patterns made by centres which provide a particular function will evolve. Centres which provide the same functions compete for customers. Customers are distributed in space so central places compete for space. As people become more mobile, and as some centres become more attractive because of the range of services offered, the space served by a particular function or

central place may change.

Functions Lower order functions include the kinds of services provided by a small general store or corner shop; higher order functions or services are provided by a departmental store.

Threshold population The minimum number of people needed to support a function.

Range of services The maximum distance over which people will travel to purchase goods or obtain a service offered by a central place. At some distance from the centre the increasing inconvenience of travel (measured by time, cost or trouble) will outweigh the value of obtaining the goods in that central place.

External economies Some central place functions or services are interdependent. Banks, for example, need to be near their customers to discuss business; shops need to be near sources of supply. If a service is located near the functions with which it has close contact it will make savings which are called external economies.

Isotropic surface A flat, featureless plain with uniform population density and with no variation of wealth and income amongst the inhabitants. This is the hypothetical landscape upon which Christaller developed his model.

CHRISTALLER'S THEORY

A certain amount of productive land supports an urban centre. The centre exists because essential services have to be performed for the surrounding area. These services are **central functions**, the places which perform them are **central places**.

Ideally each central place will have a circular service area. Circles do not fit together well. The closest regular geometrical figure to the circle which will completely fill an area is a hexagon. So Christaller envisaged a hexagonal pattern of central places and service areas.

In order to explain variations in settlement size and importance Christaller postulated the existence of an isotropic surface upon which small nucleated settlements were originally evenly distributed. If the whole area is covered with market areas, **hexagonal networks** grow up, with each village receiving trade equal to three times the trade produced by its own population. The total trade value is known as the **k-value**.

Table 14 *Hierarchy of settlements*

Settlement form	Distance apart (km)	Population	Tributary area size (Km²)	Population
Market hamlet (Markort)	7	800	45	2 700
Town centre (Amtsort)	12	1500	135	8 100
County seat (Kreidstadt)	21	3 500	400	24 000
District seat (Bezirksstadt)	36	9 000	1 200	75 000
Small state capital (Gaudstadt)	62	27 000	3 600	225 000
Provincial head capital (Provinzhaupstadt)	108	90 000	10 800	675 000
Regional capital city	186	300 000	32 400	2 025 000

Christaller recognised seven typical size settlements (Table 14) and stated that the number of central places followed a norm from the largest to the smallest in the following order 1 : 2 : 6 : 18. . . . The larger the central place, the larger is its trade area. So each larger class of settlement in the table was spaced on a hexagon of the next order size. The distances between similar centres in the table increase by √3 over the smaller preceding class.

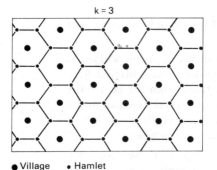
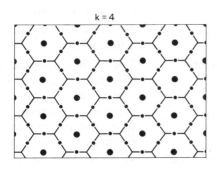
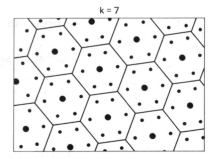

● Village • Hamlet

Fig. 89 Christaller landscape

Determining k-values

Once a k–value is established in an area it is fixed (uniform) for all levels of the hierarchy. The landscape which evolved would be one of three patterns (Fig. 89):

❶ k = 3 landscape. This is one in which the principal influence is the **marketing principle**. All areas are served from a minimum set of central places. The reason why k = 3 is because the settlement's trade area is composed of its own population plus an area which creates twice as much trade as its own population, i.e. one-third of the surrounding trade areas: so $k = 1 + (\frac{1}{3} \times 6) = 3$.

❷ k = 4 landscape. This landscape is based on the **transport principle**. As many places as possible lie on main transport routes connecting the highest order centres. $k = 1 + (\frac{1}{2} \times 6) = 4$.

❸ k = 7 landscape. All the complementary regions are clearly separated. The trade area of a central place is composed of its own and its tributary settlements' population. This pattern is based on the **administrative principle**.

THE LÖSCH MODEL

The Christaller model is very rigid. It maintains that settlements in certain regions are related exactly according to fixed k-values. Lösch produced a more sophisticated model which made central place theory more flexible.

Lösch called the pattern of hexagons **lattices**. By superimposing lattices based upon different principles on each other he produced a pattern of **sectors**. Six sectors contained more higher order centres than others. These he termed **city rich sectors**. Six others were sparsely populated – the **city poor sectors**. So Lösch introduced a variable k hierarchy. However, in adopting this approach it became harder to support the concept of a clear-cut hierarchy of settlements as shown in Table 14.

LIMITATIONS TO THE CHRISTALLER MODEL

One vital contribution the Christaller model made to our understanding of settlements was its emphasis on the concept of centrality. Because it is so inflexible, it is not completely satisfactory. Factors which disrupt this model include:

• **Transport centres** Many towns developed as stopping points on roads, railways and water routes. Along major routes central places are frequently strung out at short distances with the tributary areas stretching out at right angles to the line of the route. The traffic stimulated demand for services, for industries such as repair workshops and warehouses and for housing. An example of this process is the development of Swindon in the railway age.

- **Centres located in relation to physical resources** Towns which exist essentially as industrial centres may be located in relation to resources such as iron ore and coal, e.g. Scunthorpe. The physical resources of sea, beaches and landscape similarly locate resort towns clustered in a particular area, e.g. south-coast resorts. Weber's location theory (see Unit 3.8) may offer a better explanation of their distribution than does central place theory.
- **Planned towns** Towns developed as a result of administrative decisions, e.g. the new towns around London do not conform to the Christaller model. Since planning rather than market forces is crucial as far as urban development is concerned in communist societies, the model may be less applicable in those countries.

The rank-size rule

Christaller developed a deductive theory which included the concept of a clearly bounded urban hierarchy. By working from empirical evidence, however, Zipf arrived at a different view of the ordering of settlements and their relationship to each other. Zipf proposed the rank-size rule.

$$Pn = P_1(n)^{-1}$$

Pn is the nth town in a series 1, 2, 3, . . . n in which the towns are arranged in descending order of size. So P_1 is the largest town. The formula used is:

If P_1 has a population of 1 000 000 then P_2 has a population of 1 000 000 $(2)^{-1}$ or

$$\frac{1\ 000\ 000}{2} = 500\ 000$$

If rank and size are plotted on arithmetic graph paper for an area the plotted points would produce a smooth curve. This contradicts the steps which the Christaller concept of hierarchy envisages. This apparent conflict arises in part from the fact that whereas Christaller was concerned with centrality, Zipf measured population. On logarithmic graph paper the perfect relationship would appear as a straight line sloping downwards at an angle of 45°.

The rank-size rule applied

Settlements are ranked in descending order of population size with the largest city first. The largest city is the primate city. The rule implies that the size of settlements is inversely proportional to their rank. So the second city will have a population half the size of that of the primate city, the third one a third of the population, and so on.

Case study: Australia

The ten largest cities are listed in descending order and size. Their actual population size is shown, together with the size estimated according to the rank-

Table 15

Rank	Chief cities of Australia	Actual size in 1983 (1000s)	Estimated size (1000s)
1	Sydney	3335	
2	Melbourne	2865	1150
3	Brisbane	1138	610
4	Adelaide	971	400
5	Perth	969	285
6	Newcastle	414	215
7	Canberra	256	170
8	Wollongong	235	150
9	Hobart	174	118
10	Geelong	143	100

size formula. Using log graph paper the perfect relationship appears as a straight line sloping downwards at an angle of 45° (Fig. 90).

The graph shows that there is no close correlation between the rank-size rule and size of cities in Australia. All the cities have actual sizes much higher than the estimates based on the rank-size rule. This is because the cities of Australia have attracted a very high percentage of the population and several are important trading ports, e.g. Melbourne and Perth.

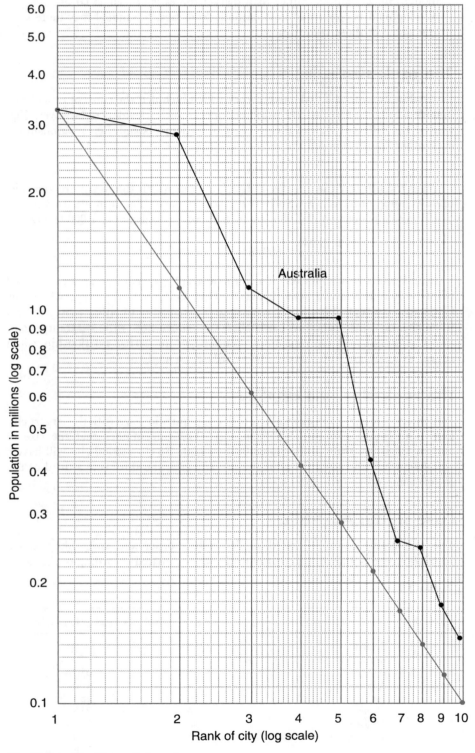

Fig. 90 Australia: The rank-size rule

3.5 URBAN STRUCTURE AND GROWTH

DEFINITIONS

Functional areas or zones As towns grow the different functions they perform tend to become spatially segregated, i.e. to occupy different areas in the town. Housing, commercial activities, industry – each becomes the chief function of a different part or zone of the town. The development of these zones is the result of various processes such as suburbanisation of industry or social segregation. Within these broadly defined functional zones finer, more detailed contrasts in land use are found. These are the results of factors such as the age of the buildings, the density of building, land ownerships and variations in commercial activities, for example, between shops and warehouses.

Morphology This is the layout of the buildings, together with the functions. Functional zones are also called morphological zones.

Urban structure The spatial relationships between the functional zones. Models have been developed which describe the structure of towns and cities. The models attempt to identify characteristics common to all towns and so help us to understand the processes which produce the structure.

MODELS OF URBAN STRUCTURE AND GROWTH

The concentric zone model (Burgess)

Burgess argued that because different types of functions have to compete with each other for limited space in the city certain functions become dominant in certain areas (see Fig. 91). So functional zones develop. These zones are arranged concentrically around the city centre. Lower status residents live near the centre of the city, higher status groups on the outer edges. Within these zones and across their boundaries there may also be **natural areas**. These are distinctive areas where a particular ethnic group has concentrated. The concentric zones may also be broken up as a result of such factors as the occurrence of high ground which, for instance, might become an attractive residential area for high status people although it is near the city centre.

The pattern is also affected by processes which operate as the town grows. For example, ethnic minorities may be absorbed into the population as a whole and move away from a ghetto. Members of other groups may improve their status and move away from the inner city zones. This process is called **invasion and succession**.

The Burgess model is regarded as a weak structural model because:
- It was developed nearly 60 years ago and great changes have occurred in the nature of cities which make the model less applicable.
- It was based on the study of Chicago and other American cities. It was therefore relevant to a particular historical and cultural context but not to

other parts of the world – it is said to lack universality.
- The model suggests that there are sharp boundaries between the functional zones. In reality these abrupt changes do not occur.
- It fails to recognise that in pre-industrial cities of countries such as India the high status groups are likely to live near the centres of the cities and the poorest families are found on the edges of the built-up areas (e.g. shanty towns).

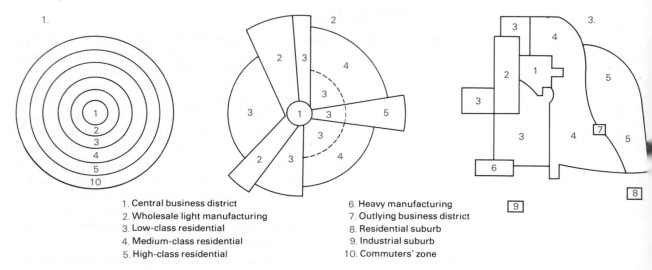

1. Central business district
2. Wholesale light manufacturing
3. Low-class residential
4. Medium-class residential
5. High-class residential

6. Heavy manufacturing
7. Outlying business district
8. Residential suburb
9. Industrial suburb
10. Commuters' zone

Fig. 91 The concentric model   *Fig. 92 The sector model*   *Fig. 93 The multiple-nuclei model*

The sector model (Hoyt)

The sector model complements the Burgess model because it considers an additional factor – direction as well as distance (see Fig. 92). It is based on the idea that accessibility to the town or city centre influences the location of functional zones. So the zones are shown in the model as sectors with wedges of residential areas developing outwards from the centre. High-grade residential areas are located in the most convenient locations and have a strong influence on the pattern of urban growth because other zones have to fit around them.

The multiple-nuclei model (Harris and Ullman)

Instead of envisaging functional zones which develop outwards from a single centre, Harris and Ullman took the view that the functional zones would develop around a number of nuclei of which the Central Business District was only one (see Fig. 93). Other nuclei might be a suburban shopping centre or old villages which have been absorbed into the growing town. So the town or city is a series of distinctive cells. The number of nuclei depends upon the size of the city.
It is argued that towns and cities developed in this way because:
- Certain activities need to occupy specific locations, e.g. large industrial complexes need cheap land.
- Some activities group together for mutual advantage, e.g. shops located in a block of shops get more customers than an isolated store.
- Some functions are incompatible, for example, the most expensive residential area is not located alongside heavy industry.
- Different functions have differing abilities to pay rents and rates. So only some functions can afford to locate near the city centre.

LAND VALUES

Within every city, land values vary dramatically. The chief factors determining values are accessibility and location.

Location

The highest land values are found in the hearts of metropolitan areas. In large American cities values often exceed $1 000 000 per acre (0.405 ha) but this only applies to a small area. The central point of greatest value is labelled the **PLVI** – the **peak land value intersection** or peak land value point. Land values drop sharply with distance from the CBD.

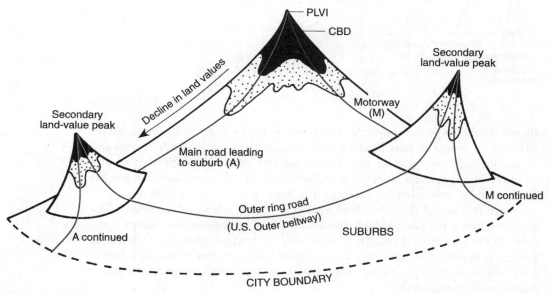

Fig. 94 Land values in a city

Accessibility

The single pattern of gradual decrease in value away from the PLVI is distorted by the location of major transportation corridors which cause higher values along their edges. Where major roads intersect, secondary land value peaks occur. Land uses reflect land values in a predictable way. The costly land in the CBD is occupied by functions that can pay high prices for space. To make this space as economic as possible, land-use functions extend vertically so the CBD is often seen as an island of high-rise development. As land values decrease outwards, the land is put to residential purposes.

Bid rent theory (Ratcliff)

This theory explains the location of functions within a town or city in terms of economic factors.

Efficiency in use is measured by rent-paying ability. Competition for different locations within the city by different functions produces the most efficient pattern of land use. So the structure of the city is determined by the financial evaluation of the importance of convenience. So rents are seen as a payment for saving the costs of transport – it envisages land use as being determined by relative inefficiencies of using land in different ways in particular locations.

In the graph (Fig. 95) each category of land user's ability to pay rent is plotted against distance from the town centre or CBD. Retail shops need to be in the centre to have maximum accessibility for all the city population. Since accessibility decreases outwards from the centre, so does willingness to pay high rents. Solicitors, accountants, etc. also like being near the centre but cannot afford the highest rents. So their offices are found on the edges of the CBD. On the graph,

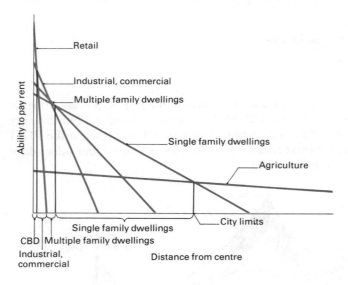

Fig. 95 Bid rent theory

therefore, the slope for commercial activities is not as steep as for retail shops. Multistorey blocks of flats produce more income than single family houses and so the flats can compete for land nearer the city centre although they cannot compete with shops and offices. Agricultural land is the least competitive and has the least steep rent/distance slope, so it is found outside the city limits.

So in this model the urban land market is seen as a land value surface. The market centre is the point of highest site value. As rent declines with distance, the value of the land falls. As the land value falls, the land use changes. This simple pattern is modified by other factors, e.g. main transportation routes have higher land values than surrounding areas; where these routes intersect, secondary commercial centres develop.

Case study: Characteristics of the CBD of American cities

The CBD may be subdivided into:

- **The core** is the most intensively used area which contains the PLVI and which is small in area. Commonly it covers only a few dozen city blocks.
- **The frame** is the surrounding support area and is much more extensive. It may take up 75% of the CBD area and contains warehouses, car parks, car sales firms and wholesalers. It usually also contains vacant land and partly used or unused buildings.

Characteristics of the core

• Intensive land use:	High buildings, land use comprised of offices, shops, hotels, theatre, banks, etc.
• Extended vertical scale:	Grows vertically rather than horizontally
• High daytime population:	Office workers, financiers, etc.
• Very small residential population:	Theatregoers, people eating out, etc. form night-time population
• Focus of intercity travel:	Main stations, bus stations, air terminals, etc.
• Centre of specialised functions:	Stock Exchanges, international buildings, etc.
• Constrained boundaries:	Dependence on public transport (rail, etc.) means that it cannot expand easily
• Limited size:	Rarely more than 1.6 km in diameter

Characteristics of the frame

• Extensive land use:	Far fewer high-rise buildings; many vacant lots
• Distinctive functional regions:	Warehouse zone; car sales lots; transportation centres; multi-family dwellings
• Extended horizontal scale:	Off-street parking and unloading facilities; movement between establishments is by car or truck
• Outside rather than inside linkages:	Support links to CBD core and rest of city Parts of the frame independent from each other
• Boundaries formed by external factors:	Frame fills sectors between railway lines and arterial roads. Tends to expand into areas of condemned housing

(after Hartshorn)

GENERAL CONCEPTS

Evolution and growth

The population of most British cities has grown over the centuries. The cities have therefore grown outwards from the centre. If old villages or towns have been absorbed into the growing city they form zones of old houses, e.g. in Norwich. So the most valuable sites – in the city centre – are occupied by the oldest properties.

Urban renewal

This is a policy designed to regenerate inner city areas. It is a response to public awareness that the scale of urban problems has now increased to a point where it threatens the functioning of major cities.

It is one of the solutions to urban decay which have been developed since 1945. It is complementary to the programmes for building new towns and overspill estates in which people from the cities were rehoused. Urban renewal is aimed at keeping people and jobs in the inner city areas.

Urban renewal may occur as **spontaneous renewal** or as **comprehensive renewal**. Spontaneous renewal occurs when demand for land in the city centre exceeds supply. Renewal is worthwhile because the new development will bring in higher rents. Much of the redevelopment of the centre of London in the City and along the river is of this type. So is the gentrification of older housing areas in London – fairly well-off people buy older houses as good investments and improve them. Comprehensive renewal may be undertaken by local authorities or by private companies. Because large sites are needed, property is often subject to compulsory purchase. Demolition is quicker than rebuilding so large cleared areas may be left as areas of **urban blight**. Comprehensive renewal provides an opportunity for well-planned rebuilding, e.g. the new city centre of Sheffield. It can also lead to the break-up of well-established communities.

DIFFERENT PERSPECTIVES

Burgess and Hoyt both developed simple models which were essentially descriptive. They were based on empirical research, i.e. on practical studies and are therefore inductive – the general patterns they show have been worked out from particular instances. When attempts were made to develop a deductive theory (reasoning from cause to effect) the bid rent theory was the result.

All the models are based on principles of market economics. They are less applicable therefore to pre-industrial cities of the Third World.

3.6 CITIES AND THEIR PROBLEMS

Definitions

Make sure that you understand the definitions in the following units: **urban structure** (3.5), **GNP** (3.10), **migration** (3.2), **central place** (3.4), **functional areas** and **urban structure** (3.5). Other definitions which are relevant to this topic are:

Inner city — The area near the centre of the city which is densely populated and which contains dilapidated housing, often in multiple occupation. The inner city is characterised by a declining industrial and economic base, higher rates of unemployment than the city as a whole, and recent loss of population. It is often a reception area for immigrants.

Residential segregration — The segregation of groups according to socio-economic status, religious beliefs or ethnic characteristics, into distinct sections of the residential areas of cities. A clearly identifiable area in which members of a single cultural or ethnic group are concentrated may also be known as a **ghetto**.

MODELS OF URBAN STRUCTURE AND GROWTH RELEVANT TO THIS UNIT

This topic draws upon knowledge from a number of related units. Models of economic development (3.10), for example, are relevant to analysis of Third World cities. Urban land use models and bid rent theory (3.5), migration (3.2) and central place theory (3.4) will all help you place city problems and issues in a sound theoretical context.

Push-pull model

This is an explanatory model of population movement into cities in which migration is seen to be the result of two sets of forces whose effects are complementary. The 'push' factors are those which encourage people to leave rural areas and include low wages, lack of work, natural disasters. The 'pull' factors are the economic and social attractions (real or imagined) exerted by towns and cities — better job prospects, higher wages, leisure facilities, etc.

PROBLEMS RELEVANT TO CITIES THROUGHOUT THE WORLD

Problems arising from physical factors

These include:
- decay and obsolescence of the oldest part of the city — the inner city, old industrial areas and derelict docklands;
- inadequate road systems and consequent traffic problems;
- provision of public services — adequate supplies of pure water, effective waste disposal;
- uncontrolled expansion into unsuitable sites — squatter settlements;
- effects of natural disasters — floods (Dacca, Bangladesh), earthquakes (San Francisco, Mexico City) or drought (Timbuktu, Tigre in Ethiopia).

Economic problems

These include:
- decline of former inner city industries and consequent unemployment;
- decline of traditional manufacturing industries;
- suburbanisation of industry and consequent land use conflicts on city edges;
- industrial growth and pollution.

Problems arising from governmental problems and planning processes

For example:
- administrative fragmentation of the city area – decisions may be difficult to make because so many authorities are involved in the administration of the built-up area;
- tension and conflict between planners and entrepreneurs who demand uncontrolled economic development;
- problems of social justice – decision-making in cities may merely reflect existing patterns of power and wealth;
- difficulty of establishing agreed criteria for change – varying groups may have genuinely conflicting interests which cause social tensions. For instance, in the redevelopment of the London docklands, the dispute over whether housing should be for locals or for 'yuppies'.

Social problems

Including:
- contrast between rich and poor can lead to political unrest;
- the contrast between suburban growth and inner city decay;
- immigration and problems relating to multicultural populations;
- housing and employment;
- squatter settlements (shanty towns).

Problems arising from population shifts

- aged and deprived elements of the indigenous population left behind in the inner city when upwardly mobile and young move away;
- emergence of ghettos and racial tension;
- squatter settlements.

Urban problems are generally complex, so although the groupings listed above provide a framework for study, important problems do not necessarily fit into a single section. For example, the problems of the inner city are the result of the ageing of the oldest parts of the city; of economic processes such as the decline of traditional industries and the establishment of new ones away from the city centre; of planning decisions which took people and jobs out of cities such as London to planned new towns; and of racial tension as the centres become multicultural. Similarly, the problem of illegal squatter settlements, which is common to many cities in the developing world, is a complex one, caused by the interplay of a number of factors.

Cities in both the developed and less-developed countries face many contemporary problems. The cities of the less-developed world, however, are faced with problems which differ in scale and intensity from those found in the wealthy industrial countries. This is because:

❶ The process of urbanisation is occurring very rapidly and on a vast scale in the developing countries.

❷ The developing countries have neither the wealth nor a sufficiently large reservoir of skilled labour with which to tackle serious problems swiftly and efficiently.

❸ Lack of an advanced technology and a modern economic infrastructure means that developing countries are less able than more advanced countries to respond swiftly to sudden crises. For instance, during the Ethiopian famine it was easier for advanced countries to get food to Ethiopia than it was to distribute that food within the country to where it was most needed.

❹ Because of their lack of wealth and international power, many developing countries are compelled to react to urban problems in ways which meet with the approval of rich creditor nations and powerful multinational companies.

PROBLEMS ARISING FROM THE RAPID GROWTH OF A CITY IN THE DEVELOPING WORLD

Case study: Cairo

Out of a total population of 53 million (1992), about 14 million live in Cairo and the city is growing very rapidly. The reasons for the size of the city population include:

❶ A very high birth rate in the country as a whole (2.9% natural increase per annum; compare the UK's 0.2 %).

❷ Mechanisation and modern farming methods reduce demand for labour in rural areas and lack of employment in the villages acts as 'push' factor.

❸ Cairo is the primate city and a magnet, i.e. a 'pull' factor. It contains all the major businesses, government offices and commercial outlets. It also has the most important and largest university population in the region.

❹ Good communications with Alexandria and the Suez Canal make imported goods cheaper than in remote areas of the country such as upper Egypt.

As a result of the in-migration Cairo has become overcrowded, polluted and unable to provide the infrastructure required.

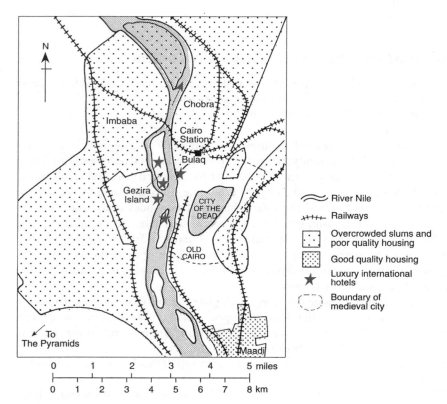

Fig. 96 Central Cairo

Housing and settlements

Unofficial settlements Many migrants (one estimate puts the figure at half a million) live in the tombs and buildings which form the cemeteries where the rich and famous were buried. This area, known as the City of the Dead (Fig. 96) is close to the centre of the city but lacks water supply, a sewage system and other basic amenities. The Mukerta cemetery alone has three primary schools to provide a basic eduation for the children.

On the city fringe there are more than 200 unofficial settlements, some so new that the government does not have any details about them. These are not shanty towns but poor quality houses made of mud bricks without water or electricity.

A third group of unofficial settlements are new additions to existing buildings. Additional storeys are added in a ramshackle manner to old buildings in the city, so that roof-top slums have been formed.

Official settlements The government has erected tall blocks of flats on the outskirts of the city but their rents are high and the cost of getting into the city to work is beyond the incomes of many people.

Nine satellite cities are being built around Cairo to encourage people to live and work at some distance from the capital. Industries are given government loans to relocate in these satellites but the response has been slow. Rents for houses are high and the cities have not developed as quickly as was hoped.

Improving the infrastructure

Cairo is very crowded and a driver's nightmare. The side streets are poorly paved and open sewers are common. Some attempts have been made to keep the centre attractive, especially on Gezira Island where some of the large international hotels have been built.

The government policy is to improve the quality of life in Cairo by building a new underground metro system and new roads, developing a new sewerage system and organising a refuse collection programme. Unfortunately, the improvements to the infrastructure cannot keep up with the growth of the urban population.

Threat of instability

Many activists seek another solution. Muslim fundamentalists are beginning to adopt policies of violence to overturn the current government which keeps state and religion apart.

SELF-HELP SCHEMES

Case study: Mexico

One of the problems in shanty towns is the lack of local initiative to improve the situation. The people who live in these illegal townships have no income, few find work and lack of basic services hinders industrial growth. For most people all their time is spent finding enough to eat and there is a constant struggle for survival against disease and malnutrition.

Government action can be hostile and attempts may be made to evict the inhabitants of shanty towns (this happened in Rio de Janeiro but met with no success as the inhabitants moved back again). In more wealthy countries such as Hong Kong and Singapore, high-rise blocks of flats have been built in large numbers and the shanty town dwellers rehoused.

In Mexico a self-help scheme, known as the Solidarity programme was launched in 1988 and has proved to be a success. This is a public investment scheme by the government which has concentrated on local public works projects such as piped water, drainage, paved roads and bridges. The programme uses local organisations and voluntary labour to channel the resources of the state and municipal governments. Cynics point to the political pay-off the scheme is having as the government has gained enormously in popularity among the poor and the migrants. One showpiece has been the shanty town of Chalco on the outskirts of Mexico City. Roads have been built, water pipes laid, new schools opened and no one living there would dream of voting for the opposition party. The Solidarity programme leaders state that they aim to motivate people to solve their own problems and make their own decisions. If people make a request they are encouraged to set up a Solidarity committee, independent of the political structure, and make a formal application. Advice and expertise is provided when it is needed. The local people provide the labour and the government the finance. There are 82 000 Solidarity committees throughout Mexico and tangible benefits have been brought to large numbers of poor people. For many, the programme is seen as an alternative to the traditional bureaucracy and red tape which result in delay and corruption.

GENERAL CONCEPTS

Urbanisation Throughout the world, people are gravitating from rural areas to cities. As far as the volume and speed of movement is concerned, the process is especially significant in the cities of the developing world.

Movement to the suburbs Movement to the edges of the cities is more than a reflection of upward social mobility. For example, many cities tackled their housing problems in the inner city areas by building new estates on the city edges. Shopping and leisure facilities and industrial estates have also moved to outer areas, where lower land prices and locational convenience near new motorways have been tremendous attractions.

Environmental considerations Concern about environmental quality may be reflected in:
- decisions to restrain growth, e.g. by the establishment of a green belt;
- regulations to restrict change, e.g. the designation of urban conservation areas which are specially protected because of their special historical or architectural qualities.

DIFFERENT PERSPECTIVES

Many of the models developed for the study of cities and their problems were developed with particular reference to modern industrial cities in advanced countries. Cities in developing countries have often grown in a different social and cultural context. For instance, the largest and most powerful cities of the developed world achieved their status as a result of the development of modern industry. The growth of many cities in developing countries, in contrast, was not based upon industrialisation.

There is a very different perspective in China and other countries with communist regimes. For example, free market economic processes such as competition for land on a bid rent basis does not apply in these countries. Their economies are 'command economies', with basic decisions about urban land-use and the functions of cities being made centrally on the basis of agreed national priorities.

3.7 AGRICULTURAL LAND USE

DEFINITIONS

A-level studies of agricultural land use are concerned with the processes which help to determine present-day patterns of farming. There is a particular emphasis on the part played by economic factors and the influence exercised by governments in deciding what is grown or produced on farmland. Some of the terms used by economists may be unfamiliar to you.

Locational rent
The difference between the total revenue received by a farmer for a crop grown on a unit of land and the total cost of production and transport of that crop. Locational rent is not the same as the rent a farmer may be charged for a unit of land by the owner.

Intensity of agricultural production
The greater the input of labour and capital on a unit of land, the greater the intensity of agricultural production.

Marginal farming
A farmer whose total revenue only just covers his total costs is a marginal producer. If the farm is located in an area where total costs of cultivating the land just balance the total revenue, it is said to be at the margin of cultivation. Beyond this margin, farming would not be worthwhile. A margin also exists between growing different crops on the same land if costs and revenue differ for each crop grown. The net income for wheat on a parcel of land may be very little or nothing but there may be a large net income for using the same land for the rearing of cattle. In this case the land is marginal for wheat cultivation and the farmer is likely to transfer his capital and labour to the rearing of cattle.

Diminishing returns
This economic law states that at a certain point in production, additional units of input will yield proportionately smaller units of output and the additional cost incurred will be greater than the additional revenue received. This can be represented as a graph (Fig. 97), where O–X represents the input and O–Y the net returns, i.e. the returns which remain after the farmer has paid his production and transport costs. At first the curve rises but with continued increases in input a point is reached at Z beyond which the net return to the farmer declines and finally assumes negative values.

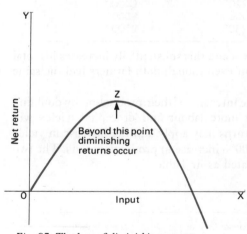

Fig. 97 *The law of diminishing returns*

ASSUMPTIONS MADE BY VON THÜNEN

Von Thünen, who farmed near Rostock in Eastern Europe in the 1820s, tried to establish why farmers behaved in a particular way in his locality. The result was a book called *The Isolated State* (1826), in which he attempted to explain how and why agricultural land use varied with distance from a market. Underlying his theories were a number of assumptions.

❶ An **isolated state**, that is land surrounded by an uncultivated wilderness.
❷ One central city as the sole market for the products of the land surrounding it.
❸ A uniform plain surrounding the city where fertility, climate and other physical factors do not vary.

❹ The plain is inhabited by farmers who supply the city.

❺ The farmers aim to maximise their profits and have full knowledge of the needs of the market.

❻ Transport is by horse and cart and the cost of transport is directly proportional to distance.

THE VON THÜNEN MODELS

Von Thünen introduced two models. The first was concerned with the intensity of production while the second examined the location of crops in relation to the market.

The intensity of production model

This is best explained by an example. Two farmers, Mr Green and Mr Brown, cultivate the same crop. They have identical inputs and yields but Brown is located 20 km from the market whereas Green is only 2 km away. Assuming that the market price for the crop is £50 per tonne and the transport cost is £1 per tonne/km, the farmers' locational rent can be calculated as in Table 16.

Table 16 Locational rent

		Farmer Green	Farmer Brown
(a)	Distance from market	2 km	20 km
(b)	Cost of production	£2000	£2000
(c)	Yield	100 tonnes	100 tonnes
(d)	Transport cost	£1 per tonne/km	£1 per tonne/km
(e)	Total transport cost (a × c × d)	£200	£2000
(f)	Market price	£50 per tonne	£50 per tonne
(g)	Total cost (b+e)	£2200	£4000
(h)	Total revenue (c × f)	£5000	£5000
	Locational rent (h−g)	£2800	£1000

The transport cost is higher for Brown and this substantially increases his total costs. Green has a higher locational rent even though both farmers had the same production costs and yields.

If both farmers decide to increase the intensity of their production by doubling their production costs, i.e. by using more labour and/or capital, yields will increase but the law of diminishing returns may apply and the increase in yields may be only 50% compared with the 100% increase in production costs. The two farmers' locational rents can be calculated as in Table 17.

Table 17 Locational rent

		Farmer Green	Farmer Brown
(a)	Distance from market	2 km	20 km
(b)	Cost of production	£4000	£4000
(c)	Yield	150 tonnes	150 tonnes
(d)	Transport cost	£1 per tonne/km	£1 per tonne/km
(e)	Total transport cost (a × c × d)	£300	£3000
(f)	Market price	£50 per tonne	£50 per tonne
(g)	Total cost (b + e)	£4300	£7000
(h)	Total revenue (c × f)	£7500	£7500
	Locational rent (h−g)	£3200	£500

By intensifying his production Farmer Brown is worse off than previously when his cultivation was more extensive, i.e. inputs were lower. His returns will therefore be greater if he adopts his previous, more extensive method of cultivation. By contrast, Farmer Green is better off after intensifying his production.

This example shows that other things being equal, the intensity of production of a particular crop will decline with distance from the market.

Von Thünen's second model

In this model Von Thünen looked at the location of more than one crop in relation to the market. The location of different crops is determined by production costs, yields per hectare, transport costs and market prices. The crop with the highest locational rent will be grown since the return will be at its greatest and the farmer will maximise his profits. One example is shown in Fig. 98.

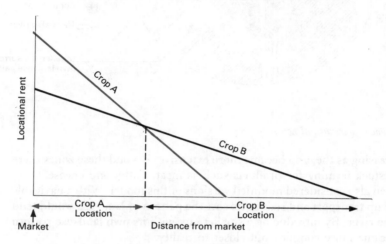

Fig. 98 Two crops with different transport and market prices

If two crops, A and B, have the same production costs and yields but A has higher transport costs and a higher market price than B, A will be grown closer to the market than B.

The explanation for this is as follows. A has high transport costs so the locational rent for A will fall more sharply with distance than will the locational rent for B. As the market price is higher for A than for B the locational rent of A at the market will be higher than for B and A will be grown closer to the market than B.

In reality production costs, yields, transport costs and the market price vary between farm products. If the farmer does not grow the crop with the highest locational rent he will not maximise his profits and may find the farm is running at a loss.

The following formula will enable you to calculate the locational rent of a crop:

$$LR = Y (m - c - td)$$

LR–Locational rent per unit of land   c – Production cost per unit of product
Y – Yield per unit of land   t – Transport cost per unit of product
m – Market price per unit of product   d – Distance from the market

SPATIAL APPLICATION OF VON THÜNEN'S MODELS

Von Thünen combined his model of intensity of production with that for spatial variations in land use and applied them to his 'isolated state'. Fig. 99 shows the theoretical pattern which would result. Nearest the city would be concentrated the production of vegetables and fresh milk because the products are perishable and the fertility of the land could be maintained by manure from the cattle and the city. Further away from the city, timber would be cut. It is bulky and so has high transport costs and a high locational rent.

In the next three zones, rye would be grown in varying degrees of intensity with

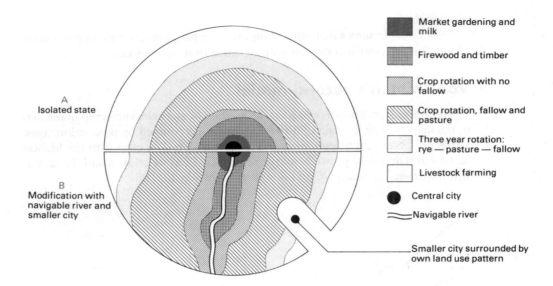

Market gardening and milk

Firewood and timber

Crop rotation with no fallow

Crop rotation, fallow and pasture

Three year rotation: rye — pasture — fallow

Livestock farming

● Central city

Navigable river

Smaller city surrounded by own land use pattern

A
Isolated state

B
Modification with navigable river and smaller city

Fig. 99 Von Thünen's agricultural zones

the yield decreasing as the crop became more extensive. Beyond these zones there would be livestock farming for products such as meat, butter and cheese.

Von Thünen also considered modified versions of this model. With a navigable river to speed up transport and reduce its cost the pattern of land-use would tend to focus on the river. By introducing a smaller city with its own land-use pattern the model became more complex but closer to reality.

Limitations to the Von Thünen model

The technological and communication improvements since Von Thünen's time have brought about changes which make the original assumptions out of date. At the same time there are also objections to the model which, with the changes, are listed below.

- There have been extensive changes in transport since 1826. Perishable goods can be carried long distances.
- Storage capacity, including refrigerated stores, has resulted in the possibility of keeping goods such as apples for months before they are sold.
- Pricing policies may encourage production away from the market. The Milk Marketing Board use differential transport charges to encourage more remote areas to produce milk.
- Cities no longer supply large quantities of manure and cheap labour for neighbouring farms. Labour has been largely replaced by machinery.
- The marketing of agricultural produce has changed drastically. Farmers sell much produce to the food-processing industry. Furthermore, governments have set up marketing agencies which help to control production by subsidising the farmer.
- Soil fertility can still be a dominant factor in the production of a crop. Although there are three sugar-beet processing plants in Norfolk, sugar-beet is not grown extensively near them. Instead it is grown on the loams of north-east Norfolk and the silts of the southern Fens.
- Decisions made by farmers are not based on complete information. The farmer achieves what to him appears to be a satisfactory level of returns. This is a satisficer solution which is dependent on two factors – the level of knowledge of the farmer and the level of uncertainty or risk in the production.
- Economies of scale tend to extend the area under one crop.

- R Sinclair has made the suggestion, based on field evidence in the Mid-west of the USA, that the Von Thünen zonations should be inverted so that the intensity of agricultural activity increases with increasing distance from the city. He argues that cities are expanding rapidly and because of anticipated expansion very little, or no investment is made on land close to them. He suggests that the inner zone should be labelled **land speculation**, and that moving from the centre the other zones should be **vacant grazing**, **field crops and grazing**, **dairying and field crops**, **specialist field grains** and **livestock**.

THE PRESENT-DAY SIGNIFICANCE OF VON THÜNEN'S MODEL

A number of geographers and economists have tested Von Thünen's agricultural zone theory in the field and support his basic concepts. Michael Chisholm cites a number of examples from different parts of the world where zoning takes place around villages. He shows that distance, irrespective of natural fertility, exercises a strong control over intensity of cultivation and that fertility is likely to be highest near a village where manure is available. Other studies have identified zones along the coast of New South Wales and around Hamburg.

J R Peet argues that the developed world of Western Europe and the north-eastern United States forms a world city with zones of decreasing intensity surrounding the highly developed area. S Van Valkenburg and C C Held show that the average yield of eight crops in Europe follows a concentric pattern, declining away from the central market (Fig. 100).

Various studies of farming in the less developed world suggest that conditions may be similar to those in the Rostock area investigated by Von Thünen.

Von Thünen's analysis is evidently still significant. He postulated a normative pattern of land use, that is, one which may be reasonably expected given a number of stated premises.

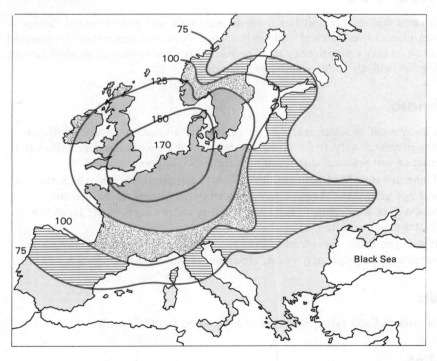

Fig. 100 Zones of decreasing agricultural intensity

GOVERNMENT INFLUENCES ON AGRICULTURAL LAND USE

Governments can indirectly influence what the farmer grows by tariffs, import quotas and other forms of import control. These controls are aimed to protect high-cost producers from low-cost imports. For example, before Britain joined the European Community there was a tariff of 0.83p per lb on imported lamb.

The government's deficiency payment system which operated in the 1950s and 1960s, together with guaranteed prices and markets for certain farm products such as fat cattle, fat pigs, milk, eggs, potatoes and cereals, meant that farmers at the margin of production for these commodities remained profitable and land which would otherwise have remained unproductive was utilised.

The EC has a complex Common Agricultural Policy which includes guaranteed prices and subsidies to member countries. However, membership of the EC means that trade barriers with other member countries must disappear. In Britain this means for example, that apple producers are no longer being shielded from the highly efficient French growers. French orchards produce 16 tonnes of apples per acre compared with only five tonnes from British orchards. This may reduce the area in Britain used for the growing of apple trees.

Other forms of government influence in the production of specific crops have included the creation of **soil banks** in the United States and the encouragement of milk production in Britain. In the 1950s and 1960s the Federal Government, concerned by the increase in crop surpluses, particularly of corn, barley and oats, introduced the acreage reserve scheme which enabled farmers to be paid for placing land previously used to grow crops in surplus supply in the 'bank'. The scheme did not achieve its purpose because farmers deposited their poorest land and continued to grow crops more intensively on the more fertile land, increasing the surpluses still further. In Britain the government encouraged milk production by setting up the Milk Marketing Board and maintaining a national pricing policy which enables small farms to remain in business and encourages dairy farming in remote areas where transport costs are high.

PHYSICAL FACTORS INFLUENCING AGRICULTURAL LAND USE

The emphasis in this unit has been on economic and governmental factors as determinants of agricultural land use but it is important to remember that physical factors also play a significant part. There are three main types of physical factors, soil, relief and, the most significant, climate.

Climate

- The amount of water available for plants and animals is highly significant. Requirements vary and evaporation rates must be considered as well as the amount and seasonal distribution of the precipitation.
- There are threshold temperatures (5°–6°C for wheat), below which the crop will not germinate. Average temperature requirements in the growing season vary from crop to crop and limiting factors such as the incidence of frost are significant.
- Winds can cause considerable damage to crops and where conditions are suitable soil erosion may occur, reducing the land available for agriculture.

Soils

An account of soil types and soil fertility can be found in Unit 2.9.

Relief

- There are handicaps to crop growing and pastoral farming at high altitudes just as there are at high latitudes. Decreasing temperatures and increasing rainfall, humidity and wind speeds are further limiting factors to be found at high altitudes. However, in tropical areas increased altitude may provide better conditions for agriculture than nearby low-lying and coastal regions.

- Slopes provide advantages and disadvantages for agriculture. Slope gradients may limit cultivation and soils may be thin but slopes facing towards the sun where soil temperatures are increased by the sun's angle may be ideal for cultivation if the gradient permits.

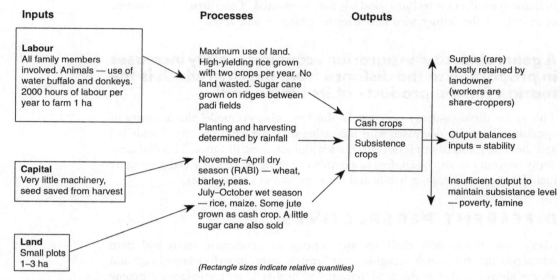

Fig. 101 Farming as a system
  Case study: Intensive subsistence (Bangladesh)

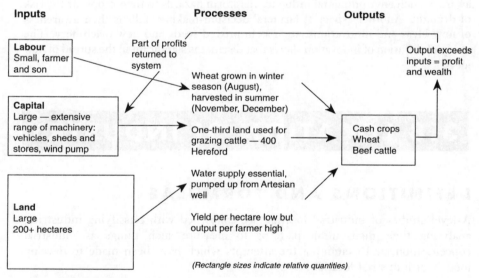

Fig. 102 Farming as a system
  Case study: Extensive commercial (Australia)

GENERAL CONCEPTS

Economies of scale are important in present-day production

There are savings in costs at a certain size of enterprise; these are known as scale economies and occur in larger units of production. The net effect of economies of scale in farming is a tendency towards regional specialisation of some activities.

Man is a satisficer rather than an optimiser

This concept, fundamental to behaviourist thinking, conflicts with the concept of economic man. It considers that instead of trying to maximise their profits, people strive to achieve a satisfactory level and establish a pattern and routine of activity which provide them with this level. They do not strive for more. This is the satisfactory situation and man is the satisficer. This state of equilibrium persists in farming until a new technological advance is adopted. This disrupts the routine of activity of the farmer who now tries to achieve a new level.

A general 'decay' in agrarian economic activity increases in proportion to the distance from the city (which is the market for the products of its hinterland)

This is the distance-decay concept. In the Von Thünen model the intensity of agricultural activity decreases with increasing distance from the city. Yields fall and the capital and labour input decreases with increasing distance. This distance-decay concept can also be applied to a number of other aspects of social geography including urban shopping habits and land use values within cities.

DIFFERENT PERSPECTIVES

Many geographers now challenge the concept of **economic man** and have developed theories which recognise that farmers have imperfect knowledge and are not always guided by the need to maximise profits. Once a satisfactory income has been achieved a farmer might be interested in more leisure time and less profit.

One problem being explored is the basis upon which farmers take decisions. This introduces such concepts as the perception of farmers – how far they are aware of such environmental influences as storm hazards to their crops, or the risk of drought. Another aspect of farmers' decision-making skills is their awareness of new ideas and innovations, such as improved seeds and new machinery. The study of diffusion of innovation shows that distance is significant in the spread of new ideas.

3.8 LOCATION OF INDUSTRY

DEFINITIONS AND FORMULAE

A-level studies of industrial location are concerned with classifying industries, analysing their distribution patterns to measure such things as industrial concentration, and examining the attempts which have been made to develop models of industrial location.

Material index

This measures the loss of weight during processing by comparing the weight of the raw material with the weight of the finished product.

$$\text{Material index} = \frac{\text{weight of localised raw material inputs}}{\text{weight of finished product}}$$

The more the index exceeds 1 the greater the significance of the cost of moving the raw material to the factory.

Location quotient

This measures the degree of concentration of an industry in a particular area. It is obtained by using the formula:

$$LQ = \frac{\dfrac{\text{number of people in industry A in area X}}{\text{number of people employed in manufacturing in area X}}}{\dfrac{\text{number employed nationally in industry A}}{\text{number employed nationally in manufacturing industry}}}$$

If 2000 people are employed in industry A in area X out of a total local workforce of 40 000 then 5% of the local workforce is employed in industry A.

If 100 000 are employed nationally in industry A and 1 000 000 are employed nationally in all manufacturing industry then 10% of the national workforce is employed in industry A but in area X the proportion is only 5%.

$$LQ = \frac{5}{10} = 0.5$$

An LQ of more than 1.0 reveals that the region has more than its share of a particular industry. Conversely, a value of less than 1 indicates that it has less than its share.

Industrial linkage

The operational contacts which exist between separate industrial firms. These contacts are strongest in firms which are pursuing the same kind of process or participating in a sequence of operations.

Some firms perform one stage in a series of operations to make a particular product, this is known as **vertical linkage**. For example, in the non-ferrous metal industry one firm refines the metal, another shapes it, another machines it and so on until the product is finished.

Horizontal linkage is common in the automobile industry where many components of a car, such as the battery and tyres, are made by specialist firms and then assembled at the automobile plant.

Diagonal linkage occurs when a firm makes a product, or provides a service, which is part of a chain of processes, but the firm is not supplying one plant as in vertical linkage. Instead, a variety of separate plants are supplied. An example is a firm which makes plastic mouldings required by a number of other firms in the district.

Firms may obtain benefits from local services and such things as a local pool of specialist labour. These firms are not necessarily linked functionally, they have in common certain services or skills which may not be available in other areas, for example the cutlery industry of Sheffield which has **common roots** in the district.

Industrial inertia

Some industries continue to survive in an area where the cost benefits they once enjoyed no longer exist. An example is the continuation of textile machinery manufacture in New England, even though most textile mills are now located elsewhere.

ADVANTAGES AND DISADVANTAGES OF INDUSTRIAL CONCENTRATION

Advantages

These can be summed up as similar industries having similar needs, for example:

❶ a local pool of skilled labour;

❷ local specialist trade associations;

❸ availability of local services such as cleaning and maintenance;

❹ local financial services and expertise which understands local requirements;

❺ local research and educational facilities;

❻ a specialist quarter where valuable links with other firms can be established;

❼ components bought in bulk may be cheaper because the supplier is also supplying other local firms. This factor and 6 are known as external economies.

Diseconomies of concentration

Although firms may find costs are lower if they are located close to similar firms, there are also diseconomies, for example:

❶ the prices of factors of production may be increased by intense local demand;

❷ labour may be strongly unionised;

❸ services and amenities may have costs which are excessive;

❹ transport congestion.

THE COSTS OF PRODUCTION

Costs of production can be summarised as follows:

- **Labour costs** These vary from place to place; their supply and productivity can also vary.
- **Entrepreneurship** The skills of the entrepreneur are more likely to be available in large cities. Managers may also have locational preferences based on such things as their personal life styles.
- **Capital** Costs of building vary; small firms cannot obtain capital easily outside their own area.
- **Energy** Some firms require vast quantities of energy e.g. aluminium producers. However, the national grid makes supplies of electricity widespread in the UK.
- **Raw materials** Improved technology may reduce costs and less raw material may be required. The cost of extracting ore from the ground is partly determined by the amount of waste which is involved.
- **Transport costs** There are two types, line haul charges and terminal charges. Various rates are imposed, e.g. mileage rate, blanket rate with stepped charges, 'postage stamp' rate, i.e. same charge over any distance.
- **Land costs** Local variations in land costs can be considerable.

WEBER'S MODEL OF INDUSTRIAL LOCATION

Initial premises (1909)

❶ Homogeneous area in terms of climate and topography.

❷ Conditions of perfect competition with large numbers of buyers and sellers.

❸ Some raw materials such as water and sand are ubiquitous, others are localised.

❹ Labour is available at fixed locations.

❺ Transport costs are dependent on weight and distance.

❻ Markets occur at specified fixed points.

❼ Man is an 'economic' animal. People tend to seek locations at which lowest costs are incurred. At such locations the highest profits will be achieved.

Weber's model illustrated by a locational triangle

It is possible to illustrate some aspects of Weber's model by using a locational triangle (Fig. 103).

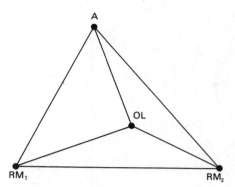

Fig. 103 A locational triangle

Assume two raw materials RM1 and RM2. 1 tonne of RM1 combines with 3 tonnes of RM2 to make a product weighing 2 tonnes which is consumed at A. In the diagram each corner of the triangle exerts a force proportional to the weight attached to it. The optimum location for the firm will be at OL which is nearer to RM2 than RM1 because it is cheaper to transport raw material from RM1 than from RM2. OL will be nearer to RM1 and RM2 than to A because of the loss in weight before the product is sold at A.

A

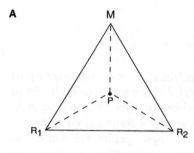

Transport costs are the same for the finished goods and for both raw materials. Factory location is equidistant from the raw material sources and market. At P transport costs are at a minimum

B

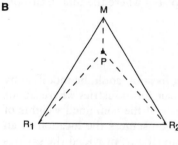

Total cost of transporting raw materials is lower than that of finished goods (for example, because raw materials weigh less). Factory P will be located closer to the market than to the raw materials

C

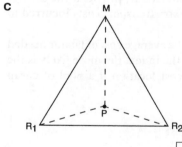

Factory P is equidistant between the two raw material sources, but closer to these sources than to the market. This is because tranport costs of raw materials are higher than for finished goods. This may happen if, for example, raw materials contain a high proportion of waste

D

Key:	
M	= Market
R1 and R2	= Raw material sources
P	= Least transport cost location for factory (Transport costs increase proportionately with distance)

Fig. 104 Applications of Weber's theory: Three industrial locations

Isodapanes

These are lines joining places with equal total transport costs. An isodapane is shown in Fig. 105, the concept was introduced by Weber. In Fig. 105, A represents the market and RM the raw material source for an industry with one raw material.

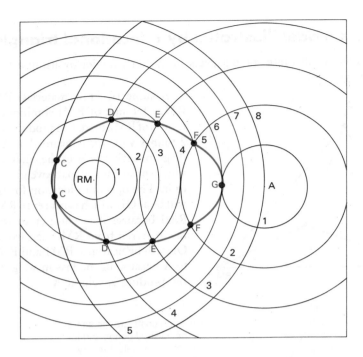

Fig. 105 An isodapane

It costs twice as much to transport the raw material from RM as it costs to transport the finished product from A. If the contour interval is the same for both sets of costs, lines drawn around RM will be closer together than those drawn around A.

At the intersecting points CDEFG of these lines, total transport costs are the same, e.g. C=2+5=7; D=3+4=7; E=4+3=7. If these points are joined an isodapane has been formed, that is, a line joining places where the total transport costs for raw material and product are the same.

Labour costs

Weber also recognised that the least transport cost location could be modified by a pool of cheap labour. This would be particularly true for industries where labour cost ratios were high when compared with the costs of the combined weights of material inputs and product outputs. In these circumstances the location of an industry would be pulled towards the pool of cheap labour, provided the savings from using cheaper labour were greater than the extra transport costs incurred in marketing the finished product.

Weber devised an index of labour costs: this is, the average cost of labour needed to produce one unit weight of output. The higher the index, the more likely is the industry to move away from the least transport cost location if a pool of cheap labour becomes available elsewhere.

Agglomeration and deglomeration

Weber also stated that the least transport cost location might be rejected in favour of a location where there were cost savings resulting from the spatial association of industries. This grouping of industries in a specific area is known as agglomeration (see above).

Although there are economies arising from industries concentrating in one area, there are also diseconomies. In recent years congestion in large industrial cities and the high price of land has encouraged many industries to leave the cities and find locations in less congested areas. This is known as deglomeration.

WEAKNESSES IN WEBER'S MODEL

❶ Perfect competition is an unrealistic concept. It assumes that demand is constant irrespective of distance from the plant. However, increased transport costs will increase prices as distance from the plant increases. When this happens demand will decrease accordingly.

❷ The model does not allow for possible spatial changes in the supply of raw materials or demand for the finished product. The supply of raw materials is rarely from a fixed point, a number of alternative sources of supply are available to the manufacturers. Weber also located the market at a fixed point but in reality the market for a finished product is scattered. Furthermore demand is not constant but varies from place to place.

❸ Transport costs are not directly proportional to distance: instead they tend to be stepped, rising suddenly at certain points. Moreover, transport costs make up a relatively small part of total costs of production for modern industry.

❹ Labour is not fixed but mobile. Weber's assumption that labour is immobile has been weakened by the growth of transport facilities and the movement of the unemployed to find work elsewhere in times of depression. Mobility is, however, limited by such things as the need to learn new skills, family ties and lack of funds to move. These limitations tend to support Weber's assumption.

❺ 'Economic man' does not exist. Many decisions are taken on a personal rather than a rational basis. Businessmen will choose satisfactory locations which enable them to operate at a profit, not necessarily the maximum profit. They are satisficers not optimisers.

MARKET AREA ANALYSIS

Weber's assumption that demand (i.e. the market), was centred on one point is unreal since demand, in practice, is spread over a wide area. A German economist, August Lösch, introduced the market area concept, that is the optimum marketing area for firms in competing industries in a given locality. He suggested that large volumes of sales could enable the manufacturer to obtain profits which would be sufficiently large to offset possible high transport costs.

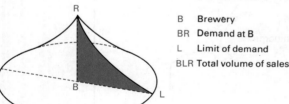

B   Brewery
BR   Demand at B
L   Limit of demand
BLR   Total volume of sales

Fig. 106 Demand in a market area: a three dimensional demand cone

For his model he assumed an isotropic plain, that is a uniform land surface with an evenly distributed population of farm households, each demanding identical goods. A number of producers of, for example, beer, located in this region would serve the population for a distance around the plant, with the price increasing away from the brewery. The market area for each brewery would be a circle with demand greatest at the centre and diminishing with distance as transport costs increase the price (Fig. 106).

A series of these trade areas will develop (Fig. 107 A).

Beyond these trade areas would be potential markets with no breweries which would encourage new producers to enter the market until the circular trade areas touch each other leaving small unserved areas in between (Fig. 107 B). The most efficient shape for the market area is a hexagon (Fig. 107 C), as this shape will give each brewer a monopoly over an area and leave no part of the region without a brewery.

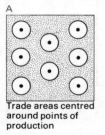

A

Trade areas centred around points of production

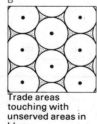

B

Trade areas touching with unserved areas in blue

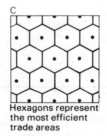

C

Hexagons represent the most efficient trade areas

Fig. 107 Trade areas

If other products are introduced into the model each will have a market area of a different size depending on the importance of transport costs and the significance of economies of scale. The different marketing areas will produce a system of networks which will form an economic region or landscape.

Lösch went on to show that by rotating these networks around a common producing centre there will be sectors where production is concentrated, containing a wide range of activities, and sectors where production will be more dispersed. These ideas link closely with the work on central place theory discussed in Unit 3.4.

Lösch went on to modify his model by introducing situations from the real world. In his theory, however, he ignored the behavioural aspects of locational choice. Instead he used the 'economic man' concept, which is unrealistic. He also ignored the situation when competing producers locate close to one another. The reasons why this may happen are discussed below.

Case study: Iron and steel, an industry tied to its raw materials

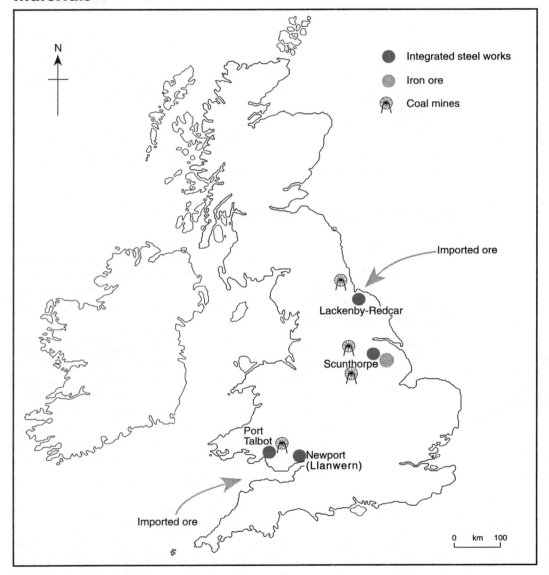

Fig. 108 Location of integrated steelworks 1992

The location of large integrated steelworks in Britain is mainly determined by accessibility to cheap iron ore which is imported or, in the case of Scunthorpe, partly obtained from the Jurassic rocks in the locality.

Coal is less important as a raw material since the introduction of the oxygen furnace in the 1950s. Government policy is important because the steel industry is nationalised. For example, the works at Ravenscraig in Strathclyde was closed in 1992 because it was considered to be inefficient.

Case study: fibreboard packaging, an industry tied to its markets

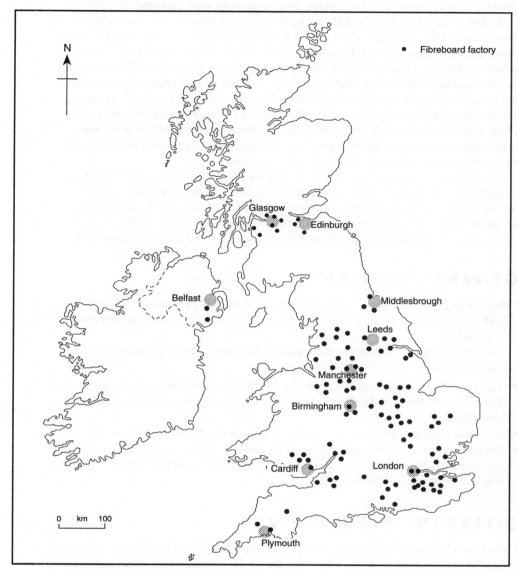

Fig. 110 Location of fibreboard packaging companies in the UK

Imported wood pulp or pulp from British forests, together with waste paper and water, are the main raw materials required to make fibreboard (cardboard, fluted board, etc.). The industry must be able to meet the changing needs of the market – manufacturers requiring packaging for their products. With low transport costs for the raw materials, using the motorway network, fibreboard manufacturers have located themselves near their customers where they have the advantage of being able to deliver the packaging quickly and know what their customers want.

LOCATIONAL INTERDEPENDENCE

Like the market area analysis approach, locational interdependence is concerned with the impact of demand upon location. Cost factors are ignored but entrepreneurial decisions are introduced to provide a behavioural aspect to the model.

The best known model was put forward by H Hotelling in 1929. He assumed that there were two competing suppliers, each having the same production costs and each capable of supplying the entire market with identical products. Demand is assumed to be totally inelastic (not affected by price changes), and the only variable cost is transport which varies in cost directly with distance.

If this situation is described by taking the example of two ice-cream salesmen on a narrow strip of beach, the location of the ice-cream stalls will significantly affect each salesman's profits. Each will have a monopoly over a certain market area, which in this case is linear, and at some point the two market areas will meet, just as the edges of the hexagons meet in Fig. 107 C. A number of alternative positions are possible along the beach for the location of the two ice-cream stalls. They could, for example, be close together, or at either end of the beach or at the mid-points of each half of the beach. The optimal solution given the assumptions listed above is for each seller to be at the mid-point of his market. At this point transport costs for customers are minimised and sales are maximised.

In reality the situation is much more complex. For example, there are likely to be more than two sellers and the population will not be evenly distributed. Centres of population will attract sellers and buyers. This results in further concentration of population and industries until diseconomies set in which will result in deglomeration with new clusters of population and industries arising in other areas.

GENERAL CONCEPTS

One of the main features of manufacturing industry is regional concentration. There are certain advantages to be gained by firms which are in close proximity to each other.

The fully comprehensive location model has been partially replaced by an appreciation that:

- Final decisons on location are made by businessmen who have imperfect knowledge of the cost-benefits involved or who have personal reasons for their choice.
- National planning policy may also play a part in the location of industry.
- Social needs may determine industrial locations in a free society and governments have sometimes intervened to redistribute industry from wealthy regions to those in need.

DIFFERENT PERSPECTIVES

Like Von Thünen with his rural land use, Weber framed his model in an isolated state with transport and labour costs to determine the location of an individual firm. Many of Weber's assumptions are unreal but his ideas highlight the importance of transfer costs and the possible different orientations of industries to materials, labour and markets.

Since Weber's time there has been a greater emphasis on location under conditions where there is not perfect competition. Lösch, for example, attempted to identify the optimum market area for firms in competing industries.

It is worth remembering that the satisficer principle gives a more realistic approach to industrial location.

Finally, do not forget that one-fifth of the world's population lives in countries which are organised as planned economies under Communist governments. By centralised planning Marxist societies eliminate the market forces which operate in capitalist countries. However, even in centrally planned economies it is necessary for decision-makers to draw up lists of priorities. Although central planning on a Communist scale does not exist in capitalist countries, and is being modified in China, the largest remaining Communist country, there is a growing tendency for governments to intervene in industrial location, encouraging developments in some regions and discouraging them in others.

3.9 TRANSPORT AND TRANSPORT NETWORKS

DEFINITIONS AND NETWORK RELATIONSHIPS

Network	A set of routes which connect junctions and termini.
Topological map or graph	Networks which have been simplified as a map or graph are called topological maps or graphs. The junctions and routes are preserved but distances and directions may not be accurate. The London Underground and the British Rail Intercity maps are examples of topological maps. By simplifying the system they are particularly useful for passengers who wish to solve routing problems quickly.
Vertex	A location on a network such as a road junction or a station. The word node is sometimes used instead of vertex.
Edge	(also known as an arc or link) A direct route connecting two vertices.
Connectivity	One important structural property of a network is the degree to which the vertices are interconnected. The degree of connection between all vertices is defined as the connectivity of the network. It is a particularly valuable concept when one network is compared with another or when changes in the same network over a period of time are being compared. A developed region with an extensive demand for transport facilities to move goods and people will have a transport network with a higher degree of connectivity than the network to be found in a less developed region where movements are not so intense.

Comparing networks

In Fig. 110 there are eight edges and nine vertices. Because the number of edges is one fewer than the number of vertices the network is described as minimally connected. If one of the edges is removed one part of the network will be disconnected from the rest. The formula for a minimally connected network is:

$$e = (v-1)$$

In Fig. 111 the network is more complex. Most of the vertices are connected to more than one other vertex and between most pairs of vertices there is more than one sequence of edges. If one edge is removed from this diagram the network will remain connected. This is not a minimally connected network so the formula given above does not apply.

Measuring connectivity

A number of different methods have been developed to measure the connectivity of networks. Of these the beta index is one of the simplest.

The beta (β) index is found by dividing the total number of edges by the total

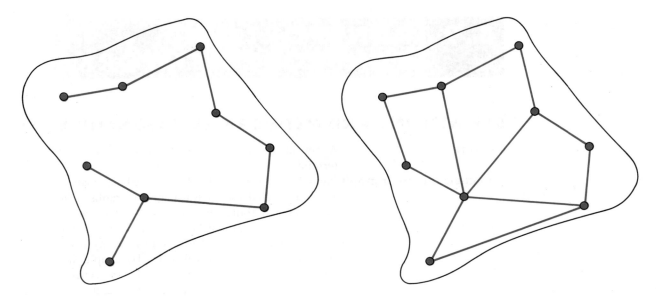

Fig. 110 A minimally connected network   *Fig. 111 A complex network*

number of vertices:

$$\beta \ = \ \frac{e}{v}$$

The beta index for Fig. 111 is $\beta = \dfrac{12}{9} = 1.33$

For a given number of vertices, the more edges there are that connect, the greater the connectivity and the higher the beta index.

The beta index has little value when complex networks are being considered. The alpha (α) index is more useful when comparing networks. To understand it you must first understand the following term:

Circuit

The additional linkages added to Fig. 110 to increase its connectivity and produce Fig. 111 have created circuitry. A circuit is defined as a closed path in which the initial vertex of the linkage sequence coincides with the terminal vertex. Another way of putting this is to describe a circuit as a path starting and finishing at the same point and traversing some or all of the network by the shortest route. In Fig. 111 circuitry exists because additional or alternative paths between vertices have been established. The number of circuits is determined by the number of additional edges added to a minimally connected network.

In Fig. 111 there are 12 edges. In Fig. 110 which had minimal linkage there were eight edges.

The number of additional edges in Fig. 111 is therefore $12 - 8 = 4$. So there are four circuits in Fig. 111 and if you remember the definition of what constitutes a circuit they are quite easy to locate on the network map.

Expressed as a formula the number of circuits is:

$$(v - 1)$$

i.e. the number of edges needed for a minimally connected network, subtracted from the number of edges actually present $-$ e.

This can be expressed as $e - (v - 1)$ which algebraically is the same as:

$$e - v + 1$$

The resulting number is sometimes called the cyclomatic number.

The alpha index compares the observed number of circuits (the numerator) with the maximum possible number of circuits for a given number of vertices (denominator). As a formula this is:

$$\alpha = \frac{e - v + 1}{2v - 5}$$

For Figs. 110 and 111 the alpha values are:

Fig. 110 $\quad \alpha = \dfrac{8 - 9 + 1}{2 \times 9 - 5} = \dfrac{0}{13} = 0$ $\qquad$ Fig. 111 $\quad \alpha = \dfrac{12 - 9 + 1}{2 \times 9 - 5} = \dfrac{4}{13} = 0.31$

There is no circuitry in Fig. 110 and minimally connected networks have an alpha index value of 0. A network with the maximum circuitry has an index value of 1. The alpha index value is normally expressed as a percentage of the maximum so that in the example given the network circuitry is 31% of the maximum.

FACTORS WHICH INFLUENCE NETWORK PATTERNS

Transport networks are built for the following purposes:

- To make a flow of goods and services possible between existing settlements – the new road network in Brazil is partly being built to connect existing settlements which previously were not connected or relied on inadequate links by water.
- To open up an area or a resource – networks were built in many parts of Africa by colonial powers to provide easy access to raw materials.
- Strategic reasons – to provide a good network of roads and railways to transport troops swiftly.

In 1963 K J Kansky identified five factors which influence network patterns. They are:

❶ **Relief** Highlands, rivers and marshland are obstacles for road and rail builders. The degree of hindrance can be registered by means of a relief index.

❷ **Shape** A country like Japan is likely to have a different network pattern from a compact country such as France. Shape can be measured statistically.

❸ **Size** In a country with a small area and a dense network, one form of transport may replace another on economic grounds. This has happened in Britain; the canals were replaced by the railways, which in turn have declined in the face of road competition.

❹ **Population** Density is important, but it must be related to the standard of living of the population. Nations with high standards of living will have denser networks than those which are poor.

❺ **Degree of economic development** Networks will be affected by such things as energy consumption and the level of imports. These will be higher in a rich country.

Kansky accepted that other factors, apart from the five already listed, can affect transport networks. Among these are political boundaries and social and historical factors as well as chance decisions.

Case study: Road network on Prince Edward Island, Maritime Provinces, Canada

Fig. 112 shows the road network on Prince Edward Island.

$$\textbf{The Beta index} = \frac{13 \text{ edges}}{13 \text{ vertices}} = 1.0$$

This is lower than would be found in a highly developed region, but higher than in many poorly developed regions. The network does not show a high degree of connectivity. **The maximum number of edges possible** would occur if each vertex was connected to every other vertex. This would produce 33 edges which is much denser than the present 13 edges.

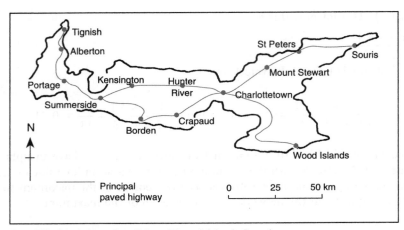

Fig. 112 Road network – Prince Edward Island, Canada

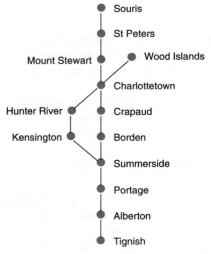

Fig. 113 Topological graph of road network

$$\text{The Alpha index} = \frac{13 - 13 + 1}{(2 \times 13) - 5} = \frac{1}{21} = 4.76\%$$

This is a very low percentage and shows that Prince Edward Island has a very simple network. It has one circuit (Fig. 112) so that it is more than minimally connected but its efficiency is low. This is partly because of the shape of the island which restricts the development of a complex network.

DEVELOPMENT AND DENSITY OF A NETWORK

Using West Africa as an example, E J Taaffe, R L Morrill and P R Gould have developed a model which identifies the stages through which a network is presumed to pass (Fig. 114).

Initially there are small scattered ports along a coast with no links with each other, although each has a small hinterland (Fig. 114a). Then one or two ports begin to grow and links with towns inland speed their growth (Fig. 114b). This process continues and intermediate centres appear (Fig. 114c). Then the vertices become interconnected (Fig. 114d and Fig. 114e), leading to a final stage (Fig. 114f) in which some links become more important than others as some cities prosper while others remain poor.

The density of a network will depend on:
• density of population;
• volume of circulation of goods and people within a region (this is related to the standard of living);
• availability of capital for investment.
Of these three factors the least important is the first.

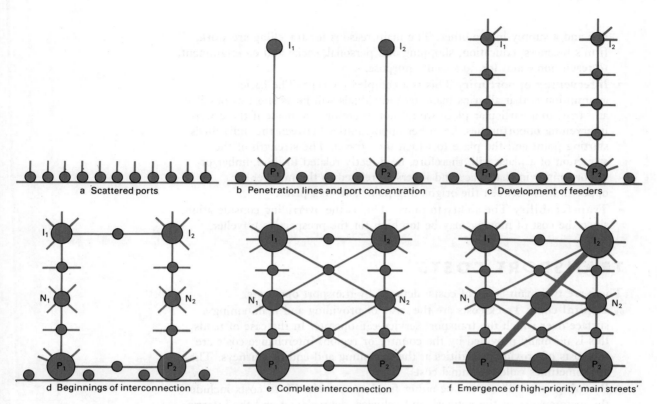

Fig. 114 Ideal sequence of network development

GRAVITY MODEL

This model gives a simple measure of interaction between places and is based solely on population and distance. It is therefore a limited interpretation of what may happen.

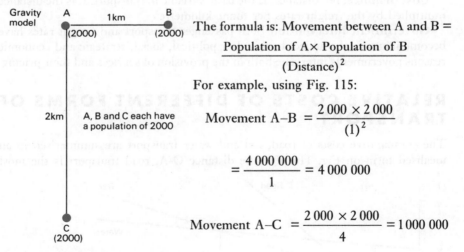

The formula is: Movement between A and B =

$$\frac{\text{Population of A} \times \text{Population of B}}{(\text{Distance})^2}$$

For example, using Fig. 115:

$$\text{Movement A–B} = \frac{2\,000 \times 2\,000}{(1)^2}$$

$$= \frac{4\,000\,000}{1} = 4\,000\,000$$

$$\text{Movement A–C} = \frac{2\,000 \times 2\,000}{4} = 1\,000\,000$$

Fig. 115 Gravity model

In this example there would be four times as many trips between A and B as between A and C.

INTENSITY OF MOVEMENT BETWEEN LOCATIONS

E Ullman identified three principles which will help to determine the intensity of movement between locations.

• **Complementarity** For two areas to interact there must be a demand in one and a supply in the other. The main reasons for travelling are work, firm's business, education, shopping and personal, social and entertainment, to reach home and for no specific purpose.

- **Intervening opportunity** This is a complex concept. The basic assumption is that all trips made by individuals will be as short as possible and trips to a particular place would not, therefore, be made if there were intervening opportunities, i.e. other opportunities between the individuals' starting point and the place to which they travel. The strength of the attraction of a place will, therefore, be directly related to the number of opportunities in that place and inversely related to the number of opportunities between the originating point and that place.
- **Transferability** The ability to move. This is the overriding consideration since the cost of moving may be too high for the prospective traveller.

TRANSPORT COSTS

There are two main types of costs incurred by transport operators.

❶ Capital costs Track costs are the costs of providing and maintaining a surface over which the transport service can operate. In the case of roads this is normally provided by the country or region. Interchange costs are the costs of providing facilities at the beginning and end of journeys. These are sometimes called terminal costs.

❷ Running costs These can be either fixed or variable. Fixed costs include the maintenance of the network and vehicles, depreciation and the interest on borrowed capital. These fixed costs would be incurred whether or not the vehicles or other means of transport were being used. Variable costs relate to the costs incurred as a result of movement in a transport system. These costs will largely depend on the distance travelled and the number of journeys which take place. Variable costs include the cost of fuel and servicing.

Cost distance, not distance, is the basic variable in transport. It is the distance multiplied by the freight rates per tonne kilometre.

Government intervention Both passenger transport and freight rates have become increasingly subject to this. For political, social, strategic and economic reasons governments intervene both in the provision of services and their pricing.

RELATIVE COSTS OF DIFFERENT FORMS OF TRANSPORT

The comparative costs of road, rail and water transport are summarised in an idealised form on Fig. 116. For the distance O-A, road transport is the most

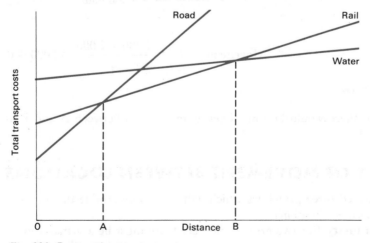

Fig. 116 Comparative transport costs

competitive. For the distance A-B, rail transport is the most competitive, while for distances beyond B water transport is most competitive.

Railways

There are high capital costs which increase with the distance to be covered by the track. Fixed running costs are also high but variable running costs are low, making rail costs more competitive over long distances.

Water transport

Costs are high over short distances because terminal costs are high but over long distances costs are lower than for railways or roads. Bulky and heavy cargoes can be carried cheaply in specialist ships such as oil tankers, bulk ore carriers and container ships. The larger the ship, the more economical it is to run. Artificial waterways involve a heavy capital outlay and continuous maintenance which makes the fixed running costs high.

Road transport

Although movement costs are higher for road than for rail over long distances, over shorter distances road transport is more economical because fixed costs are low and terminal costs are much lower than for rail or water.

Air transport

Capital costs are high and so are terminal costs but speed makes air transport attractive for passenger travel and certain types of goods. The great advantage of air transport is that it is three-dimensional and as a result routes are more direct.

Pipelines

There is a heavy capital outlay and high fixed costs. Carriage over long distances by water is much cheaper than by pipeline.

GENERAL CONCEPTS

Shrinkage of distance This, the result of improvements in technology, is a continuing phenomenon. Expressed positively it has been described as space convergence and this concept is highly significant to geographers in the study of spatial relationships.

Route network This concept introduces a systems approach to the study of transport and provides a more coherent viewpoint than the examination of individual routes in isolation.

Relative costs are very important in determining the nature of a transport network. Route networks will develop where the economic demand is sufficiently strong, despite physical difficulties.

DIFFERENT PERSPECTIVES

The study of transport networks follows a recent trend in geography away from regional synthesis towards viewing phenomena as part of a system. The links between elements in the system form networks and the study of these networks leads to a greater understanding of relationships within a system.

3.10 DEVELOPING COUNTRIES

DEFINITIONS

A developing country is not easy to define. It is generally agreed that developing countries make up most of the continents of Africa, Asia and Central and Southern America. These countries contrast economically with the developed rich, advanced, industrial countries of Western Europe, North America and Japan.

The Gross Domestic Product (GDP) of a country is calculated per capita by dividing the value of all the goods and services produced in that country by its total population.

When we compare the volume of goods and services which one individual, group or nation receives compared to others, we often use the phrase *standard of living*. This is not easy to measure or express as a figure. One way of comparing countries is to use estimates of income. Most countries calculate their Gross National Product (GNP).

GNP = net value of all goods produced and all services rendered in one year in a particular country. The country's exports are subtracted and the imports added. In addition, 'invisibles' (financial services, insurance premiums, etc.) are included (Fig. 117a).

Here is a recent table of the world's richest and poorest nations ranked by GNP per capita (in US dollars).

Table 18

	1983	1990		1983	1990
Switzerland	16,440	30,270	Bhutan	80	190
Germany	*13,590	16,500	Chad	120	190
Sweden	13,520	21,710	Bangladesh	130	180
Denmark	12,950	20,510	Ethiopia	140	120
Norway	12,650	21,850	Nepal	140	170
Belgium	12,180	16,390	Burma	170	500
France	11,730	17,830	Mali	190	260
Netherlands	11,470	16,010	Burundi	200	220
USA	11,360	21,100	Rwanda	200	310

* calculated for the former FDR (West Germany)

The table shows that changes in the GNP per capita can be considerable over a short period of time. The GNP can go down as well as up.

PQLI is the Physical Quality of Life Index which has been formulated by the Overseas Development Council (ODC). It is calculated by averaging three social characteristics of the population of a country: literacy, life expectancy and infant mortality. Each is given an index scale of 0–100

e.g. Infant mortality   Country with highest rate in world (Cambodia) = 0
                               Country with lowest rate in world (Sweden) = 100

      Life expectancy   Sierra Leone shortest life expectancy = 0
                               Norway with longest life expectancy = 100

Literacy rates run from 0–100 and are also counted.

There are many other indices which could be used to measure quality of life, e.g. health statistics, but this provides a relatively single and clear basis for comparison and unlike GNP and GDP focuses on social rather that purely economic factors (Fig. 117b).

Some criteria for economic development in the Americas

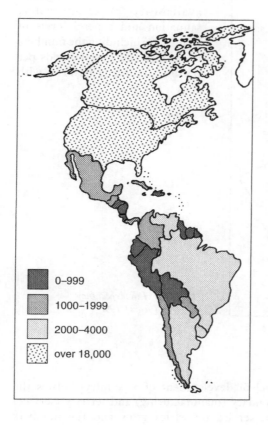

The range of GNP per capita is extreme. Haiti, with $360, is the lowest and the USA with $19,800, is the highest. All the countries of South and Central America have per capita GNPs of less than $3,500. Mexico has a GNP which is $\frac{1}{12}$th that of its neighbour, the USA.

Legend:
- 0–999
- 1000–1999
- 2000–4000
- over 18,000

Fig. 117a GNP (US$) 1990

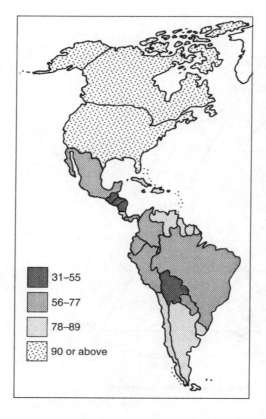

Colombia, Guatemala, Belize, Honduras and Nicaragua have the lowest ratings for development, using the PQLI formula. There are other differences to be seen when maps a and b are compared.

Legend:
- 31–55
- 56–77
- 78–89
- 90 or above

Fig. 117b PQLI 1990

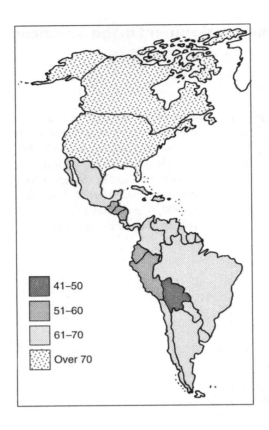

Life expectancy depends on a number of factors including diet, availability of clean water, sanitation and general levels of health care including the numbers of doctors and hospital beds per person. Compare Fig. 117c with Figs a and b.

Fig. 117c Life expectancy at birth (years) 1990

Employment structure

One criterion for showing the level of development of a country relates the numbers involved in primary, secondary (manufacturing) and tertiary (service) industries. With increased wealth, service industries grow and the numbers

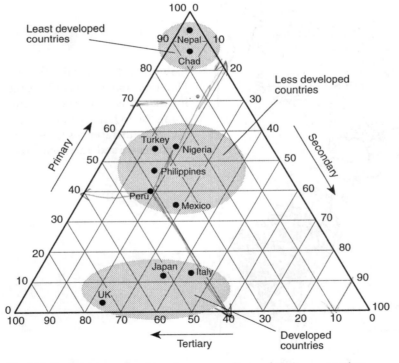

Fig. 118 Percentages employed in primary, secondary and tertiary occupations

employed in primary industries fall, possibly due to more mechanised farming or reliance on imported foodstuffs. Capital investment may reduce the numbers employed in secondary industries.

To understand how to read Fig. 118, we will take the example of Peru with 40% employed in primary, 19% in secondary and 41% in tertiary occupations. Read the primary percentage horizontally, the secondary at 7 o'clock from the secondary edge and tertiary at 11 o'clock to the horizontal baseline. Now you add India to the graph, 71% primary, 18% secondary, 11% tertiary.

Table 19

Rank (% employed in primary industry)	Country	GNP per capita 1988 (US$)
1	Nepal	170
2	Chad	160
3	Turkey	1,180
4	Nigeria	720
5	Philippines	546
6	Peru	920
7	Mexico	1,640
8	Italy	14,953
9	Japan	15,030
10	UK	13,329

Table 19 shows the relationship between the percentage in each country on the graph (Fig. 118) employed in primary industries and the GNP per capita. The ranking shows some discrepancies but, like the graph, the developed countries form a distinct group, as do the two least developed countries – Nepal and Chad.

SOME MODELS OF ECONOMIC DEVELOPMENT

A number of models have been built to describe and explain the process of development. The models are attempts to simplify a very complex situation so that we may understand why some countries have remained poor. The models also help us to examine the interrelationship of the factors which affect development and the stages in the process by which some countries have become more advanced. Models are useful in planning for future development and in pointing out ways in which the economic and social gaps between rich and poor countries may be narrowed.

The vicious circle model (Nurske)

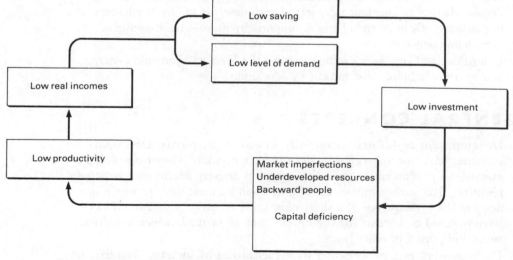

Fig. 119 Vicious circle theories of development

This model highlights the problem of lack of capital in developing countries. It does not explain why processes occur in developing countries and suggests that nothing changes.

Rostow's model

This is concerned with the economic growth of countries as part of a single process of development. A key stage in the model is take-off – when old ideas give way to forces of economic progress. So the problem of developing countries is how to achieve take-off. The model is criticised because it ignores social factors.

Myrdal's model

This is also called the cumulative causation model. The model suggests that economic development leads to an increase rather than a decrease in the difference between regions. Two main effects of rapid growth of a thriving region are **spread effects** – surrounding regions benefit from the greater demand for foodstuffs and raw materials, and **backwash effects** – capital and people move to the thriving regions so other regions are worse off.

THE BASES OF DEVELOPMENT

- Industrialisation is seen as the main agent of change.
- Vast amounts of capital are needed for industrialisation. These are obtained: either through international aid schemes (World Bank) or by private investment by foreign firms (multinationals).
- Trade agreements help development – guaranteeing markets and/or prices, e.g. EC arrangements for former British colonies.

STRATEGIES FOR DEVELOPMENT

❶ National plans such as those in India and Tanzania may aim at balanced growth (trying to keep a balance between the different parts of the economy) or unbalanced growth (rapid development of key sectors such as iron and steel).

❷ Low technology strategy involves the modernisation and expansion of traditional industries mainly to meet home market demands, e.g. the textile industry in village India.

❸ Export stimulation or import substitution occurs when countries have to decide whether to encourage exports of raw materials to obtain currency to buy other goods or to spend less on imports by making their own goods to meet home demands.

❹ Countries like Cuba have decided to leave the Western economic system and to try to achieve development by revolution.

GENERAL CONCEPTS

- **Development is defined essentially in economic terms.** Developing countries have not undergone modern industrialisation. They have obsolete methods of production so their poverty is not entirely due to poor national resources. But such countries are characterised by mass poverty which is not just the consequence of a short-term crisis or national disaster. The poverty could be lessened by the introduction of methods which are already successfully used in other lands.
- **Development is a progressive transformation of society.** Countries try to achieve development by means of deliberate planning of large-scale

economic and social change. The use of natural resources is coordinated and ways of trying to catch up with the wealthier nations are devised. However, development is not the same as economic growth. Economic growth may mean **quantitative** change, i.e. the increase of existing means of production; development means **qualitative** change – new forms of economic activity are created.

- **Development has a social meaning**. It involves creating the conditions which make it possible for the people of a country to realise their human potential, so that they get enough food, receive sound education which trains them for work, have good job opportunities and the right to take part in independent government.
- **Economic links** between developed and developing countries are maintained through international trade, international aid and the investment of capital.

DIFFERENT PERSPECTIVES

- **Development may be seen from an economic perspective.** Problems are analysed in a rational manner, plans are formed as a result of statistical forecasting; decisions are made about resource allocation.

   This approach is fraught with difficulties. Conditions beyond the control of the planners may change rapidly and to such an extent as to make the plan less practicable, e.g. the rise in world oil prices has seriously affected development policies. When the plan is finalised it may be extremely difficult to implement it because of problems such as civil disorder or the lack of enough skilled people.

- **Development may be viewed from a social perspective.** The main concern is then to seek ways to overcome problems of overpopulation, hunger, malnutrition, etc.
- **Underdevelopment in some countries is the direct result of the ways in which wealthy capitalist countries have developed.** This is the radical Marxist view. Wealthy countries are said to use the resources of the poorer countries to their own advantage and to exploit the developing world.

No single perspective gives a complete picture of the real situations in Third World countries or of the process of development. People and groups with different sets of beliefs and values see economic and social problems in different ways. For example, a member of the government of the People's Republic of China will have very different ideas on how to tackle development problems from the ruler of an oil-rich Arab state. It is important therefore that we are aware of the existence of different viewpoints, explanations and solutions to development problems.

Chapter roundup

Although this chapter is divided, for convenience's sake, into ten units, there are many links between the units and with units in the other chapters. For example, Unit 3.3 has close links with Unit 3.4 because the theoretical landscapes of Christaller and Lösch offer economic explanations of the revolution of rural as well as urban settlements. In a similar manner Unit 3.5 has close links with Unit 3.8 and Unit 3.4. These are only a few of the many interrelationships which occur between topics. A theme which runs through many aspects of human geography is the problem of the distance separating locations, how this space can be traversed and the sociological and economic significance of the links which are formed.

Transport and transfer costs play a very important part in industrial location theory and feature in the Weber model which is described in the unit on Location of Industry (pages 188–192). Transport costs and distance are also central to the von Thünen model of rural land use (see pages 179–184). The description of the network development model (Unit 3.9), based on the evolution of the transport network in West Africa provides a valuable basis for research into similar networks in the developing world. Many countries in the less developed world have networks superimposed by colonial powers and this is an important factor in our studies of these areas.

Chief examiners complain that answers to questions about human geography are sometimes superficial and lack precise examples or detailed knowledge. We suspect this weakness may occur because some candidates place too much emphasis on newspaper headlines or TV coverage of topical events. For example, if you are asked to give details of aid programmes being used to help developing countries, it is not sufficient to write down Bandaid in Africa. Far more information is required about the type of aid, who administers it and the countries or regions where it is being distributed. In this chapter we have concentrated on models, formulae and concepts, and provided a number of examples to illustrate the main points. You will need to supplement this information with case studies you have examined and places you have visited on field trips or as course work exercises. Examining boards emphasise the need for a balanced range of case studies across the developed and the developing world.

Illustrative questions and answers

1   What factors affect the distribution and density of population (a) in a small area you have studied of not more than 100 square kilometres; (b) in an area of continental size?

(in the style of the University of Cambridge Local Examinations Syndicate, A Level)

Tutorial note

The question is clearly divided into two parts which will have equal weighting. Each part has two sections – distribution and density. The question requires good knowledge of two areas of contrasting size. It also tests your ability to select the most significant factors when they are operating at quite different scales. For the small area it is best to choose the district in which you live or one which you have studied in detail on field work.

Suggested answer

Distribution is concerned with location – where people are found, whereas density relates to the number of people living in the area.

$$\text{Density} = \frac{\text{number of people}}{\text{unit area}} \quad \text{e.g. number of people per km}^2$$

(a) I have chosen the small market town of Hailsham (population about 18,000) in East Sussex. The town lies near the A22, about 15 kilometres north of Eastbourne.

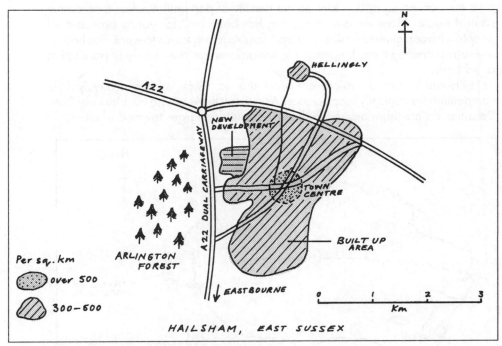

Fig. 120 Population density in Hailsham, East Sussex

Hailsham developed on a low sandstone ridge on the landward rim of Pevensey Levels, a marshy area with heavy clay soils. The distribution of the rural population reflects the agricultural possibilities offered by the geology and soils. Pevensey Levels are grazing areas used for sheep and cattle mainly in the summer when the farmers rent fields for their stock. There are consequently few farms on the marshes. To the north of Hailsham the lighter, better drained soils provide grazing and arable land. There is a therefore greater density of farms in the north of the area and the nucleated village of Hellingly.

Human and economic factors resulted in the growth and development of Hailsham as a central place. It still has a weekly stock market and serves the surrounding rural area. The modernisation of road transport in the 1930s encouraged the development of ribbon settlement along the main roads, except along the by-pass (A22) where planning restrictions forbade residential development. Building is also totally restricted to the west of the A22 where the Forestry Commission has planted Arlington Forest. Some building has recently been permitted close to the by-pass to make room for an industrial estate and residential housing to the north-west and west of Hailsham. The town has expanded rapidly in recent years. This is partly due to the proximity of Eastbourne, a major retirement and retail centre, as well as a coastal resort. The retirement function has spilled over into Hailsham and much of the new building is for elderly in-comers.

The density of population reflects the factors outlined above but other factors have also influenced the pattern. One is historical. Prior to expansion the town was characterised by Victorian terraced houses. Expansion has not involved replacement of this old housing stock. As a result the central town area and the ribbon development along the main roads within the town are areas with the highest density.

Socioeconomic factors have also influenced the expansion of the town. In the past the local authority had a housing policy which concentrated council housing in the town on a large estate to the south of the town centre. This now forms a high-density area. The private housing was mainly geared to the lower end of the market – high-density bungalows for people who were retiring but could not afford the higher prices in Eastbourne. Although the bungalows occupy small plots the occupancy rate is low, so the density of population is less than on the council estate. More expensive housing has been built for young professional people who commute to Eastbourne and neighbouring towns to work. The houses are surrounded by more land than the bungalows and the density of population is not high.

Hailsham is not a major service centre so there is comparatively little competition for centrally located sites. As a result there are no tall blocks of flats. Densities do not therefore reach the levels found in larger towns and cities.

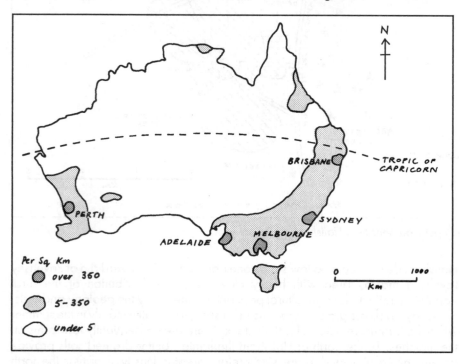

Fig. 121 Population density in Australia

(b) The distribution of population in Australia is shown on the map above. As the map shows, the distribution is peripheral, being mainly around the coasts. It is also, in the main, outside the tropics with the eastern coastlands more heavily populated than those of the west. This pattern is the result of the interaction of physical and human factors.

Physical The overwhelmingly important factor is climate. Because of its latitude, most of central Australia is a tropical desert which discourages settlement. Large areas are totally unpopulated except for small groups of aborigines. In the west the desert stretches to the coastlands but on its eastern flank it is bordered by hills and a grassland region. In the north there are small areas of tropical rainforest, much has now been cleared for cultivation.

Human Until recent decades Australia operated a 'whites only' policy, restricting immigration from Asia, the nearest land area to the north. White settlers found the humid tropics in the north a difficult area in which to live and the area has developed less rapidly than the south-east and south-west. Economic factors have also played an important role in determining the distribution of population. The settlement of the interior areas of western and north-eastern Australia is closely linked to the exploitation of mineral wealth. The peripheral pattern is partly a reflection of former colonial ties with Britain when ports were the main points of exchange for exported food (wheat) and industrial raw materials (wool), and the import of manufactured goods.

The settlers of Australia originated mainly in western and central Europe. The majority were urban dwellers and attracted to the cities. Although the immigration pattern has changed, with larger numbers coming from southern Europe and Asia, the same magnetic attraction of the larger urban areas still applies. A striking feature of the population geography of Australia is the dominance of the major cities, Brisbane, Sydney, Melbourne, Adelaide and Perth, in and around which the densities are as high as in countries with much larger total populations. Ten million people live in these five cities, out of a total population of just over 17 millions. By contrast, many interior areas are sparsely populated and very few people are attracted to these areas which are inland and often many thousands of kilometres from one of the coastal cities.

2 Fig. 122 is a model of urban development in a Western city in the nineteenth century.

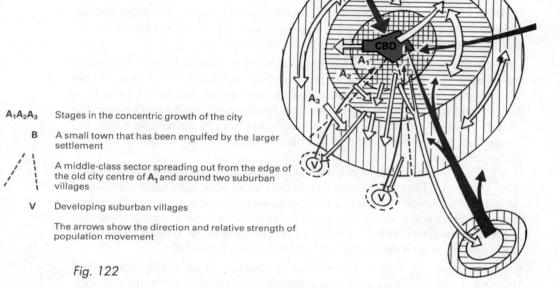

A₁A₂A₃ Stages in the concentric growth of the city

B A small town that has been engulfed by the larger settlement

A middle-class sector spreading out from the edge of the old city centre of **A₁** and around two suburban villages

V Developing suburban villages

The arrows show the direction and relative strength of population movement

Fig. 122

(a) (i) Identify the three principal types of population movement.
 (ii) Suggest reasons for each type of movement.

(b) (i) How might the pattern of population movements have changed in the twentieth century?
 (ii) What might have been the effects of these changes on the structure of the city?

(c) Contrast concentric zones A₁ and A₂ in terms of their present-day residential character, both:
 (i) inside the middle-class sector;
 (ii) outside the middle-class sector.

(in the style of Oxford and Cambridge Schools Examination Board, AS Level)

Tutorial note

The question tests your understanding of the changes that have taken place in Western cities in the last 100 years. To answer the question you must first study the diagram carefully. Do not be put off by the apparent confusion in the diagram, spend a few minutes interpreting it with the aid of the key. You are asked about the principal types of population movement so you must study the flow arrows carefully, noting their thickness, because the bolder the arrows, the more important is the movement they represent. Your answer plan should follow the structure of the question precisely, using the same letters and numbering.

Suggested answer

(a) (i) The three main movements are rural to urban migration; inter-urban (urban to urban) and intra-urban (within the city).

(ii) The reasons for each type of movement are as follows.

Rural-urban The growth of industry and commerce in the nineteenth century attracted workers from rural areas.

Inter-urban There was a counterflow from cities to other urban areas where jobs offering more money and opportunities were available and where new businesses could be started. Subsidiary businesses or industries could also be developed in other urban areas. Hence the movement in the south-east sector of the diagram, away from the larger city to the smaller urban centre. Moreover in the smaller urban centre, land would be cheaper and housing probably of a better quality.

Intra-urban As residents of the city became socially upwardly mobile, they moved to better residential areas – often in the suburbs away from the CBD. The building of new housing estates and improvements in communications encouraged movement outwards from the centre. The expansion of the CBD also displaced people who had to move elsewhere in the city.

(b) (i) In this century the pattern of population movements will have changed in the following ways. Greatly increased movement out to suburbs. Movement out to rural areas which form a commuting belt into the city. Movement away from the city centre as the result of new housing developments on the city's edge. The decline of inner city industries, encouraging people to move away from the centre. Low quality inner city housing would attract overseas immigrants with little money to spare.

(ii) There will be a decline in the inner city, creating problem areas of low-quality housing. The city will extend outwards, absorbing local communities and neighbouring towns. There will be a development of modern industrial zones in the outer city area or, with government funding, in the inner city problem areas. A green belt will be created around the city restricting further outward extensions and resulting in new commuter centres beyond the green belt.

(c) (i) In zone A_1, within the middle-class sector, large family houses will disappear. The buildings will change their functions and become, for example, solicitors' and accountants' offices. Housing is replaced by business and commercial buildings as the CBD expands towards the middle-class sector.

In zone A_2, within the middle-class sector, the area is likely to be subject to gentrification when some of the middle class move back towards the city centre as land values and house prices rise sharply in the favoured residential suburbs. The areas the middle class move from may be invaded by lower income families who can afford these older houses, but could not afford good quality modern suburban houses. The large houses will be sub-divided into flats, apartments, student hostels and so on.

(ii) Outside the middle class sector in A_1, the area becomes part of the twilight zone. Local industry has declined, the indigenous population has moved elsewhere and the area has become one of multicultural immigration. Many former buildings will have been removed to make way for comprehensive development – council estates or prestigious schemes such as the London Dockland development.

Zone A_2, outside the middle-class sector, is invaded by the upwardly mobile immigrant community. As younger people move to newer and better residential areas, the elderly indigenous population is left behind.

Question bank

1 (Time allowed: 45 mins)

	Total Dependency Ratios[1]			Old-Age Dependency Ratios[2]	
1	Turkey	70.1	1	Sweden	26.6
2	Ireland	67.4	2	Norway	24.2
3	Iceland	57.3	3	UK	23.3
4	Norway	56.5	4	Denmark	23.2
5	Portugal	56.3	5	Belgium	23.1
6	Cyprus	55.6	6	Austria	22.8
7	Spain	54.6	7	West Germany	22.7
7	Sweden	54.6	8	Switzerland	22.1
9	UK	53.2	9	Greece	22.0
9	Greece	53.2	9	Italy	22.0
11	Italy	52.8	11	France	21.3
12	Belgium	52.4	12	Luxembourg	20.8
13	France	51.8	13	Spain	20.0
14	Denmark	50.4	14	Portugal	19.5
15	Malta	49.9	15	Ireland	18.8
16	Austria	48.9	16	Netherlands	18.7
17	Netherlands	47.5	17	Cyprus	18.0
18	Switzerland	46.6	18	Iceland	17.0
19	Luxembourg	44.5	19	Malta	15.8
20	West Germany	44.0	20	Liechtenstein	14.0
20	Liechtenstein	44.0	21	Turkey	8.5

[1]Total Dependency Ratio $= \dfrac{\text{Persons } 65 \text{ and over} + \text{children under } 15}{\text{Persons } 15 - 64} \times \dfrac{100}{1}$

[2]Old-Age Dependency Ratio $= \dfrac{\text{Persons } 65 \text{ and over}}{\text{Persons } 15 - 64} \times \dfrac{100}{1}$

Fig. 123 Dependency ratios, Western Europe, 1984

(a) Study Fig. 123. Why does the ranking of the countries on the Total Dependency Ratio vary so much from that of the Old-Age Dependency Ratio? (6)

(b) (i) Define the terms overpopulation and underpopulation. (4)
(ii) With reference to **two** countries, discuss the extent to which national population policies have sought to achieve optimum population. (20)
(iii) How can cultural and moral values sometimes hinder the operation of what in purely economic terms would be appropriate population policies? (5)

(Northern Ireland Schools Examinations and Assessment Council, A Level, June 1990)

Pitfalls

Be careful when defining overpopulation and underpopulation. Your definitions should be as succinct as possible and not long, rambling paragraphs. Examples may help to clarify your explanations.

In (b) (ii) note the word 'optimum'. Do not assume that you must write only about countries that are trying to reduce the birth rate. Some countries, such as Australia, are prepared to receive carefully selected immigrants to increase the total population.

Do not ride a particular hobby horse when answering part (b) (iii). You may, for example, have strong views about laws concerning abortion but this is not the place to air them. Give a balanced assessment, being as objective as possible.

Points

(a) Define the terms 'Total Dependency Ratio' and 'Dependency Ratio' and remember that the dependency ratio does not include those who are unemployed. The key point which should determine your answer is the differentiation between the economically active and the non-economically active. In developing countries the dependency ratio is likely to be higher than in a developed country.

Make sure you give a balanced viewpoint when answering (b) (iii). Cultural aspects might include age of marriage, type of family unit (nucleated, etc.), family size (smaller in some countries with high living standards) and so on. Moral issues will include religious beliefs, moral attitudes towards family planning and moral attitudes imposed by governments, e.g. China.

2 (Time allowed 22 mins)

Study Fig. 124 which shows a basic migration model.

(Adapted from: Lee (1966), *A Theory of Migration, Demography 3*)

Fig. 124   A basic migration model (attracting factors are shown as +, repelling factors as −, and neutral factors as 0)

(a) State *two* attracting and *two* repelling factors which encourage migration from *Less Developed Countries*. (4)

(b) Draw an *annotated* population pyramid to illustrate the probable effects of emigration on the population structure of the country of origin. (6)

(c) (i) Suggest *two* physical and *two* human factors which might be described as intervening obstacles to migration. (4)
(ii) Outline how such intervening obstacles have been increasingly subject to change. (6)

(University of London School Examinations Board, AS Level, June 1991)

Pitfalls

The examiners' report on the answers to this question states, 'This question was typical of those set on a popular human topic with which candidates often feel confident but do not score highly'. The report points out that one of the reasons for scoring low marks is lack of detail and making statements which are not sufficiently specific. For example, the question in (a) asks for two reasons why emigration from less developed countries is attractive. Answers just listing 'employment' and 'housing' score low marks. Fuller and more specific answers scoring full marks would be 'Waged employment in industry', and 'Joining extended family with shared accommodation available.'

The population pyramid required in (b) must be annotated. That is, it will require not only age bands to be labelled but also comments such as 'Lower numbers in young adult age ranges.'

(c) (ii) Needs careful thought and some good examples to show how attitudes can change to immigrants.

Points

The examples given in the 'Pitfalls' section above should be noted. Whereas parts (a) and (b) deal with emigration from less developed countries, part (c) uses the word migration. This will mean you can give examples of obstacles to internal migration, such as civil war in Ethiopia and physical disadvantages in northern Canada.

3 (Time allowed: 25 mins)

Fig. 125 below illustrates the principal features of a commuter village.

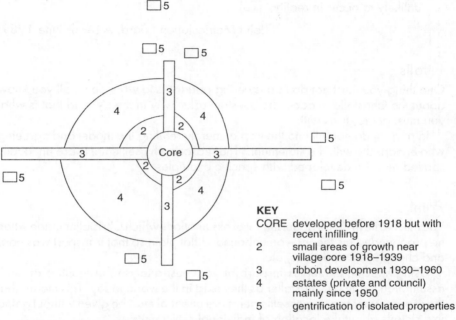

KEY
CORE developed before 1918 but with recent infilling
2 small areas of growth near village core 1918–1939
3 ribbon development 1930–1960
4 estates (private and council) mainly since 1950
5 gentrification of isolated properties

Fig. 125 The principal features of a commuter village

(a) Outline **one** way in which the inflow of commuters has affected the form of the village illustrated in Fig. 125. (3)
(b) Describe **two** ways in which the pattern of migration to rural areas in the Developed World has changed since 1945. (6)
(c) With reference to specific examples suggest why, in the developed world, migration to rural areas is not always welcomed by the existing inhabitants. (6)

(The Associated Examining Board, AS Level, June 1990)

Pitfalls

Do not try to answer part (a) without first looking carefully at the diagram provided. Use the key to identify the features listed and remember you are only asked to outline one way the form has been affected. If you try to answer the question by providing a list you are wasting valuable time and will lose marks.

Part (b) requires careful reading. The key words are 'changed since 1945'. Writing a paragraph on generalities about why people choose to migrate to rural areas will gain you no marks.

Part (c) should present no problems if you know something about the socio-economic issues involved.

Points

Write a few sentences about the one way you have chosen, e.g. ribbon development.

In part (b) you should consider such aspects as the increasing scale of migration, the escalation of second home ownership and improvements in mobility making travelling longer distances possible.

Part (c) requires specific examples, which can come from the UK. You may have come across examples of second homes in the Peak District or elsewhere when you were on holiday or doing field work.

4 (Time allowed: 45 mins)

(a) Why, in theory, might settlements of equal size be equally spaced? (10)
(b) Referring to specific examples, discuss the factors which make the pattern unlikely to occur in reality. (15)

(Joint Matriculation Board, A Level, June 1989)

Pitfalls

One thing you must not do in answering part (a) is to write down all you know about the Christaller model. The question asks 'why in theory' and that is what you must get to grips with.

In part (b) do not fall into the trap of merely refuting the model and agreeing wholeheartedly with the statement. The reasons why settlements are unequally spaced must be developed with specific examples.

Points

You must write in detail about the set of assumptions which Christaller made when he propounded his theory – an unbounded flat plain so that transport was easy and cheap in all directions, etc.

Using specific examples in part (b) you must analyse the realities of each assumption made by Christaller as they exist in the world today. This means that the reasons why spacing of settlements are unequal must be given without going into details about the location of individual settlements.

5 (Time allowed: 35 mins)

(a) Select any **one** model of urban structure
    (i) Describe the pattern of land use; (5)
    (ii) Outline the principles upon which it is based. (5)

(b) With reference to specific examples, assess the applicability of this model. (15)

(The Associated Examining Board, A Level, June 1990)

Pitfalls

There are two problems to consider when answering this question, the first is which model to select and the second is which specific examples to use when answering (b). In some ways the sector model (Hoyt) is straightforward since it includes the features of the concentric zone model (Burgess). However, the multiple nuclei model also has much to offer, particularly if you can give some good examples from large cities.

You should be able to give at least three examples of urban structures which either confirm or refute the model you have described in (a).

Points

Draw a sketch of the model you have chosen and label it clearly.
Describe each of the sectors in detail and their position on the model.

For part (a) (ii), provide information about the model's background and whether it was based on examples from the United States or elsewhere. Explain the principles on which it is based, for example the sector model is based on the idea that accessibility to the city centre influences the location of functional zones.

When answering (b) give precise information about the zones in the cities you have chosen and for each one assess whether it complies with the assumptions in the model.

6 (Time allowed: 45 mins)

The table below shows selected inner and outer city indicators for London. Explain the problems of inner city areas in the developed world which are suggested by the information provided in the table.

	Inner London	Outer London
% population change 1971–1981	−18.4	−2.7
Population density (persons/ha)	92.4	19.6
% persons born in UK	72.0	93.1
% households comprising OAPs only	23.6	23.2
% children living with only one adult	13.9	5.8
% children with mothers working full time	20.7	12.4
% households lacking inside WC	3.2	1.2
% persons unemployed	13.4	5.6

(University of London School Examinations Board, AS Level, 1990)

Pitfalls

This question does not ask you to write all you know about inner cities. It concentrates on the problems and gives you a table of inner city indicators for London.

One danger is to focus too closely on the figures in the table and work out the precise difference between a figure for Inner London and the same figure for Outer London, this is not needed. You should analyse the data or manipulate it to show you understand it, but do not simply repeat information given in the table without adding your own interpretation.

Points

Start off by writing a short explanation to show you know what is meant by the inner city and its contrasts with the outer areas of the city.

Then be systematic and write a short paragraph on each section of the table pointing out the differences between the inner and outer parts of London and explaining each problem as it appears in the table. Try to make generalisations from the details. For example, the percentage of households comprising OAPs only is concerned with the problem of the aged who are living on fixed, and usually low incomes. Their problems include the general problems of the care and extra help which elderly people may need.

Finish off with a final paragraph summarising the inner city issues, but not repeating what you have written. Examiners only award marks once!

7 (Time allowed: 40 mins)

(a) Outline the main assumptions of the Von Thünen model. (10)
(b) To what extent does the model help in an understanding of the pattern of present-day agricultural land-use? (15)

(University of London School Examinations Board, A Level, June 1991)

Pitfalls

Part (a) of the question does not want to be decorated with sketches of the circular patterns suggested in the model. Nor is there a need to write several pages about the model. As the examiners' report states, 'Little of this embellishment served a useful purpose. It was bad examination strategy as it took time from work elsewhere in the paper.'

(b) Do not make the mistake of dismissing the model as irrelevant. There are many aspects of it which are replicated in the real world – see the relevant paragraphs in Unit 3.7.

Points

Answer (a) by writing short paragraphs, preferably numbered to provide a structure, setting out the main assumptions of the von Thünen model. This approach can get you 10 marks very easily.

Part (b) needs to be approached with caution. You must point out the limitations to the model at the present time. After writing at some length about the limitations you must then add further paragraphs pointing out the present-day significance of the model as expounded by Chisholm and others. It is also worthwhile adding some sentences about the notion of constructing an ideal model as a framework against which the complexities of real world situations can be measured.

8 (Time allowed: 45 mins)

'Weber's model of industrial location is of limited use when examining the location patterns of manufacturing industries established *since 1950*.' How far do you agree with this view?

(Oxford and Cambridge Schools Examination Board, A Level, June 1991)

Pitfalls

The easiest mistake when answering this question is to assume that Weber based his model entirely on transport costs. Transport costs lie at the heart of his model but there are other important factors such as labour costs and that many raw materials are localised and not ubiquitous.

The key words in the question are 'since 1950' and the examiners' report notes that many answers did not focus on the location patterns of manufacturing industries established since 1950.

Be sure you give detailed examples to support your arguments and do not assume that Weber's model is totally outdated.

Points

Start by giving a brief summary of Weber's model of industrial location and the premises on which it is based.

This summary should be followed by explanations of the reasons why the model is not always appropriate at the present time. Back up your explanations with actual examples of industrial locations. Some good examples which can be quoted to show the model is limited in its application but in some cases is still appropriate, are: the manufacture of paper; iron and steel works locations in Western Europe; manufacture of electronic goods; manufacture of sugar from beet; manufacture of jam; the location of aluminium smelters; location of car manufacturers. It is up to you to sort out which of these give strength to Weber's model and which weaken it!

9 (Time allowed: 15 mins)

Study the graph below, Fig. 126, which shows the relationship between the distance and costs of transporting goods by lorry, train and barge, and distance in a developed country.

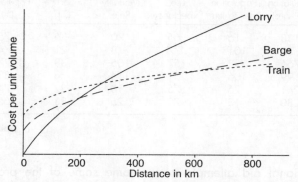

Fig. 126 Distance /Cost graph

(a) (i) At what distance does lorry transport cease to be the cheapest?
(ii) At what distance does barge transport cease to be the cheapest? (2)

(b) Why do transport costs increase more slowly as distance increases? (2)

(c) Outline **three** factors, **other** than distance, which affect transport rates. (6)

(d) How might a government alter the structure of transport costs in order to encourage the carriage of goods by rail? (5)

(The Associated Examining Board, A Level, June 1991)

Pitfalls

The simple comparative line graph is not difficult to interpret but you must be accurate. Careless reading of the graph could result in no marks for part (a). Part (b), according to the examiners' report, was rarely done correctly. This was because only the best candidates considered other factors about costs, apart from transport costs increasing with distance.

Section (c) is not difficult but the reasons must be explained and elaborated upon.

Section (d) may encourage vague replies. Be specific and do not include increasing fuel costs. Such costs would also have an effect on road transport. The question uses the term the structure of transport costs . This means that you cannot suggest greater investment in the railways as one means of encouraging the carriage of goods by rail.

Points

In (a), make accurate estimates of the distances. The examiners do not expect you to be completely accurate because the graph is not that precise, and you are allowed certain tolerance limits.

Sections (b), (c) and (d) require you to show your knowledge of the many factors that affect transport costs and the various ways in which a government can encourage one type of transport by financial and judicial methods.

10 (Time allowed: 40 mins)

(a) Study Fig. 127.

(i) Select from the table (Fig. 127), **three** sets of statistics which would be useful in deciding whether a country is Developed or Developing.
Explain in detail how the statistics you have selected can indicate the level of development of a country. (9)

(ii) Many of the statistics in the table were obtained from national censuses. With reference to named countries, outline the problems of conducting a census in a **Developing** country. (6)

	Population (millions)	Population per sq km	Life Expectancy	Infant Mortality Rate	Population under 15 (%)	Urban Population (%)	Adult Literacy (%)
Brazil	138	16	65	70	36	75	78
France	55	101	77	8	21	74	100
India	766	233	57	105	38	27	41
Nigeria	99	106	51	114	na	33	34
USA	241	26	75	10	22	74	99
USSR	280	13	70	25	23	66	100

na = not available

Fig. 127

(b) 'International aid attempts to overcome some of the problems facing Developing Countries.'

(i) Describe the different ways in which international aid is organised.

(ii) Discuss the viewpoint that international aid does not always benefit the receiving country. (10)

(Scottish Certificate of Education, Higher Grade, May 1991)

Pitfalls

(a) Do not expect all the sets of statistics in the table to be useful when making your selection. Remember that having made your selection you have to explain why those particular sets are useful. When making your selection look carefully at the countries listed and decide which are part of the developing world and which are not. If the same statistic, or one very close, applies to a developed as well as a developing country you may have selected the wrong set.

For (ii) your knowledge of developing countries should help you to decide what problems arise in trying to get accurate statistics. Although you may not know of actual problems encountered in specific countries, most developing countries can be taken as examples.

In part (b) keep (i) and (ii) separate. In (ii) you are asked to discuss. This means you should attempt to give a balanced view because the statement that aid does not always benefit the receiving country is not necessarily true in every circumstance.

Points

Having made your selection in (a)(i), give a detailed explanation of why each set can help to indicate the level of development of a country. Note that your selection is not limited solely to developing countries.

In (ii) put yourself in the position of a census collector in, for example, an African country such as Tanzania. Think of the problems involved in collecting the information where transport is limited, people may be illiterate and records of basic information such as rates of birth are not kept.

In (b)(i) do not give a list of organisations but attempt to describe the various methods by which international aid is organised to reach the countries that need it. Try to classify the various ways in which aid is organised.

(ii) The viewpoint that international aid does not always benefit the receiving country partly relates to the type of aid given. Some forms of aid may not encourage the people to fend for themselves. Other forms of aid may be targeted at one group of people, e.g. expectant mothers, and fail to help other groups equally in need.

CHAPTER 4

REGIONAL AND ENVIRONMENTAL ISSUES

Units in this chapter

Chapter objectives

When you have studied the units in this chapter you should be able to:

*   understand the concept of a problem region and why such regions occur;

*   explain the reasons why some regions in the UK have declined in recent decades;

*   describe the problems that have arisen as a result of regional decline;

*   describe the measures taken by the government and the EC to assist the problem regions;

*   describe the changes that have occurred in two problem areas, South Wales and the Scottish Highlands;

*   understand the changing distribution of population in France;

*   explain the causes and effects of inequalities of wealth in the regions of France;

*   appreciate population issues in a developing country;

*   describe the reasons for, and problems resulting from urbanisation in a developing region – West Africa;

*   describe the agricultural economy of India;

*   understand what is being done to improve agriculture in the developing world;

*   explain some of the regional problems in Brazil and the strategies being adopted to improve the less-developed regions;

*   understand the concepts of exploitation and conservation and their application to regions of the developed and developing world;

*   explain the different forms of pollution and their sources;

*   describe some of the measures being taken to reduce pollution.

Relevance of the units

The focus in this chapter is the contribution that geography can make to an understanding of some contemporary issues and problems concerning people and environments. One of the major issues in countries of both the developed and developing world is that of differences between regions. These differences result in spatial inequalities within a country which require solutions at a national level. Unit 4.1 looks at some of the inequalities in employment that are to be found in the UK and examines the various ways in which assistance is given to problem areas and also examines the economic problems of the inner cities. Unit 4.2 looks at some of the regional problems that exist in France and the measures being taken there to develop the peripheral regions. Unit 4.5 looks at regional development strategies in Brazil, a developing country that has tackled its problems in distinctive ways, some of which affect the Amazonian rainforest.

In the Developing World there are also population issues and the problems that result from rural–urban migration. Unit 4.3 looks at these issues and problems as they occur in West Africa.

Another problem of the Developing World is to improve the efficiency of food production to feed the increasing population and provide a surplus for export. Unit 4.4 examines the problems of agriculture in India and the Green Revolution and its effects. There is also a case study of the multi-purpose development of the Narmada Valley.

Units 4.6 and 4.7 look at the issues which relate to the environment and some of the solutions that are being used to reduce exploitation and pollution.

Throughout this chapter you will be faced with contemporary issues and problems which will make you more aware and knowledgeable about such topics as unemployment, migration, pollution and conservation at local, national and global levels.

Key ideas and concepts

One of the important concepts you must understand is that of a problem region: how a problem region can be identified and the issues that can be found in such regions. Linked with this concept is the corollary that regional problems are best tackled by governments and more prosperous regions can be affected adversely as a result.

There are a number of concepts linked with population. They include the concepts of optimum and under- or overpopulation. Key ideas associated with migration are explored in Unit 4.3 with particular reference to migration in the developing world.

Population pressure and the concept of internal disequilibrium are examined in Unit 4.4 in connection with agricultural developments in India. Population pressure is closely connected to the availability of resources and internal disequilibrium is directly related to the degree of population pressure.

The concept of a perceptual frontier exists in Brazil as it did in the United States in the nineteenth century. The interior is still largely undeveloped and the 'frontiersman' attitude still prevails. This concept helps to explain the Brazilian attitude to exploitation of the rainforest which is seen by many Brazilians as an area similar in its potential to that of the prairies of North America in the nineteenth century.

The concept of conservation and its areas of conflict with exploitation are matters which regularly capture the headlines and generate programmes on TV. Similarly the concept of pollution, its causes and effects are further examples of the relevance of geography on a local, national and global scale.

4.1 UNITED KINGDOM: REGIONAL PROBLEMS

WHY SOME REGIONS HAVE DECLINED

❶ During the nineteenth century there was a period of rapid industrialisation based on the availability of coal and the ease with which raw materials could be obtained, either locally or from overseas. As a result, major manufacturing and urban centres developed in Central Scotland, the North-East, South Lancashire, West Yorkshire, the Midlands and South Wales. London also became an important industrial centre as well as the commercial and administrative capital.

❷ After World War I the attraction of the coalfields for industrial development steadily weakened. The more traditional exports of cotton textiles, coal, ships and heavy engineering products became less profitable as overseas countries developed their own industries. The pattern of world trade changed and the market for some products such as steam locomotives and rolling stock contracted severely.

❸ As people in advanced industrial societies have increased their personal wealth during the last three decades there has been a rapid expansion in the demand for consumer goods such as television sets, refrigerators, cars, washing machines, lawn mowers, typewriters and many other goods which are to be found in a modern home. The attraction of coalfield locations has weakened as consumer demand has changed. Proximity to markets or supplies of components is more significant and the emphasis has shifted to southern England, especially Greater London where the market and materials are available.

❹ World trade has also grown for such exports as aircraft engines, lorries, electrical products and electronic equipment. Commonwealth countries have become less significant as customers for British goods, but trade with Western Europe has increased.

❺ Improved transport facilities, particularly the door-to-door flexibility of road transport, the construction of a motorway network and the development of deep-sea container facilities have all strengthened the Midlands and the South-East and made them the most economic locations for new and expanding industries.

❻ The energy required by the growth industries can be obtained from the 400 kV grid of the generating companies, National Power, PowerGen and Nuclear Electricity, the pipelines of British Gas and transmission pipelines from coastal refineries installed by the petroleum companies. The accessibility of energy supplies to practically all parts of Britain has given manufacturers the opportunity to locate their plants close to the major demand centres for their products, such as London and the South-East, where net personal incomes amount to 35% of the national total, or in the Midlands which accounts for a further 16% of the national total.

❼ The size of the labour market in London and the Midlands is also important. It means that the possibility of obtaining the right sort of skills was greater in these regions than elsewhere in the country. The skills required for the consumer industries, many of which use conveyor belt techniques, were not to be found in the traditional heavy industries of South Wales and the North. As industry declined on the coalfields, labour from these areas migrated to the South-East and Midlands and has been trained to fulfil the needs of the new industries.

❽ Apart from employment in manufacturing industries, there has been a considerably enlarged demand for specialised services such as banking, insurance, government services and the retail trade which has increased employment opportunities in these occupations. The long-standing dominance by London of this sector of the economy facilitated expansion of services in this region rather than elsewhere.

⑨ Decline has not been confined to industrial areas; some rural areas have also become problem regions. The two largest rural regions which have experienced economic deterioration are the Highlands and Islands of Scotland and west and central Wales. In these regions the economy is relatively unbalanced, there is little employment available and local incomes and opportunities are therefore limited. Remoteness has inhibited investment and the major primary activities, agriculture, fishing and forestry employ few people. As in the traditional industrial regions, the demand for the products of these rural regions has declined, not because consumer demand has changed (there is still a need for the primary products these regions can produce such as meat and timber), but because primary products can be obtained more cheaply from overseas. The lure of high wages and improved amenities in the industrial cities has encouraged migration from these areas.

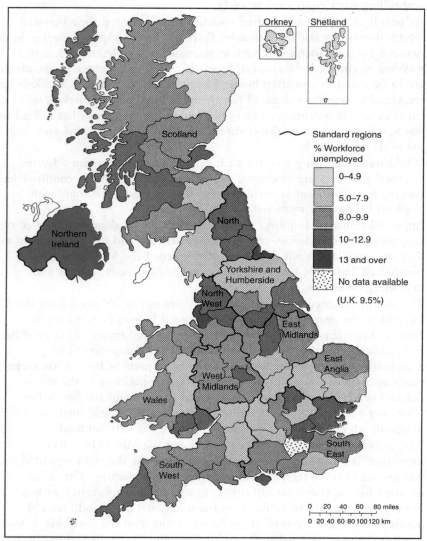

Source: *Employment Gazette, June 1992*

Fig. 128 Unemployment, April 1992

RESULTANT PROBLEMS

The regions which have declined during recent decades display a number of symptoms which classify them as problem regions:

- High rates of unemployment which reach over 15% of the labour force in some cities (Fig. 128). The worst-hit regions have been those which grew up on the coalfields. Recently unemployment has risen in service industries, affecting London and some rural counties such as Cornwall.
- Net migration to other parts of Britain and overseas has resulted in a steady fall in the total population of these regions (see Fig. 129). Between 1971 and 1981 there was a 2.9% decrease in population in the North region, compared with a 0.5% increase in the total population of England and Wales. It can be argued that there were decreases in the population of Greater London and the West Midland conurbation during the same period but these changes were caused by movement from the congested city regions to the neighbouring suburbs or rural hinterlands.
- Higher unemployment and lower average wages have reduced the purchasing power in the problem regions with average weekly expenditure 20% or more less than in the more prosperous regions.
- Economic stagnation and decline has affected the infrastructure of the less

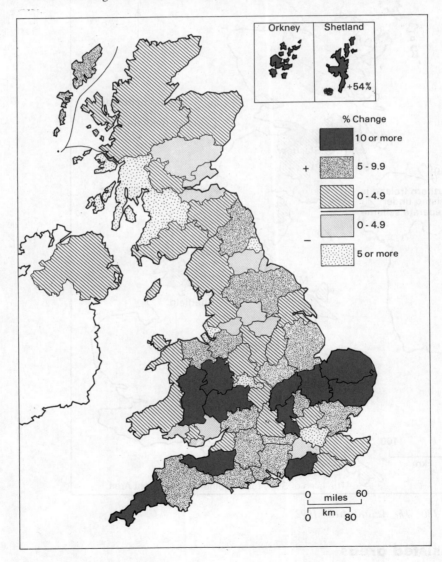

Fig. 129 Population changes 1971–1981

prosperous regions. Lack of investment and low levels of personal wealth have resulted in poor housing, fewer amenities, derelict mines and factories and a decline in the level of public services which contrast with the comparatively higher standards of the more prosperous areas.

• Transport services are less viable because there have been few new developments and a decline in the economic structure. The improvement and extension of the existing transport network is discouraged except in higher population density areas such as London. Consequently transport costs are increased making the regions less attractive locations for new or expanding firms.

GOVERNMENT ASSISTANCE

State assistance to the problem regions has been of considerable significance in the last thirty years. The nature and scale of the assistance changes from time to time and the areas shown on Fig. 130 are subject to modification as circumstances alter.

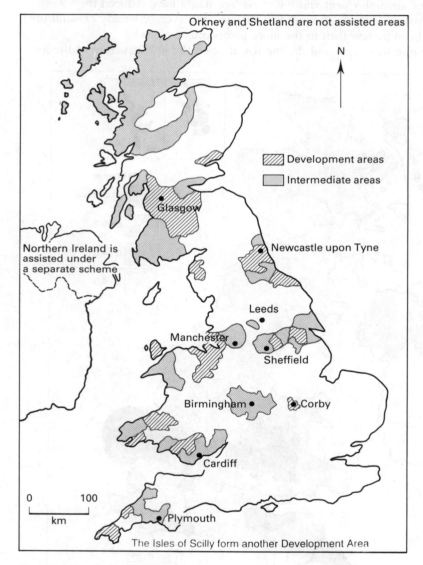

Fig. 130 *The Assisted Areas, 1992*

Assisted areas

The government has identified two categories of problem areas based on the scale of difficulty; they are the Development Areas and Intermediate Areas. The level of assistance is less for the intermediate areas. Money has been allocated to diversify and restructure employment. In addition, a number of inducements has been offered to attract industries to these areas.

- Industrial estates have been built ahead of demand with rent concessions to industrialists.
- Grants and loans are available with tax concessions to new enterprises.
- Financial aid is available to train employees in skills required by new industries.

Selective assistance in the regions is given for certain investment projects undertaken by firms while Regional Enterprise Grants are available to firms with fewer than 25 employees to support investment and innovation.

The English Industrial Estates Corporation provides industrial premises in England where private sector provision is inadequate.

The Rural Development Commission in England promotes economic and social development by providing small factories and workshops and giving technical advice.

In Wales the Welsh Development Agency promotes industrial development in urban areas and the Development Board for Rural Wales provides factories, key workers' housing and advice for small businesses.

In Scotland the Scottish Enterprise and Highlands and Islands Enterprise provide a wide range of support to industry, operating mainly through a network of private-sector-led Local Enterprise Companies.

In Northern Ireland the Industrial Development Board provides training grants, exemption from local taxation and other help for manufacturing companies, as well as grants to retain good management.

New towns

In order to accommodate residents of the assisted areas in new housing and provide a suitable urban infrastructure, the government designated 14 new towns to these regions. They include Skelmersdale and Warrington in the North-West, Peterlee and Aycliffe in the North-East and East Kilbride and Glenrothes in central Scotland. These new towns have played a significant role in attracting manufacturing investment into regions of high unemployment.

Urban regeneration

Since 1981 there has been increasing action by the government to tackle the social and economic problems of inner city areas. Government policy is aimed at spending public money on inner city renewal by coordinating attempts to tackle environmental dereliction and encouraging private enterprise.

Enterprise Zones

Since 1981 the government has set up 27 Enterprise Zones. Each zone runs for a period of ten years and has the following benefits:
- exemption from the business rate (local property tax);
- 100% allowances for corporation and income tax purposes for capital expenditure on industrial and commercial buildings;
- a much simplified planning system;
- a reduction in government requests for statistical information.

The earliest zones have ended their ten years of support and others are not likely to be formed.

Urban Development Corporations (UDCs)

Eleven UDCs have been set up in order to reverse large-scale urban decline. The

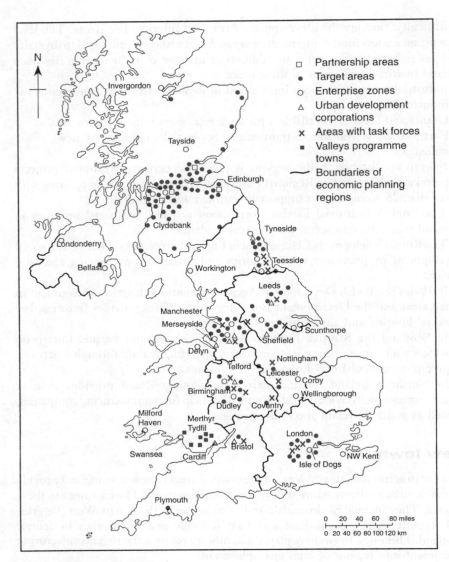

Fig. 131 Urban policy initiatives

first two were established in London Docklands and Merseyside in 1981. The other nine are at Trafford Park (Greater Manchester), Teesside, Tyne and Wear, Black Country (West Midlands), Cardiff Bay, Bristol, Leeds, Central Manchester and Sheffield. The last four were set up in 1988–89. Large government grants and secured private investment commitments enable derelict land to be reclaimed and houses, offices and industrial floorspace to be provided.

Urban Target Areas

The government has introduced an Urban Programme which allocates money to selected local authorities on the basis of a 75% grant to cover spending on approved projects. The programme is directed at economic, social, environmental and housing problems and the areas targeted are those where the problems are greatest and the levels of deprivation most severe.

Action for Cities Initiative

This scheme was started in 1988 for England and Wales and provides £4,000 million a year to be spent on the inner cities.

City Challenge

Under this programme, set up in 1991, local authorities are invited to submit plans for regenerating their city neighbourhoods by tackling the problems of physical decay and poor quality of life. Over a five-year period the best proposals will receive government funding which will be combined with spending by the councils themselves, the private sector and other bodies.

In Scotland four Partnerships have been set up – in Dundee, Edinburgh, Glasgow and Paisley. These aim to improve the type and tenure of housing available for local people, to improve employment prospects and to tackle social and environmental problems on the estates.

In Northern Ireland a Belfast Action Team has been set up and the Laganside Corporation was established in 1989 to regenerate Belfast's riverside area. In Wales the Cardiff Bay Development Corporation was set up in 1987 to redevelop an area of south Cardiff, once the commercial centre.

City Action Teams

Eight City Action Teams (CATs) have been established in England to coordinate and target government programmes to regenerate inner cities. They act as a central contact point with government for business, voluntary and community organisations.

Task Forces

There are also 16 Task Forces in England to bring together and focus the efforts of government departments and the local community to regenerate inner cities. Each Task Force consists of a small team of five or six civil servants based in the most deprived parts of an inner city area. So far they have committed some £80 million to over 3 000 projects and, in time, they will hand over their functions to local organisations.

Garden Festivals

A number of Garden Festivals have been funded in Assisted Areas with the aim of improving the environment and attracting tourists. The first was held at Liverpool in 1984. This was followed by Festivals at Stoke-on-Trent in 1986, Glasgow in 1988, Gateshead in 1990 and Ebbw Vale in 1992.

Welsh Valleys Programme

In 1988 the Welsh Development Agency introduced a programme to improve the economic, social and environmental conditions in the valleys of South Wales.

ASSISTANCE FROM THE EUROPEAN COMMUNITY

Britain's membership of the European Community since 1973 has made a variety of EC measures available to the assisted areas. These measures are designed to ameliorate the problems of less prosperous parts of the Community and to create a market within which there is equality of competition whatever the national or regional location. The aim is to see that similar regions with similar problems get similar assistance and no attempts are made to prop up enterprises which are out of date or inefficient. Membership of the EC imposes constraints upon the member governments since the Commission has the power to examine state aid and to rule whether or not it is in accord with EC policy.

Britain's assisted areas are eligible for a variety of financial aids administered from Brussels and the role and magnitude of this help is steadily increasing.

Loans from the European Investment Bank

This bank will lend up to 40% of the fixed capital costs of major projects at low interest rates. It will also lend money to modernise undertakings or to develop new economic activities. For example, the bank is to help finance British Aerospace's share of the development of the new A-330 Airbus with £150 million of credit funding.

Grants and loans from the European Coal and Steel Community (ECSC)

Money is available for the coal and steel industries or for other industries which would create jobs for redundant coal miners or steel workers. When, in 1979, the British Steel Corporation closed its plant at Shotton in North Wales, funds from the ECSC helped to improve the Corporation's redundancy scheme and support retraining schemes. In 1983 the National Coal Board borrowed £14 million to invest in the Nottinghamshire coalfield.

European Regional Development Fund (ERDF)

The fund supports projects in less prosperous regions of the Community in the context of regional development programmes. About half of ERDF grants are for infrastructure projects such as motorways and industrial estates. The rest goes to industrial projects such as the modernisation of a motor vehicle components factory in Antrim. Tourism and related projects also benefit. For example, ERDF money helped the development of the Merseyside Maritime Museum at the Albert Dock in Liverpool.

European Social Fund (ESF)

The ESF was set up to assist vocational training, retraining and resettlement schemes in the EC, particularly for school-leavers and the unemployed. The UK has received grants for handicapped immigrants, creating new jobs for young people and improving working conditions. Sometimes ESF grants are combined with funds from the ERDF. For example, Bradford received an injection of money to improve the environment and revitalise an inner city conservation area by bringing in new residents and constructing offices and hotels.

CASE STUDY – SOUTH WALES

In the nineteenth century, the economic vitality of South Wales stemmed from two basic industries – coal mining, and iron and steel. Much of the coal was exported and steel furnaces provided the raw material for a number of specialised steel processing industries such as tin plating, galvanising and the production of sheet steel.

Because of its narrow industrial base, South Wales was less diversified than its two main competitors, Central Scotland and the North-East. In 1970 there were 52 pits operating in the region employing 42 600 men. By 1992 only 3 pits were operating. The number of blast furnaces dropped from 15 in 1970 to 7 in 1989, only those at Newport and Port Talbot remaining in use. In the same period employment in the iron and steel industry declined from 60 000 to 22 000.

Government assistance to the region has been channelled in recent years through the Welsh Development Agency which is responsible for approving new schemes for funding. The largest amount of investment has taken place in Mid Glamorgan, the county with the highest unemployment rate. Communications have been improved with the building of the M4 which reaches as far as Swansea and Llanelli. Improvements have also been made to the existing road network including the Head of the Valleys (e.g. through Merthyr Tydfil) road.

Good labour relations, high productivity and the financial incentives offered by Development Area grants have attracted a number of firms to move to South Wales or to develop there. Ford has opened an engine plant at Bridgend in Mid Glamorgan, aided by a grant from the European Regional Development Fund. The project has brought 1800 new jobs to the area.

No fewer than eight Japanese manufacturers have moved to South Wales, e.g. Panasonic and Sony in the Cardiff area and Aiwa at Blackwood to the north. In the Newport area, Plessey Marine is providing 500 jobs making defence electronics. Other firms with new factories in Gwent are Inmos (electronics), Ferranti (computer programming) and Mitel Telecom.

Cardiff, founded on iron production and the export of coal has been revitalised by new roads schemes and the conversion of the steelworks site at East Moors into a factory complex. Although unemployment is higher than the national average, employment in the service industries has maintained its importance (Fig. 132).

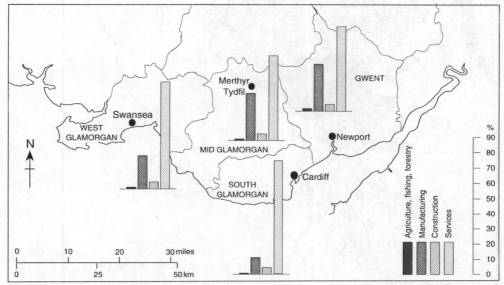

Fig. 132 Employment in South Wales, September 1989

Source: *Digest of Welsh Statistics 1991*

Case study – The Highlands and Islands

The Scottish administrative areas of Highland, Western Isles, Orkney and Shetland (see Fig. 133) have a total population of only 277 000 compared with 5.1 millions for the whole of Scotland. The population declined steadily after 1861 and it is only in the last two decades that it has begun to increase. With the exceptions of Caithness and Nairn all districts recorded higher populations in 1981 than in 1971.

The main problems of the region are its remoteness, lack of resources, poor facilities for industrial development and limited industrial base. Although this rural region has been classified as a Development Area, the exploitation of the North Sea oil and gas fields since 1974 has brought economic benefits to some parts of the region but not to others.

The Shetland and Orkney islands have benefited most and have low levels of unemployment, while the Western Isles have unemployment rates well above the UK average (see Fig. 134).

The table overleaf shows the number employed by companies whose output is wholly related to the North Sea oil industry.

Oil production has fallen from 120.7 million tonnes in 1986 to 86.3m tonnes in 1990 and the rig construction programme which benefited the Clydebank yards is now running down. Nevertheless, investment by the oil companies has had a multiplier effect and completely reversed the economic position of Orkney and

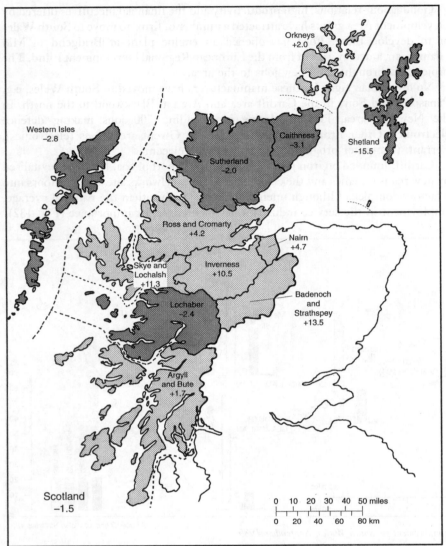

Source: *Scottish Economic Bulletin 1991*

Fig. 133 Highlands and Islands population change 1981–1990 (%)

Shetland which are in danger of having their traditional values swamped by the changes taking place there. Shetland experienced a 54% increase in population between 1971 and 1981 compared with 10.7% in Orkney and 6.3% in the Western Isles. The increase in Shetland was related to the immigration of construction workers at the Sullom Voe terminal and once the work was finished there was a fall in employment (Fig. 134).

Table 20 Numbers employed by North Sea oil industry

Administrative region	June 1980 (thousands)	Dec 1990 (thousands)
Highland	4.4	4.0
Islands	3.5	2.1
Fife	0.8	2.2
Grampian	32.3	49.7
Strathclyde	2.7	2.1
Tayside	1.8	1.8
Central & Lothian	0.9	0.3

Crofting, the traditional agricultural system of the islands and western coastlands was assisted by the Highlands and Islands Development Board. There

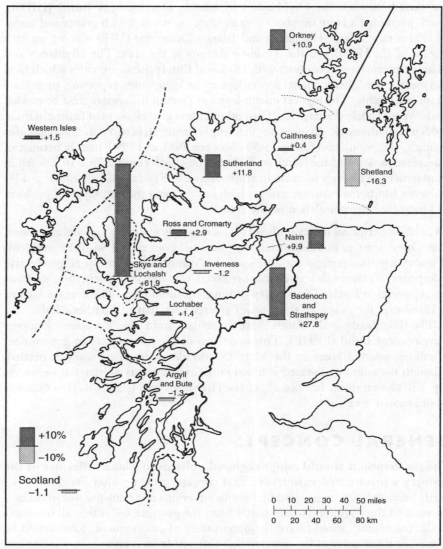

Western Isles +1.5

Caithness +0.4

Orkney +10.9

Shetland −16.3

Sutherland +11.8

Ross and Cromarty +2.9

Nairn +9.9

Inverness −1.2

Skye and Lochalsh +61.9

Lochaber +1.4

Badenoch and Strathspey +27.8

Argyll and Bute −1.3

+10%
−10%

Scotland −1.1

0 10 20 30 40 50 miles
0   20   40   60   80 km

Source: *Scottish Economic Bulletin 1991*

Fig. 134 Highlands and Islands employment change 1981–89(%)

has been some consolidation of crofts to form viable farm units. Grants have been made for fishing and the development of fish-processing plants. This assistance is necessary since fishing is an important means of livelihood in most crofting communities. Money from the ERDF and the government has been used to improve the infrastructure, including roads, drainage and public transport. Small integrated programmes have been introduced involving work with the farmers and fishermen on such projects as a new pier on North Uist to improve facilities for shellfish and lobster boats.

Away from the crofting coastlands, cattle and sheep rearing, arable farming, tourism and forestry are the staple forms of livelihood. Assistance has been given to farmers and the tourist industry has been encouraged by the building of hotels and the development of Aviemore as an all-year-round tourist and sports centre.

Forestry has not provided the employment prospects which were once considered possible and the supply of timber for the paper and wood pulp industry of Fort William has proved costly, resulting in the closure of some plants. The Inverness area has proved attractive to firms which do not depend on local raw materials such as manufacturers of components used in telecommunications.

Help for the Highlands and Islands

Government aid Between 1965 and 1991 government aid to the region was channelled through the Highlands and Islands Development Board (HIDB), which promoted a large number of small-scale enterprises with grants and loans. In 1991 a new Board, Highlands and Islands Enterprise (HIE) was set up by a merger of the HIDB and the Training Agency in the area. The Highlands and Islands Enterprise will contract with ten Local Enterprise Companies which have also been established. These are independent companies reporting to private sector-led boards. The highest unemployment rates in the region must be tackled by the Western Isles Enterprise. Throughout the region closures of firms can make sudden and dramatic changes to the employment structure. In Shetland, for example, the population fell by 15.5% between 1981 and 1990, mainly because of a decrease in demand for labour at Sullom Voe which resulted in a 16.3% fall in employment. The high increase in employment in Skye and Lochalsh (Fig. 134) is due to additional manufacturing which has reduced the employment problem and increased the population of the area.

EC aid The regional policy of the EC is increasingly affecting regional assistance. The Community is not concerned with national policies but with the problems of less prosperous regions with the goal of a 'common market' for all productive enterprises, whatever their national or regional locations. At present there are wide discrepancies in levels of prosperity within the Community. The average income in Hamburg, for example, is six times greater than that of Southern Italy.

The Highlands and Islands have benefited from the European Regional Development Fund (ERDF). This is only available for projects in government scheduled assisted areas so the State can decide where the money is needed, although the amount allocated is based on EC assessments of material needs. As Fig. 130 shows, most, but not all, of the Highlands and Islands Region qualifies as an assisted area.

GENERAL CONCEPTS

The government should adopt regional policies to make fuller use of the country's productive resources. This concept grew up after World War II, partly because it was considered that public supervision of land-use was in the best interests of the community, and partly from the growing belief that all members of the community should have the opportunity of employment. Jobs should be created in those parts of the country that suffered from economic stagnation and high levels of unemployment. There was a corollary to this idea, assistance to some regions could only be effective if limitations were imposed on growth in the more prosperous parts of the ocountry. As a consequence restrictions were put on new factory and office developments in the Midlands and the South-East. Regional policies have had a significant influence on the spatial distribution of economic activity in Britain but the recent decline in overseas and home demand has resulted in setbacks to regional policy and brought about a relative deterioration in the once prosperous West Midlands.

4.2 FRANCE: POPULATION AND REGIONAL DEVELOPMENT

POPULATION DISTRIBUTION AND CHANGE

Total population

In 1990 France had a population estimated at 56.6 millions, an increase of over

4.2% in eight years. By European standards the population is growing relatively fast, with the result that 20% of the population is under fifteen years old. Another 38% is in the 15 to 39 category which includes the years when child-bearing is at its peak. The number of elderly people has also increased as a result of a reduction in the death rate.

Distribution and density of population

As Fig. 135 shows, although there are considerable variations in the population density the overall density is remarkably low. In 1988 there were 102 persons per square kilometre compared with 246 in West Germany, 324 in Belgium, 356 in the Netherlands, 190 in Italy and 223 in the United Kingdom.

The greatest concentration of population occurs in the Île de France where the Paris metropolitan area dominates the rest of France as well as the surrounding region. There are also high densities in the lower Seine valley and the Pas-de-Calais. The other major zone of relatively high densities is in the Rhone valley and along the Côte d'Azur. On Fig. 135 the distribution within the Rhone-Alpes and Provence-Alpes-Côte d'Azur regions is more concentrated than it appears when more refined statistics are examined. The central and southern Alps have very low densities whereas the Mediterranean coastlands from Marseilles to the Italian frontier and the region around Lyons and Grenoble are areas of relatively high population densities.

The regions with the lowest densities include the upland regions of the Massif Central, the Pyrenees, Lorraine and Auvergne. These regions of low density are essentially rural areas not influenced by neighbouring urban agglomerations.

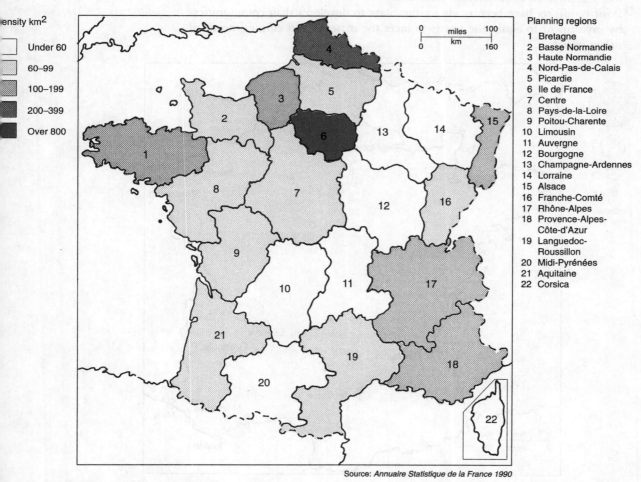

Source: Annuaire Statistique de la France 1990

Fig. 135 Population density 1990 by planning regions

However, even in rural areas the more productive farmland supports higher population densities – the main examples being fruit and vegetable growing along coastal regions of Brittany and the Rhône valley, the viticulture of Bas-Languedoc and the arable farming of Alsace.

The dominant feature of the population pattern is the distribution of urban centres, particularly those which have absorbed smaller rural communities to become major urban agglomerations. (The word **agglomération** is used in the French Census to describe clusters of urban communes – districts with some self-government and a mayor.) The fifteen largest urban agglomerations are shown in Fig. 136. The map indicates the size and significance of the Paris urban region, nearly eight times as large as the Lyons region which is the next largest agglomeration. Five of the agglomerations are coastal ports which have rapidly increased their share of French industrial development and trade in recent years. They are Rouen, Nantes, Bordeaux, Toulon and Marseilles, the last-named agglomeration being the largest port complex in France.

Urban agglomerations have increased in size at the expense of rural areas and there has been a significant shift towards the polarisation of the French economy within urban centres.

There are a number of reasons for the migration from rural areas.

❶ The consolidation of agricultural holdings and increased farm mechanisation has led to a fall in the demand for agricultural labour.

❷ The growth of industries and tertiary services in urban areas has attracted people from rural areas where work is more difficult to obtain.

❸ The movement of young people to the towns to obtain work leaves rural areas with low birth rates. This results in an excess of deaths over births in many areas such as the Massif Central.

❹ Positive efforts have been made by the State to develop urban communities by investment to equip the towns to meet the material and cultural needs of urban society.

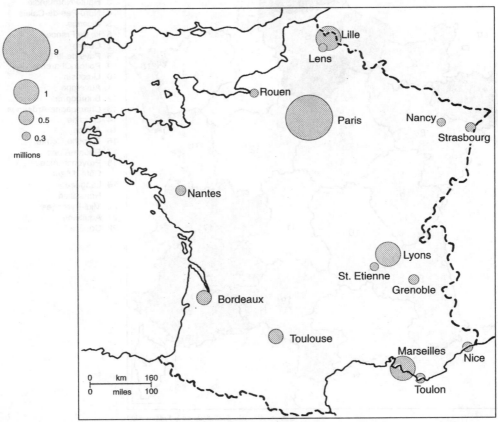

Fig. 136 Relative size of the fifteen largest urban agglomerations 1990

❺ The depletion of rural population results in the erosion of services, particularly those such as clubs and recreational amenities which enrich the quality of life.

Movement of population

Fig. 137 shows the percentage change in population which took place in the seven

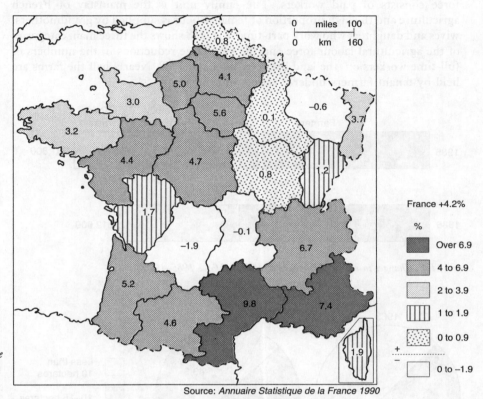

Source: *Annuaire Statistique de la France 1990*

Fig. 137 Percentage change in population 1982–1990 by planning regions

years between 1982 and 1990. The trend shown on the map has been caused by inter-regional migration in addition to natural increase. The Paris agglomeration is no longer the magnet for migrants which it used to be. Decentralisation policy to relieve some of the congestion in Paris has resulted in population movement to some of the surrounding départements, particularly in the Centre region.

More significant, however, has been the migration to the planning region of Rhône-Alpes and the neighbouring region of Provence-Alpes-Côte d'Azur and to Languedoc-Roussillon. The increase in these regions is particularly significant since it consists to a large extent of migration from other regions rather than natural increase which is lower here than in parts of northern France. The climate of the Midi with its warm winters and long hours of sunshine has attracted specialist industries and tertiary services as well as retired people. Furthermore the area has also been attractive to overseas immigrants such as Algerians. At the same time the older industrial regions of the Nord and Lorraine have become zones of exodus with a decline in the overall population in Lorraine and virtually no change in Nord-Pas-de-Calais. In the Massif Central the population of Limousin showed a slight decline.

What Fig. 137 does not show is the continual decline of many of the rural areas, with the loss of young people, and the rapid increase in the population of the urban areas where work is available. In 1990, 74% of the French population lived in settlements with populations of over 2000, whereas in 1931 the urban population only just equalled that of the rural communes. In recent years the population of many French cities, except Paris, has increased rapidly. Marseilles, Bordeaux, Toulouse, Nantes and Toulon have expanded at rates above the national average. Even higher growth rates were experienced by small cities such as Aix-en-Provence and Perpignan. Most of these increases were the result of net migration and not natural increase.

AGRICULTURE

The agricultural labour force

Over 40% of French agricultural holdings are farmed by owner-occupiers who depend on family labour to work the holdings. Little more than 13% of the labour force consists of paid workers. The family unit is the mainstay of French agriculture and the high proportion of female labour is supplied by grandmothers, wives and daughters who work part-time. Fig. 138 shows the three main categories of the agricultural labour force and the very large reductions in the numbers of full-time workers on the land between 1963 and 1988. Nearly half the farms are held by tenant farmers under a variety of schemes.

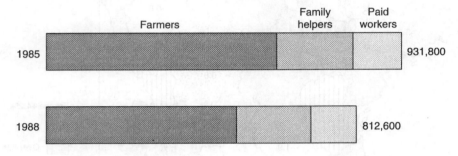

Fig. 138 Changes in the full-time agricultural workforce 1985–1988

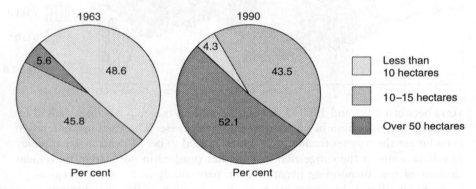

Fig. 139 Size of agricultural holdings

Farm size

In 1990, nearly 4.3% of French farms were less than 10 ha in size. Many of the smaller farms were little more than large gardens providing specialised products such as vines, flowers, fruit and market garden crops. The highest proportion of French farms are over 50 ha in size. As Fig. 139 shows, about 52% of the holdings are in this category. The relatively small size of French farms has encouraged cooperative schemes for bulk purchasing and marketing.

Agricultural problems

There have been strenuous efforts by the government to rationalise the structure of farming. The modernisation programme has been particularly concerned with the following aspects of farming.

- **Redistribution and consolidation of property** Many farms are fragmented, with small fields restricting the use of machinery. The consolidation programme funded by the government comprises two organisations to promote consolidation. The first, formed in 1960, consists of the Sociétes d'Aménagement Foncier et d'Établissement Rural (SAFER). These societies buy land offered for sale and use it to enlarge farms which are too small to operate efficiently. The second, formed in 1963, is known as Fonds d'Action Social pour l'Aménagement des Structures Agraires (FASASA). This fund offers incentives to farmers to retire at 60, subsidises farmers moving to areas where operators are scarce and retrains operators who wish to leave non-viable farms. Fig. 138 shows that there has been a drop in the size of the agricultural labour force while Fig. 139 shows changes in the sizes of holdings indicating that there has been considerable progress towards larger and medium-sized holdings.

- **Increasing the level of technology** The State has invested considerable sums in rural electrification and the improvement to water supplies. Teams of agronomists and engineers promote agricultural advancement, but the individual cooperation and initiative of the farmers is essential. In remote areas and on smallholdings where little capital accumulation is possible, investment in fertilisers and new machinery is extremely limited.

- **Meeting the needs of the market** Membership of the Common Market has heightened the need for French agriculture to increase productivity to remain competitive with the other members of the Community. Marketing boards for commodities such as grain and wine have been set up and a network of regional markets serves the main consuming areas. French farms are still geared to polyculture (the growing of a variety of crops) together with livestock rearing, and it has proved difficult to encourage farmers to change to new crops. Specialisation is only to be found in some regions such as the limon-covered plains of the north-east (grain) and Languedoc (viticulture). In the lower Rhône valley, irrigation schemes have vastly increased the area under intensive cultivation of fruit and market garden crops. Considerable effort has gone into improving quality, maximising yields and the packaging of produce.

- **Resistance to change** Sporadic outbursts by French farmers against the importation of, for example, British lamb or Irish beef are evidence of the reluctance of many farming communities to accept rationalisation and adopt larger farm units. Historically these communities of small farmers have been the backbone of French food production and they have retained considerable political influence. The movement towards organic farming may help to prolong the existence of many inefficient small farms provided they can retain the quality of output which has been sacrificed for quantity by many of the larger agro-businesses.

Industrial regions

France possesses very few extensive industrial regions on the scale to be found in Britain or West Germany. The largest industrial agglomerations are: (a) the Paris region; (b) the Nord-Pas-de-Calais coalfield with extensions around Lille, Tourcoing and Roubaix; (c) Lorraine with discontinuous industrial centres between Longwy in the north and Nancy in the south, extending eastwards to the German frontier; (d) Lyons and the neighbouring scattered industrial centres in the Loire coal basin.

In addition to these industrial regions there are port industries based on the import of raw materials such as crude oil and iron ore, facilities for re-export and transport inland, and local demand. The ports which have developed as industrial centres are Marseilles, Bordeaux, Nantes, Le Havre and Dunkerque. The inland ports of Rouen and Strasbourg have similar characteristics. Finally there are a number of minor industrial centres, some with a wide and others with a narrow range of industries. Their locations are dispersed and they draw on local skills and obtain raw materials and energy resources from elsewhere. They include Toulouse, Grenoble, Rennes, Clermont-Ferrand and Dijon.

RELOCATION OF INDUSTRY

Industrial development in France took place in the nineteenth and early twentieth centuries on or near the coalfields and iron ore resources. These developments, together with good routes, particularly those converging on Paris, encouraged industrial growth in the north and east of the country. As a result, three-quarters of the industrial capacity was east of a line from the département of Normandie to Haute-Alpes. Except for the seaports there was an absence of large industrial plants in the centre, the south and west and a corresponding deficiency of labour, capital and business enterprise. Since the end of World War II there have been considerable changes in the distribution of industry. These changes have been the result of two major forces. The first was the **decline of the basic industries** such as wool and cotton textiles, iron and steel, heavy engineering and shipbuilding. At the same time there has been an **expansion in demand** for aerospace products, electronics and consumer goods which are not dependent on nearby coal or raw material supplies.

The second influence on industrial location has been the State which has set up **planning regions** (see Fig. 140) and introduced a succession of national plans. State assistance to industry in certain areas and State measures to improve the quality of life in the poorer regions have helped to bring changes to industrial location.

Some industries which were concentrated in a few localities (for example, car manufacture) have been encouraged to disperse, in some cases to areas of declining industries such as the Nord coalfield, to prevent large-scale unemployment.

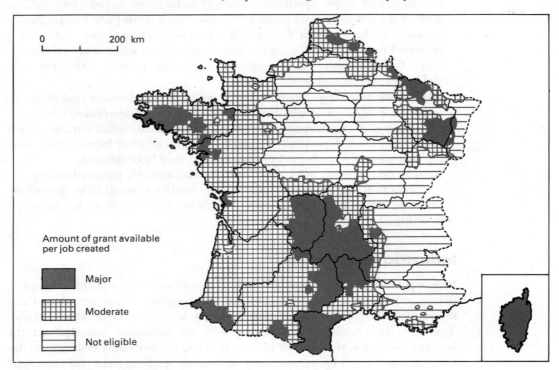

Fig. 140 France: regional variations in government aid to industry

CORE AND PERIPHERAL REGIONS IN FRANCE

The core-periphery concept

Different rates of development occur in the regions of many countries. There is one region where economic development shows most progress, this is the 'core' region. In other parts of the country progress is slower, and these regions are comparatively under-developed when compared with the core region. These outer regions form the periphery because they are on the edge of the economic development of the core region. They form backwaters of spatial inequality which need support from the core if they are to develop and contribute substantially to the economy of the country.

Core and periphery in France

In France the centralisation on Paris over many centuries has resulted in the Paris Basin developing as the core region of the country. In this region there is the most extensive industrial development, the main commercial and business centre of the country and the focus of routes from other parts of France and Europe. The peripheral regions are those remote from the Paris Basin where industrial development has been limited and rural development hampered by such factors as poor communications, difficult terrain and inefficient farming methods. Regions which form the periphery include southern Brittany, Corsica, the Massif Central and the Pyrenees.

Solving the core-periphery problem

The French government has taken a number of steps to encourage growth in the peripheral regions. Fig. 140 shows how government aid is distributed with some areas receiving major grants, others receiving moderate and a third group receiving no grants at all. As in Britain, industrial expansion is the keystone of regional development. Grants are given to firms for each job created within a fixed period. In addition improvements are made to the local infrastructure, and farming is being reorganised along the lines already described. Communications between the core and the periphery are also being improved, notably by building new railway links for the TGV network.

The underlying policy is one of decentralisation away from Paris and the Paris Basin – the core region. Growth is encouraged in the peripheral regions, the intention being to implant self-sustaining industrial growth in the provinces which will, in the long run, be beneficial to the rest of France. This 'spread' effect results from increased spending powers and economic recovery in peripheral regions stimulating an increase in the demand for goods and services in other regions.

Fig. 140 provides clear evidence of the regions of France which make up the periphery. They fall into two broad categories: peripheral rural regions such as Corsica, south Brittany and the Massif Central, and old industrial regions where heavy industries have closed down, such as the north-east and Lorraine.

Developments in one peripheral region – The Massif Central

The planning regions of Limousin and Auvergne, which cover much of the Massif Central, form the most extensive rural problem area in France. The main difficulties of the area can be summarised as follows.
- Physical conditions and a limited natural resource base which restrict the agricultural and industrial potential of the region.
- Rural depopulation, leaving the older people behind.
- Lack of comprehensive road and rail networks.
- Small farm units, uneconomic to work – over 90% of the farms are less than 50 ha in size.
- Lack of urban development except in cities like Clermont-Ferrand and Limoges which are peripheral to the region.

Improvements to the area are taking the following forms.
- Consolidation and enlargement of farm holdings and the encouragement of older farmers to retire.
- Setting up of agricultural cooperatives.

- Introduction of improved livestock breeds.
- Afforestation of upland regions.
- Encouragement of tourist industries, particularly winter sports.
- Improvements in communications.

In other problem areas similar measures are being introduced, where appropriate.

GENERAL CONCEPTS

France is a country of urban communities

This is a relatively recent concept. France used to be considered as essentially an agricultural nation with a relatively static population which was concentrated in the northern half of the country. But changes which have been taking place since 1945, in particular the rapid increase in the total population, have rendered this picture inaccurate. These changes have brought about new patterns in French regional and national life.

The French Government is a major instrument of planning and change

This concept is also new. France was the first country in Western Europe to introduce national economic planning. This planned economy has resulted in extensive changes to the spatial distribution of people and employment. An urban hierarchy has emerged and this, together with the existence of distinctive regions, forms the basis for planned development at national level.

French society has proved to be more dynamic in the last three decades than previously. With so much rapid change, it is important to make sure that, when studying the geography of France, you have up-to-date information.

4.3 WEST AFRICA: POPULATION ISSUES

DEFINITIONS AND FORMULAE

Urbanisation	There is no simple definition of urbanisation. Broadly speaking, it is the proportion of the population living in towns and the increase in the population of town dwellers compared with that of rural dwellers. As a result of this process there is an increase in the number and size of towns and cities. The rate of urbanisation is accelerating. It is estimated that 42% of the world's population lives in urban areas compared with 29% in 1950.
Birth rate	This is the number of live births per thousand of population during a particular year. Birth rates vary from about 12 to 50 throughout the world. The birth rate is over 40 in all the countries of West Africa. We need to know the birth rate, together with the death and net reproduction rates, because together they indicate whether a population is likely to grow or decline.

Death rate

This is the number of deaths per thousand of population during a particular year.

Migration

Spatial movements that involve a change of place of residence and the crossing of a political boundary. Residential moves which do not result in crossing such a boundary are usually referred to as mobility rather than migration. **Out-migration** and **in-migration** refer to internal migration from or to a given area within a country. **Internal migration** refers to a change of residence within a country.

Net reproduction rate

This is the average number of female children born to every woman in the population. This measure recognises that many children do not live long enough to become parents, many women die when they are still young enough to have children and some who are alive are too old to have children. NRR is a measure of whether a society is reproducing itself. If NRR = 1 the population is stable; more than 1 indicates a growing population; less than 1 means that the population is in decline.

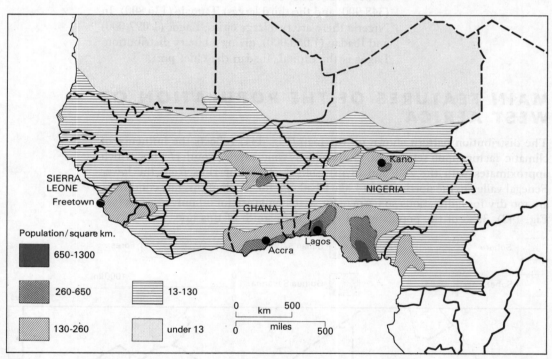

Fig. 141 West Africa: rural and urban population

Population density

This measure relates the size of population to the area of land on which it lives.

$$\text{Pop. density} = \frac{\text{number of people}}{\text{unit of area}}$$

It is expressed as the number of people per square kilometre or square mile, e.g. the present density in Britain is about 229/km². This figure is the average number of people per square kilometre of the country. It does not recognise the difference in density between city areas and the Highlands of Scotland. Fig. 141 shows that in West Africa the

243

density of population increases southwards from the Sahara to the Gulf of Guinea.

Primate city

The largest city in a country or region. It is also the centre of political affairs, trade and economic, social and cultural activities. According to the **rank-size rule** the size of settlements is inversely proportional to their rank. The assumption is that the second largest city will have a population half the size of the primate city. The third largest city will have a population one-third the size of the primate city and so on.

As a formula:

$$Pn = \frac{P1}{n \text{ (or R)}}$$

Pn = the population of the city
P1 = the population of the largest (primate) city
n (or R) = the rank-size of the city.

In Ghana the population of the primate city, Accra, is 859 600. The second largest city is Kumasi (348 900) and the third largest Tumale (136 800). In Nigeria there are two large cities, Lagos (1 097 000) and Ibadan (1 060 000), giving a binary distribution. Lagos is the capital, Ibadan the chief port.

MAIN FEATURES OF THE POPULATION OF WEST AFRICA

The distribution pattern shown on the map (Fig. 141) reflects the influence of climatic factors upon settlement. Human life is concentrated south of a line which approximates with the 200 mm (8 in) isohyet. This line runs from the lower Senegal valley to the north-east of Lake Chad. To the north of this line conditions are too dry for cultivations so permanent settlements are found only at oases (see Fig. 142). 33% of the population of Africa lives south of this line.

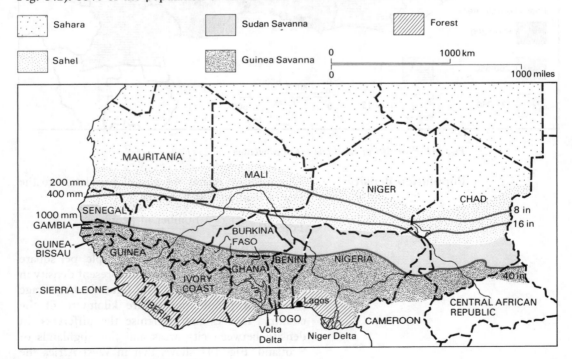

Fig. 142 Vegetation zones of West Africa

The colonisation of West Africa by European nations intensified the pattern of increasing concentration near the coast of the Gulf of Guinea. The rainforest climate of the area encouraged the growth of commercial crops such as cocoa and rubber. Ports were established to handle trade with Europe.

The population of West Africa is growing rapidly but, since the density of population was low compared with other parts of the world, the problems caused by the rapid growth are not as severe as in Asian countries. The rates of growth in West Africa do not differ as much between countries as they do between districts within the same country.

The basic picture today is of a concentration of intensive economic activities and of people in scattered 'islands' which are separated by vast areas in which little change has occurred.

Before the establishment of colonies in the nineteenth century there were few towns in West Africa except in the lands of the Hausa in Northern Nigeria (e.g. Kano) and in Yorubaland (e.g. Ibadan and Oyo). When colonies were established, existing towns became administrative centres. Those which were developed as river or coastal ports or rail termini grew fastest. The largest became colonial capitals. Since independence, national capitals have grown rapidly as political and administrative centres. They now attract immigrants from other parts of the country.

Urban growth is now the most widespread process. The number of town-dwellers doubles every ten to twelve years. Urban populations are characterised by a high proportion of young people (15–45 years old) who have migrated from the rural areas.

RURAL–URBAN MIGRATION

In 1975 only 25% of the people of Africa lived in urban regions. By AD 2000 it is estimated that 40% of the population will be urban. This change involves the massive redistribution of people to certain key receiving regions. The primate cities and their surrounding regions are the major magnets.

Reasons for this movement include:

❶ **The influence of colonial contacts** In colonial times the spatial structures of the economies of different territories were focused upon a small number of port cities. These cities became the centres of newly established transportation systems and gradually became the largest internal markets and the centres of manufacture. Rural–urban migration focused upon these nodes. So urbanisation was not common to all developing world centres but specifically to those which became centres of the Western form of 'modernisation'.

❷ **The effects of independence** Since independence, the domination of these cities has increased. Multinational companies have been attracted by cheap labour, e.g. females for the textile industry, so factories have been located in or near the largest urban agglomerations. The 'developed' urban regions have therefore become even more attractive to migrants.

❸ **Perceptions of high wage opportunities** These have attracted rural people who also believe they will have a better life style in the big city. The migrants have also acted as sources of information about job opportunities and wages for families and friends they have left at home. If they feed back positive information to their home areas it stimulates further migration.

❹ **Transfer of money** Money sent back to their families also stimulates migration. The money reinforces optimistic perceptions of the opportunities offered by the city. If the money is used to educate the young they have wider horizons and are more likely to move away.

GENERAL CONCEPTS

Optimum population, underpopulation and overpopulation

These concepts relate to the law of diminishing returns. It is argued that as long as the techniques used remain the same, the application of additional capital and labour will lead to a proportional increase in output. This applies both to agricultural land and to industries. There is a point of maximum return, which is the optimum (best) situation.

Optimum population is therefore the point at which a country has achieved a density of population which with the given resources and skills, produces the greatest economic welfare (the maximum income per head). If the population is greater than this, the country may be said to be overpopulated. If it is less, it is underpopulated. In the case of both underpopulated and overpopulated regions, the standard of living is lower than it would be if the optimum prevailed. In West Africa it could be argued that the Sahel region is overpopulated. Liberia could be said to be underpopulated because mining development is held back by a limited supply of labour.

Demographic transition

This is the change from a low total population experiencing high birth rates and high death rates to a high total population experiencing low birth and low death rates. There are four main stages recognised in this process.

Most of the countries of the developing world, including those in West Africa, are in the second stage of the demographic transition. Modern farming techniques produce more food and modern medicine has been introduced, so death rates have declined. Birth rates are still high, partly because large families are socially prestigious.

DIFFERENT PERSPECTIVES

The Malthusian perspective

When the population of Britain was increasing rapidly, Thomas Malthus published an essay on population in which he argued that the rate of increase in food supply could not keep up with the rate of growth in population. He forecast that unless population growth was checked there would inevitably be starvation, disease and war. But the agricultural revolution and the spread of farming to the grasslands of the southern hemisphere increased food supply dramatically. The fate outlined by Malthus seemed to have been put off indefinitely.

In the developing world today the supply of food has increased, e.g. the Green Revolution but the increase has not kept up with the rapid growth of population. So in areas like West Africa the relationship of food supply to population is a crucial problem.

The demographic transition theory

This provides a comparative perspective. The theory is based on observations and descriptions of what has happened in Europe and North America in particular. There is no guarantee that what has happened in other parts of the world in the past will be repeated in the developing world today. For example, mortality declined in Europe and North America because housing and health conditions improved. In West Africa it is the result of the application of modern medicines. At present there is little evidence of a decrease in fertility which is a key part of the transition from Stage 2 to Stage 3.

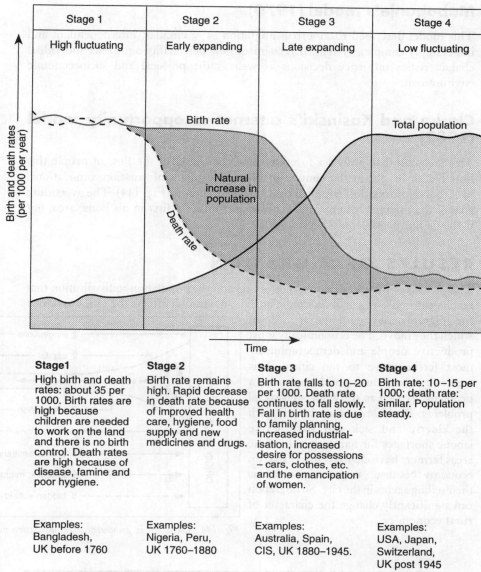

Fig. 143 *Demographic transition model*

Stage 1	Stage 2	Stage 3	Stage 4
High fluctuating	Early expanding	Late expanding	Low fluctuating

Stage 1
High birth and death rates: about 35 per 1000. Birth rates are high because children are needed to work on the land and there is no birth control. Death rates are high because of disease, famine and poor hygiene.

Stage 2
Birth rate remains high. Rapid decrease in death rate because of improved health care, hygiene, food supply and new medicines and drugs.

Stage 3
Birth rate falls to 10–20 per 1000. Death rate continues to fall slowly. Fall in birth rate is due to family planning, increased industrialisation, increased desire for possessions – cars, clothes, etc. and the emancipation of women.

Stage 4
Birth rate: 10–15 per 1000; death rate: similar. Population steady.

Examples:
Bangladesh, UK before 1760

Examples:
Nigeria, Peru, UK 1760–1880

Examples:
Australia, Spain, CIS, UK 1880–1945.

Examples:
USA, Japan, Switzerland, UK post 1945

MODELS OF MIGRATION

The Todara model (1969)

This seeks to explain and predict the volume of rural–urban migration in terms of the difference in income between the formal wage-earning urban and rural sectors. The effects of this difference are modified by the expectation of migrants about getting a job in the urban sector. It is criticised because it only considers economic motivation and ignores the fact that many new immigrants survive by earning money in the informal sectors of the economy.

The Amin model (1974)

This is a model of labour migration which sees internal migration as a form of involuntary transfer from the rural to the coastal regions of Africa as a result of the unequal investment of international capital into export crop producing areas. It is criticised as being crude and oversimplistic.

Mabogunje's model (1970)

This model described rural–urban migration as a circular, interdependent and increasingly complex system. It recognises how personality and other individual characteristics influence decisions as well as the physical and socioeconomic environment.

Clarke and Kosinski's alternative opportunity model (1982)

This suggests that in order to understand the causes of the flow of people this flow has to be put in the context of flows of capital, information, innovations, profits and information supplied by returning migrants (Fig. 144). The overriding goal of the migrant is to maximise his opportunities – first in his home area, but if this is not possible, elsewhere.

RESULTS OF MIGRATION

The process of migration is self-reinforcing and the population redistribution that results can cause regional economic change. Migration affects the cities to which the migrants move and the areas from which they move. The economically most productive people and demographically most fertile move to the cities. This creates massive housing and employment problems as well as the associated social problems. Rural areas may be left with the elderly and sick and have severe labour shortages for harvesting. In some areas farmers have changed to a cash crop economy because migrants can act as their selling agents in the city. So migration can significantly change the character of rural economies.

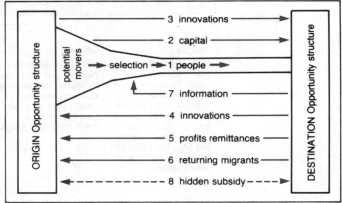

Fig. 144 Spatial flows associated with population mobility

4.4 INDIA: DEVELOPMENT ISSUES

India is one of the chief agricultural countries of the world and its agricultural produce is one of its main sources of wealth. Agriculture is likely to be the mainstay of the Indian economy for the foreseeable future. 70% of all Indian workers depend on farming for their livelihood and farming provides 46% of the national income.

Subsistence is still an important factor in the farming economy. Small farms retain about two-thirds of their crops for food for the family; large farms sell about two-thirds of their produce. The crops which are grown are therefore determined by two main factors. They are (i) the need to provide food for the family, (ii) market factors – the saleability and profitability of different crops. 45% of the country is cultivated; 15% is double-cropped. So the possibility of extending the cultivable area is very limited. Much of the remaining 55% of the land area is made up of mountains, deserts and land which has been built over. Efforts therefore have to be concentrated on intensification of agriculture. Population pressure combined with unscientific farming methods has meant that much land is being overworked. Nearly 25% of the cultivated land suffers from soil erosion, 66% of the arable land needs soil conservation measures.

TRADITIONAL PRACTICE AND FARMING METHODS

Traditional practices and expertise built up over the centuries in different parts of the subcontinent reflect physical environmental factors, especially climatic and hydrological (water supply) rhythms and the growing conditions required by the crops. Traditional methods include cattle used as draught animals; an emphasis on grain production; the 50/50 division of the crop between landowner and farmer; the farmer's division of his own share – some sold to pay the interest on debts, some kept for seed; hand-sowing; transplanting, weeding and harvesting with a primitive plough; little or no fertiliser. These traditional practices are now being challenged by pressures for change.

Irrigation

This is the means whereby essential water is provided in farming areas which have marked dry seasons and/or extreme variability. Although temperatures throughout the year in most parts of India permit crops to grow, rainfall is strongly cyclical and monsoon rain unreliable in amount and occurrence. So irrigation has always been a vital factor in the agricultural economy of India. Fig. 145 shows the areas which are most prone to drought.

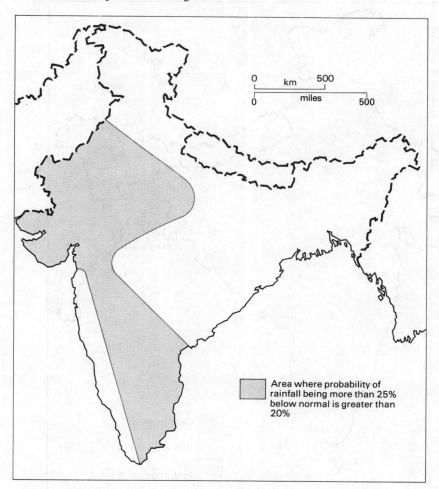

Fig. 145 India: main area prone to drought

Fig. 146 shows the distribution of the traditional methods of irrigation. Some of them date back for thousands of years – the canal system of the north-west was part of the Indus civilisation of 4000 years ago. The tanks of the south and south-east are also part of India's cultural inheritance.

The type of irrigation is dependent on certain physical factors.

- The availability of surface water in the form of river systems has allowed the development of canal irrigation, e.g. in the Punjab.
- Relief and the nature of the terrain may also determine the techniques used, e.g. in Kashmir nearly all the irrigation is by **kuls** – leads led off from mountain streams along terraced areas with wooden aqueducts taking the water across ravines.
- Floods also provide a source of irrigation with flood channels diverted to lead the water into the fields.
- The hard rock terrain of south India has encouraged the construction of tanks dammed by earth or granite blocks in shallow valleys.
- The depth of the water table is also important. Ancient wells exist in areas where the water table is high and easily reached but a low water table makes this technique useless.

The use to which the water is to be put also influences the type of irrigation method used, e.g. in the south the water is stored in tanks to provide water for use immediately after the rainy season to allow rice and sugar crops to grow. The tanks are not intended for long-term use during the dry season.

In recent years, new methods of irrigation have been developed.

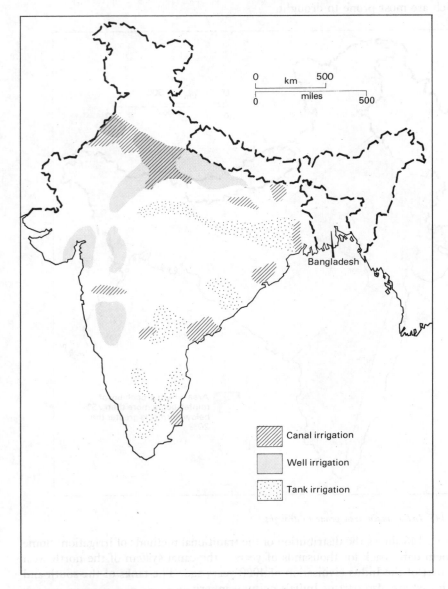

Canal irrigation

Well irrigation

Tank irrigation

Fig. 146 Distribution of main types of traditional irrigation

AGRICULTURAL REGIONS

There are four main regions:

❶ The Himalayan zone (rainfall 1000–2500 mm per annum). The main crops are wheat, maize and rice. Seed potatoes and fruit are also grown.

❷ The dry zone (less than 700 mm rainfall per annum). The chief crops are millets, oil seeds, wheat, maize, groundnuts, cotton and gram (chick peas).

❸ The sub-humid zone (rainfall 700–1250 mm per annum). Sugar cane, tobacco and rice are important crops in addition to those grown in the dry zone.

❹ The wet zone (rainfall more than 1250 mm per annum). The main crops are rice, tea, jute, sugar cane, spices, oil seeds, gram, millets and wheat.

MODERNISATION OF AGRICULTURE

The aim of modernisation is to achieve greater efficiency in agriculture. Modernisation is therefore concerned with both the physical conditions of the environment, such as water supply and soil fertility, and with socioeconomic conditions, e.g. the size of landholdings, availability of credit to buy new equipment, education levels which give the people skills necessary to put new ideas into practice.

In order to increase efficiency in Indian agriculture, four major problems had to be faced.

❶ The need to increase the availability of a guaranteed water supply. In recent years, major developments have occurred in the extension of irrigation. Major barrage schemes such as the Bhakra–Nangal scheme provide water to irrigate 2.6 million ha. The sinking of tube wells and the increasing use of small electric pumps by farmers to tap deeper wells than could otherwise be reached have also made important contributions to the expansion of the

Table 21 India: Regional variations in use of irrigation and irrigation techniques

Region	Canals % Indian canal irrigated area	Tanks % Indian tank irrigated area	Wells % Indian well irrigated area	Others % other irrigated areas of India	Total % of Indian irrigated area
North West Haryana, Himachal Pradesh, Jammu & Kashmir, Punjab, Rajasthan, Delhi	27	5	28	5	22
North Centre Bihar, Uttar Pradesh	26	12	39	42	31
North East Assam, Manipur, Meghalaya, Nagaland, Tripura West Bengal	11	8	–	21	7
West Centre Gujarat, Madhya Pradesh, Maharashtra	10	10	20	6	13
South and South East Andhra Pradesh, Kerala, Karnataka, Orissa, Tamil Nadu	26	65	13	26	27
Totals	100	100	100	100	100

irrigated lands. Table 21 shows the regional variations in the use of irrigation; the farmers choosing the type most suitable for their particular area.

❷ The need to increase yields. The increasing provision of irrigation has been accompanied by the introduction of high yielding variety (HYV) crops. India was one of the developing countries which introduced the Green Revolution. This revolution is described in detail below.

❸ Essential land reforms. Rural areas are overpopulated and there is not enough land. The operational landholding worked by a family is often too small to provide the food they need. In rice lands a family holding may be less than 1 ha and even in the less productive and less intensely cultivated dry lands of West Gujarat the holdings are no more than 6 ha. This situation is worsened by conditions of tenancy. Many farmers are sharecroppers and landlords expect their rents but are only prepared to make minimal investment in the land. This problem applies to about 20% of the total farmland.

Attempts have been made to achieve land reforms but well-intentioned laws have proved difficult to enforce. Attempts have been made to transfer land ownership to the farmers who work it, to limit rents to 20% of the output, etc. But in a large country in which tenants have traditionally regarded landowners as their social superiors, real changes are difficult to achieve.

❹ Farmers' need of capital for modernisation. The modernisation of agriculture is dependent upon the availability of capital for investment. Farmers need money to sink tube wells, buy electric pumps to raise water, buy the HYV seeds and the fertilisers and pesticides which go with them. The importance of investment is shown in the model of agricultural improvement (Fig. 147).

Despite the establishment of rural cooperatives and efforts by central government the problem of capital has not been solved. As prices for fertilisers, pesticides, etc. have increased, poor farmers have applied less to the land and this in turn has decreased HYV yields.

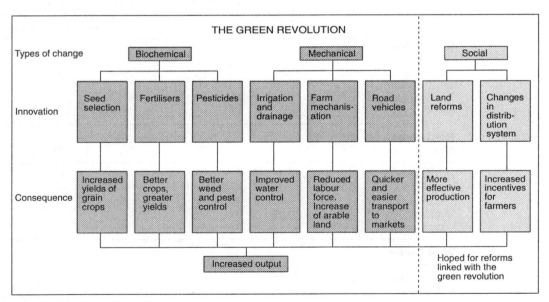

Fig. 147 The Green Revolution

The Green Revolution in India

The Green Revolution started in the late 1960s in a number of countries in the developing world including India. It was based on the introduction of high-yielding varieties of wheat and rice. These new hybrids had been developed in Mexico and were introduced in India in 1966/67. By 1973/74, more than half of the wheatlands had been sown with new varieties. In the Punjab, the 'granary of India', wheat production rose from 2.5 million tonnes to 5.4 million tonnes as a result of increases in yield.

In regions such as the upper Ganges where water depth can be carefully controlled, high-yielding rice strains were very successful. By 1973/74, 25% of the rice land was sown with HYV seeds and in some areas yields increased by 93% in the first six years. HYV strains of millets and maize were also developed.

In addition to HYV seeds, India began a programme of farm modernisation. Tractors were introduced, communications improved and some small farms were consolidated as larger holdings. Quantities of   fertilisers were used and pesticides introduced to control pests and weeds. Irrigation projects improved water control and farm machinery was imported to deal with tasks such as threshing and pumping away surplus water. The innovations and consequences of the Green Revolution are summarised in Fig. 147. Unfortunately, the hoped-for social changes have not been as extensive or far-reaching as it was hoped. Efforts aimed at land reform had a very limited success because of social, religious and political difficulties. Efforts were made to provide guaranteed markets and there was a significant development in the creation of credit facilities for farmers. Despite these measures there is considerable rural overpopulation and standards of living in farming areas are extremely low. People have continued to migrate to the towns and cities and many small farmers are permanently in debt. The Green Revolution has increased food supply but it has not solved any of the underlying social, economic and political problems of India. The benefits and costs of the Green Revolution in India are shown in the chart below.

Benefits	Costs
• Doubling of wheat and rice yields	• HYV seeds not suited to drought or waterlogged soil
• An extra crop is possible in some regions	• Heavy applications of fertiliser and pesticides essential, increasing costs and environmental pollution
• Need for fertilisers has created new industries and jobs	• Mechanisation has increased unemployment
• Wheat, rice and maize have improved diet and give greater variety	• Some HYV crops are not so pleasant to eat
• Farmers who can afford seed, tractors and fertilisers have a higher standard of living	• Farmers unable to afford tractors, etc. are relatively poor, especially those with the smallest plots
• Irrigated areas have increased	• Environmental costs such as salination, pollution of rivers by fertilisers and pesticides, increased risk of soil erosion
• Improvements in roads	• Not all areas can benefit from irrigation
• More food for the poorer people	• High cost of fuel restricts number of farm vehicles
	• Gap between rich and poor, between landowners and landless

A model of agricultural improvement

Fig. 148 shows the relationship between agricultural improvement and the general economic development for a developing country. Apply the model to the factual information on agricultural development in this section. Work out how the changes in agriculture relate to (a) the industrial development of the country (b) the urbanisation of the population.

DEVELOPMENT PROJECTS

Narmada Valley project

As part of its economic strategy, India has pursued major development projects

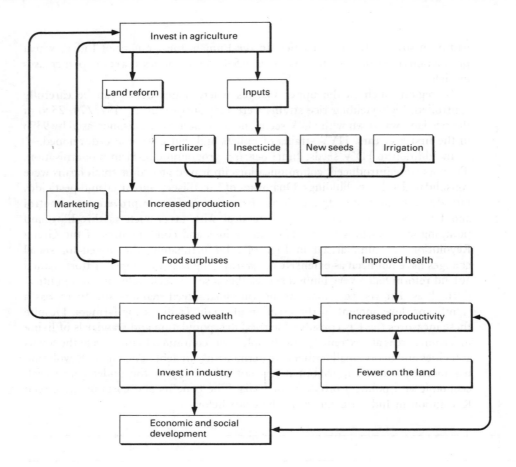

Fig. 148 A model of agricultural improvement

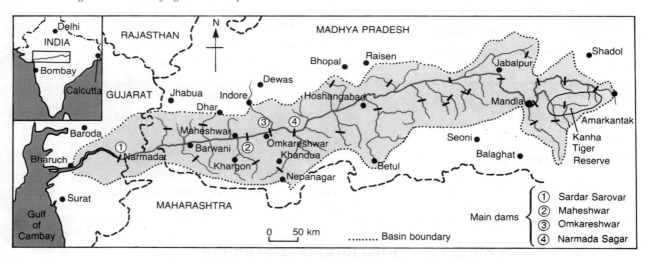

Fig. 149 Narmada Valley project

as a means of increasing national wealth and standards of living. Fig. 149 shows the Narmada Valley in which such a project is now proceeding. The Narmada river has a drainage basin of 98 000 sq km and this basin at present supports 20 million people.

The development of the plan consists of the construction of 30 major dams, 135 intermediate size dams and 3,000 minor ones along 1,300 km of the river. The total effect will be to flood 6,000 sq km – an area about the size of Devon. More than a million people are to be resettled. The project is intended to provide three things: drinking water, water for irrigation, and hydroelectricity for the state of Gujerat. It is being supported by international aid from the World Bank.

Until recently, comprehensive multipurpose development projects were seen as the key to rapid social and economic development in the developing world. There was little or no opposition to proposals which made significant contributions to regional development. Today feelings are more mixed. Reported attitudes to this project include:

- 'The most significant development milestone of the decade.' (Indian editor of an environmental magazine)
- 'We are not fighting to stop a dam, we are fighting for social justice.' (a sociologist)
- 'Environmentalists are anti-progress, anti-Gujerat and anti-national.' (a dam builder)

Cost-benefit analysis When a project of this type becomes controversial, vested interests overstate their cases. A less emotional view can be gained by analysing the benefits which can reasonably be expected as a result of the development and the social and economic costs that will have to be paid.

Benefits	Costs
• Bring good quality drinking water to Gujerat to replace a diminishing supply from silted-up tanks and rivers	• 2000 sq km of farmland will be lost through flooding
• Vast increase in water available for irrigation which will increase agricultural production and farmers' incomes	• 3500 sq km of forest will be lost by flooding
• Additional power available for industrial development in Gujerat	• 1.5 million rural population will be displaced
• Provides a permanent improvement in water supply, dams are planned to last 200 years	• Traditional ways of life of three tribal groups destroyed
• Re-housed villagers will have more modern homes	• Flood irrigation schemes of this type cause waterlogging and soil salinity problems
• Timber-felling provides ready money for development and jobs	• Wildlife will be displaced. Rescue operations as the water rises will not be able to save all the animals living in the area
	• Man/animal conflicts will become serious as traumatised wild animals seek food in fields and villages

Alternative solutions

In place of large-scale, prestigious development projects which have drastic effects upon existing environments and communities, some scientists suggest that less capital-intensive, smaller-scale improvements would be more effective. For the Narmada Valley it has been suggested that significant and lasting improvements could be achieved by:

- The wise use of groundwater.
- Building more water tanks and de-silting existing tanks, ponds and lakes.
- Adoption of dry-land farming techniques so that there is less demand for irrigated water.
- Afforestation which would protect soils and help soak up monsoon rains.

The benefits of this approach would be:

- The de-silting work would provide many local jobs.
- Local communities would not be displaced, traditional ways of life would not be disrupted.
- Afforestation would reduce the rate of siltation.
- New forests could be properly managed to provide a permanent income for the region.
- Wildlife habitats remain undisturbed.
- India would incur less debt.

Associated problems

Decision-making in developing countries in relation to major development plans is often complicated by issues not strictly related to the direct benefits and costs incurred. These include:

- Political pressures – local and national politicians may gain support as a result of a prestigious scheme.
- The influence of important absentee landowners.
- The size of the profits that major companies can get from large capital intensive development projects.
- Pressures from organisations such as the World Bank which has considerable expertise in supporting large scale projects but no comparable infrastructure for handling small loans.
- The lack of vast sums of capital available within the country for investment in development projects.
- The buying-off of local opposition by commercial and political agents.
- The use of the media to influence local attitudes to the project.

GENERAL CONCEPTS

The Green Revolution

This was an attempt to intensify agriculture. Many authorities believe that the best hope of improving food yield in the developing world is through the intensification of farming in existing cultivated lands rather than by attempting to extend the agricultural areas. The revolution was a complex process whereby low-yielding traditional agricultural practices were transformed by the introduction of new technology and national economics.

Population pressure

This is the condition of disequilibrium between the size and rates of growth of population on the one hand, and the availability and rate of development of resources on the other. It is not synonymous with population growth. If technological advance and social and political development occurs, this may result in increased resources becoming available, thus, although there is an increase in population, there is a decrease in pressure.

Internal disequilibrium

The degree of this that exists between people, economies and resources is directly related to the amount of population pressure. It is partly the result of increased heterogeneity which has occurred as a result of the introduction of modern sectors into the economy and the social and political structures of the country. In India, for example, modern development has resulted in the creation of a small, highly privileged sector of the population localised geographically in the major cities. They are the government officials, politicians, professional people, etc. Their ways of life and standards of living are related to international links more than to traditional culture and their policies and activities are dependent on foreign aid, investment and overseas markets. The existence of this sector in the primate cities magnifies the extent to which those cities attract migrants through their wealth and quality of life. India's major cities account for two-thirds of her urban growth.

DIFFERENT PERSPECTIVES

The demographic perspective

The Malthusian view of the relationship of population to resources is relevant to the present situation of rural population in India. In Western Europe the technological advances of the Industrial Revolution made the projected situation described by Malthus seem unlikely. Some hope that the present agricultural and industrial development of India will have a similar effect to the Industrial Revolution in Europe.

The technological perspective

This is symbolised by the Green Revolution (see above). This perspective sees India's economic and social salvation in the implementation of rational and scientifically based development programmes.

4.5 BRAZIL: REGIONAL STRATEGIES

BASIC ECONOMIC FACTS

Brazil is the fifth-largest country in the world by area, the sixth by population. It takes up nearly half of the continent of South America but much of its territory remains empty or thinly populated. Despite its emptiness Brazil is now the major manufacturing country in South America. Its major industrial region is the São Paulo–Rio de Janeiro region (south-east Brazil). Brazil does not have the developed energy resources necessary to match its size and ambitions. Coal production is the equivalent of that produced by two large efficient pits in England; its oil production is only 4% of Venezuela's; it has only 4% of the hydro electricity available per head of population that Norway has.

From the late 1960s Brazil's economic growth rate has been one of the most rapid in the world. Its population growth has also been rapid so the gross domestic product (GDP) is still very low compared with the Western industrial nations.

ECONOMIC CYCLES

The economic development of Brazil has been characterised by a series of cycles. In each cycle a particular resource has been intensively developed in one part of the country. The intensive development has led to the exhaustion of the resource and the region in which it was located has been abandoned as a centre of economic interest. The main cycles have been (in chronological order):

Brazil wood

This first attracted the Portuguese to the north coast of Brazil. The wood yielded a dye which was sent back to Europe. This was followed by the exploitation of the Amazon Forest, especially for its wild rubber trade. The **rubber cycle** brought great wealth to those who controlled the trade until alternative sources of high quality plantation rubber in South-East Asia became the world's suppliers, e.g. Malaysia and Indonesia.

Sugar cane

This cycle developed in the north-east in the Recife–Santos area. For 150 years up to 1700 this was Europe's chief source of sugar. It was unable to meet the competition of the plantations set up in the West Indies and the sugar economy of north-east Brazil declined.

Gold and precious metals

Deposits were found in the eighteenth century in Minas Gerais state and exploited until they were largely exhausted. Only in recent years has Minas Gerais become an important mining area again with iron ore and bauxite mining.

Coffee

The coffee boom of the nineteenth century began in the Paraiba valley and then spread to São Paulo. This boom came to an end in the 1960s when much of the stock was diseased, there was no suitable empty land upon which to extend coffee growing and emergent countries such as Kenya competed successfully with Brazil for western markets. Land used for coffee-growing at the peak of the cycle has now reverted to poor quality farmland.

Industry

Much of the capital generated by the coffee industry was invested in the growth of modern manufacturing industries in the south and south-east.

Forests

The newest of the cycles which is still in operation. Amazonia and its tropical rainforest is seen as a massive economic resource from which vast profits may be made quickly. Deforestation, the development of mining, the introduction of heavily subsidised cattle ranching and building of roads and air strips has brought fundamental changes to Amazonia and its people.

REGIONAL DIFFERENCES

Economically the country is dominated by the coastal areas. 90% of the people of Brazil live within 900 kilometres of the sea. The 'core' region is the São Paulo–Rio de Janeiro-Belo Horizonte triangle in which the new industrialisation and other aspects of modernisation have been concentrated. This region contrasts dramatically with other regions which are largely undeveloped or having to cope with high population growth rates unmatched by economic development.

Economic regions may now be distinguished which are different from the traditional geographical regions (Fig. 150). Each economic region is characterised by a particular stage and type of economic development.

Eastern heartland

The economic core of the country including São Paulo state, Minas Gerais state, and Rio de Janeiro. The region contains 10% of Brazil's area, 40% of its population, and its average wage is 150% that of the country as a whole. 66% of Brazil's industries are located here and it provides the market for 75% of Brazil's manufactured goods.

The north-east

When plantation agriculture was important and prosperous this was the chief economic region of Brazil. It is now in long-term decline and is getting steadily poorer than other regions in the country.

The north

This is a resource frontier not yet integrated into the Brazilian economy. It is being transformed rapidly and fundamentally but in ways which are attacked by many as ill-conceived and unacceptable at national and international levels.

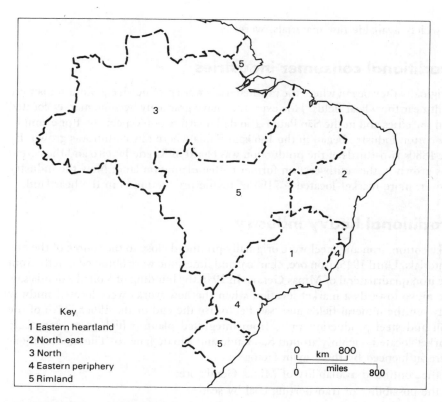

Fig. 150 *Economic regions of Brazil*

Eastern periphery

The southern sub-tropical half of this region is an area of established family farms and small industries. The northern tropical half has been isolated and underdeveloped. It is now beginning to develop as part of Rio de Janeiro's sphere of influence.

The rimland

This frontier region is a transition zone between the heartland, the north-east and the north. The traditional cattle-rearing economy is being improved and, as new roads are built across the rimland, economic development is commencing.

MODERNISATION OF AGRICULTURE

Agricultural productivity is increasing as a result of technological change. The government is subsidising this development. As farm labour has decreased (as a result of rural–urban migration) mechanisation has increased. Farms have also changed from a grazing to an arable economy in many areas and this has stimulated mechanisation further. A national plan for the manufacture of tractors, the production and distribution of fertilisers through agricultural service centres, and Federal and State programmes of technical assistance have encouraged greater production. Financial bodies have been established to arrange loans for farmers. New marketing arrangements and new roads mean that the additional produce can be marketed more efficiently.

Nevertheless, some regions remain agriculturally backward, especially the north-east. The expansion of commercial agriculture in many areas is severely limited by remoteness from suitable markets.

INDUSTRY

Industry began to develop in Brazil in the middle of the last century, on the proceeds of the coffee boom. The first industries, concerned with the processing of widely available raw materials, were:

Traditional consumer industries

Originally they began where the raw materials were produced, e.g. flour mills were built near the wheat fields. However, they have gradually become market-located – in the cities and in the São Paulo–Rio de Janeiro region especially. For example, the cotton industry began in the 1860s in Bahia where raw cotton was grown. By the 1880s two-thirds of the production was based in Rio de Janeiro and the cotton was grown in the south-east on former coffee plantation land. Now the industry is even more market-located – 71% of textile production is in the heartland.

Traditional heavy industry

Like cotton, iron and steel were originally produced close to the source of the raw materials. Until 1945, iron ore, charcoal and limestone were obtained chiefly from the iron quadrilateral of Minas Gerais. In 1946 the building of Volta Redonda saw the move towards a market location when the new works were located midway between the mineral fields and São Paulo. By the end of the 1960s, 25% of the iron and steel production came from integrated plants which were essentially market-located – mainly around São Paulo and Rio de Janeiro. The new locations were influenced by three main factors:

❶ the continued availability of Minas Gerais ore;

❷ the possibility of transporting coal by sea;

❸ the markets for steel in the São Paulo–Rio heartland.

Industrial 'take-off' after 1964

In 1964 a military government took over Brazil. It was determined to bring economic and political stability to the country and to achieve economic growth. Inflation was checked, overseas investors encouraged to invest in Brazil and great incentives were given to manufacturing industries. By the 1970s Brazil had one of the highest economic growth rates in the world. At first, existing industries were expanded. Soon, however, economic growth involved the introduction of new industries – in particular, cars and petrochemicals – of which Brazil is the leading Latin American producer. The government has encouraged foreign firms to establish plants in Brazil and the import of finished vehicles, etc. is discouraged by high import duties. The plants were established in the heartland, close to the major internal markets. As well as new industries, new roads, hydroelectric power stations and a telecommunications network have been developed. There is now a dualism in the manufacturing economy of Brazil – modern efficient plants in the heartland, traditional small industries, closely related to the availability of raw materials, elsewhere.

The rise in oil prices, the world recession of the early eighties and falls in commodity prices as demand decreased had serious economic consequences for Brazil. High levels of inflation and indebtedness and increasingly difficult social problems produced changes in political attitudes and policies. In 1985 democratic elections were held and the country moved from a military dictatorship to elected civilian rule. The present government hopes to achieve more permanent progress and to move away from unplanned 'stop-go' policies. Prestigious but expensive projects such as the new road to Peru for the export of Amazonian timber have now been revised or abandoned.

REGIONAL DEVELOPMENT PROGRAMMES

Attempts were also made to decrease regional disparities. One such attempt was the building of a new capital city.

Brasilia

The capital of Brazil used to be Rio de Janeiro but it ceased to be so in 1960. The Brazilian government decided to build a new capital for their 'new' nation, and Brasilia was built on a site 1,600 km inland from Rio. This decision signified the Brazilian determination to develop the interior – the focus of economic development was switched from the coastal areas to the centre of the country. The establishment of Brasilia has provided a major magnet on the edges of the undeveloped areas, deflecting population flow from the Rio de Janeiro–São Paulo axis and encouraging economic growth in new areas. New land transport links between Brasilia and the heartland of the south-east assist in this.

Attempts have been made to develop other parts of Brazil. For example, new highways were begun in the less developed regions such as Amazonia. Regional development administrations, financed by national taxes, have been established. SUDENE in the north-east and SUDAM in the north are two of these organisations. Their programmes include road building, the installation of power stations, settlement schemes for new farmlands, building schools, developing ports and encouraging new industries. Although progress has been made, however, these regional programmes have not lived up to expectations.

DEVELOPMENT PROBLEMS

The less-well-developed regions have not shared fully in the economic boom and the development gaps between the regions have not been narrowed. The differences between the rich and poor which are most obvious are the differences between cities such as Rio de Janeiro and the least developed areas. The main economic problems are:

❶ The north-east has a large population but little employment.

❷ The need to mobilise the resources of the Amazon basin.

❸ The west is not fully settled and should take people from the overpopulated north-east.

❹ Continued expansion of the south and south-east will depend on the creation of bigger markets within Brazil. This means that other parts of the country have to acquire more purchasing power.

❺ Urbanisation – the movement of people to the cities, and rapid population growth within the cities has resulted in the development of shanty towns (favelas) in which poverty, crime and other social problems are concentrated.

Environmental degradation, e.g. the large-scale destruction of the Amazon forest by tree felling, the expansion of cattle ranching, the development of mineral resources, is fundamentally altering the geographical character of the region. Environmentalists claim that the destruction of the forest would deplete the earth's supply of oxygen, huge areas would suffer from soil deterioration, wildlife would be destroyed and traditional Indian cultures would disappear. International concern has now been aroused. This concern is not confined to issues of conservation or the fate of the Amazon peoples but is also related to the question of the global atmospheric and climatic effects of the destruction of the largest tropical forest in the world.

GENERAL CONCEPTS

Perceptual frontiers

Brazil still has a relatively small population for its total area and in some respects an exploitive 'frontiersman' attitude still prevails. No region within Brazil has had a concentration of natural resources and locational advantages sufficient to make it the permanent supreme focus of the country. Brazil has a history of different discoveries in different locations, offering apparent possibilities of great wealth. But these opportunities have never quite lived up to expectations and over time this has led to a speculative approach to economic development once summed up as the search for 'El Dorado'.

Core/periphery phenomenon

This is the situation in which major contrasts in economic progress have developed between a core region in the country and the underdeveloped interior which is almost totally outside the activities of a modern industrialised country.

The empty heart

This is best illustrated by the distribution of population (Fig. 151). It is important,

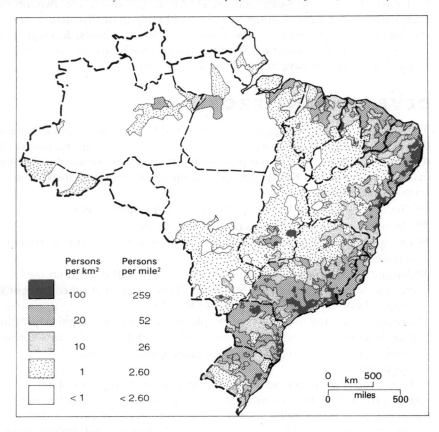

Persons per km² / Persons per mile²
- 100 / 259
- 20 / 52
- 10 / 26
- 1 / 2.60
- < 1 / < 2.60

Fig. 151 Brazil: population density

however, to distinguish between areas with very little potential for development, e.g. the semi-arid north-east interior and areas such as Amazonia with major untapped resources. The concept is also complicated by the fact that north-east Brazil is an area of difficulty. In terms of its potential for development it is already overpopulated, although it appears on the map to be thinly populated.

Views about the present economic activities and future potential of Brazil vary enormously. Some geographers see the progress made in recent years as an 'economic miracle' similar to that of Japan. Other geographers see a different picture – the empty interior, the decaying older agricultural communities of the north-east, the shanty towns, the widespread poverty. So Brazil is an enigma.

4.6 EXPLOITATION AND CONSERVATION

DEFINITIONS

Conservation

The protection of natural resources and the natural environment for the future. This includes the effective management of resources such as soils, minerals, landscapes and forests to prevent their over-exploitation and destruction. Conservationists are increasingly concerned with the preservation and protection of whole habitats as well as of endangered individual rare species. They practise careful environmental management to achieve and maintain an ecological balance and do not concentrate on passive protection.

Exploitation

The unwise or careless utilisation of hitherto unused or under-used natural resources for commercial purposes. Exploitation involves freedom for the operation of market forces with profit a prime motive and only limited concern for the effects of either the scale or rate of economic change involved. In developing lands exploitation has been essentially a short-term commitment to a region to make the most profitable use of minerals, land and other valuable resources, with little regard for the need to establish sustainable economic activities which over the long term could bring about comprehensive development without too great an ecological or social cost.

Tropical rainforest

A type of forest dominated by very tall trees that grow near the Equator. The plant cover is rich, varied and quick growing in response to the climatic conditions of all the year round rainfall (above 1500 mm) and consistently high temperature (25–30°C). These forests contain commercially valuable hardwood such as mahogany.

TFAP

(The Tropical Forest Action Plan of the United Nations Food and Agriculture Organisation (FAO).) It is jointly sponsored by the United Nations and World Bank. It is designed to establish global tropical forest conservation and development programmes. It aims to obtain finance for these programmes from national governments, private industries and international organisations.

EXPLOITATION AND CONSERVATION– AN EXAMPLE IN THE DEVELOPED WORLD

The rapid industrialisation of Britain in the nineteenth century created similar impatience to create economic wealth and similar conflicts of interests as those encountered in the developing world today. At that time there was also a lack of awareness of, and concern for, the environmental effects of large-scale exploitation of previously unindustrialised areas. As a result, in recent times work has had to be done to repair the environmental damage caused more than a hundred years ago. A prime example of the reclamation of land laid waste by industrial exploitation was the Lower Swansea valley project. The area was the site of major smelting and refining factories in the nineteenth century. The works were abandoned and decayed. They were surrounded by waste heaps containing traces of arsenic and other poisonous materials so there was little or no vegetation cover. The project was based on scientific research at Swansea University and the conservation programme designed to reclaim this industrial wasteland involved the removal of major eyesores, the grassing of waste tips, afforestation and the education of the children of the area in conservation issues and concern for the environment.

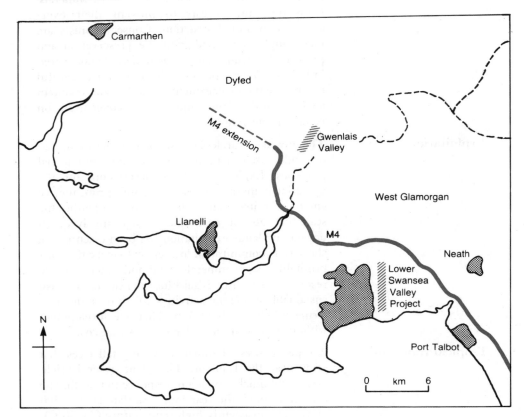

Fig. 152 Development projects in the South Wales region

Present-day environmental concern and pressure for effective conservation policies have not, however, removed the problems caused by industrial exploitation in this part of Wales. A major industrial raw material need in Britain today is for stone and aggregate for the building industry. The extension of the M4 motorway westwards in South Wales created an intense local demand for aggregate and construction companies were eager to extend quarrying operations. In some cases permission for quarrying was granted before planning controls came into existence. In the 1960s, Intermediate Development Orders (IDOs) were issued which can be activated today without any fresh enquiries. The Gwenlais Valley in Dyfed is threatened by an IDO. The valley ridge is an area of Special Scientific Interest (SSI) and in the valley there are five working farms. A major construction company has the legal right to destroy the entire valley through quarrying.

This is a major issue in other parts of Britain too. It was estimated that 280 million tons of aggregate would be needed each year by the year 2005. This target was passed in 1988. The most suitable materials and quarries are located in regions of beautiful scenery and even in National Parks. As pressure for building materials increase many counties have to make decisions about conflicting interests. You would find it useful to make a cost-benefit analysis similar to the one in Unit 4.4

to demonstrate conflict and pressure on the environment resulting from this type of exploitation in an area known to you.

An example from the developing world – general features

Concern over exploitation and conservation issues currently focus upon what is happening to the tropical rainforests. Most tropical rainforests are found in developing countries. These countries are deeply in debt to international banks and the governments of wealthy developed countries. They are therefore desperately anxious to exploit new sources of income in order to tackle major internal economic and social problems.

The destruction of the rainforest is the result of a multi-faceted process of exploitation. Valuable timber is a source of immediate profit but the land which is cleared also offers possibilities for profitable cattle ranching until the soil is exhausted. The heavy rainfall and nature of the terrain makes possible massive hydroelectricity projects in some locations. The forest areas also contain valuable mineral deposits. The entire programme of exploitation is underpinned by the creation of a transportation network of new roads along which timber, minerals and meat may be exported, and air strips which make even the most remote areas accessible. Construction and transportation in turn offer the possibility of huge profits.

The tropical rainforests are being destroyed at an alarming rate (Fig. 153). Half the world's tropical forests have now been removed, mainly in the last 40 years. Every 60 seconds 40 ha is said to be destroyed and it has been forecast that at the present rate of removal all the rainforests will have disappeared within 30 years. Accelerated cutting rates were reported in 1988 in the Philippines, Sabah, Sarawak, Thailand, Madagascar and the Ivory Coast. So the problem is not confined to the Amazon.

The exploitation of the rainforests has become the subject of much criticism by countries of the developed world which have become more conservation-conscious recently. However, the advanced countries have already destroyed most of their natural environments and they play the major role in creating pollution through their industrial activities. They also use up the world's natural resources most rapidly. Despite this, the developed countries have the finance and the

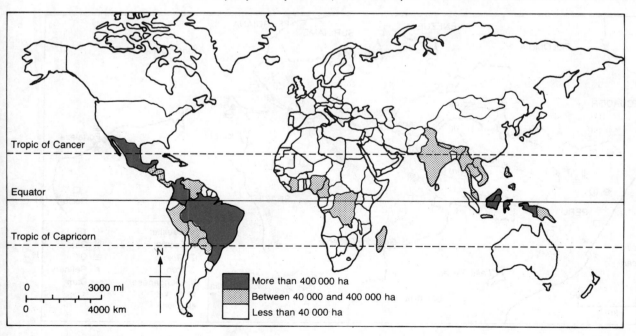

Fig. 153 Annual destruction of the rainforests

expertise in science and technology to work with the developing lands to conserve and manage the remaining forests. Some of this work is now being fostered by international agencies and by the implementation of agreements to international conventions designed to set good standards of utilisation and conservation. Working in parallel with official organisations are voluntary associations such as the World Wide Fund for Nature (WWF) and Friends of the Earth (FOE) which share the concern for the maintenance of our natural environmental heritage.

The destruction of the Amazon forest

The rate at which this forest is being removed is indicated by the fact that in three months in 1989 a rainforest the size of England, Scotland and Wales combined was cleared. Much of the clearing is by burning which scientists have calculated contributes 7% of the entire world emission of carbon dioxide which contributes to the greenhouse effect (see Unit 4.7).

There are currently four main aspects of the economic exploitation and industrialisation of the Amazon:

❶ The clearance of forest to make space for commercial cattle ranching. Until recently this was supported by the government of Brazil which subsidised clearance and did not tax farm incomes. This activity has attracted farmers from other regions who see better prospects, e.g. the farmers of the south who produced soya beans as a cash crop but have been replaced by mechanised techniques. It also attracted land speculators who saw huge profits in the heavily subsidised process of clearing and using the land.

❷ The use of timber for commercial purposes. Logging camps, new saw mills, forest tracks along which felled timber is dragged to mills and collection points and the creation of new roads along which the timber is exported have all contributed to the destruction of the forest. The timber has a ready market in the furniture and building industries of the developed countries.

❸ The development of hydroelectric power resources. The prime mover in this has been Brazil's northern region electricity company, Electronorte. The Amazon region is seen as Brazil's chief future source of cheap power which will contribute significantly to the development and prosperity of the

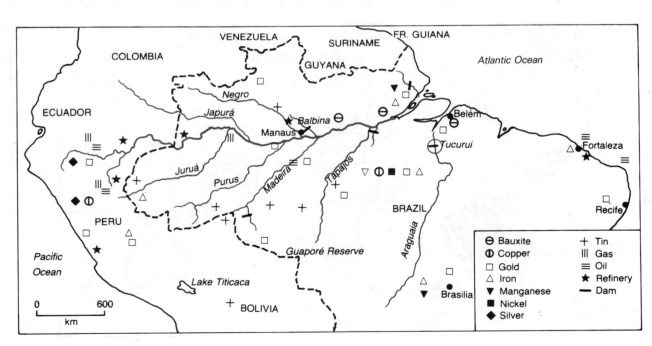

Fig. 154 Distribution of mineral resources in the Amazon region

country. Virgin forest has been flooded and new dams built. Tucurui, built in 1984, is now Brazil's largest man-made lake (the size of Dorset) and has the world's third largest dam.

❹ Mineral exploitation. Fig. 154 shows the distribution of important mineral resources within the Amazon region. Mining has involved forest clearance and the displacement of indigenous peoples. Industrial processes have also damaged the environment. In gold mining, for example, mercury is used in the extraction process and mercury poisoning has affected rivers and streams.

The effects of government policy

Until recently the central government strongly favoured the rapid industrialisation of the Amazon. This was seen as the way to tackle Brazil's international debt problems and to ease social and economic pressures internally by offering new opportunities to the unemployed and poor. Consequently policies were adopted which favoured developers and speculators. These included:

- the subsidising of ranchers who cleared forest;
- exempting farm income from tax;
- approving major schemes such as the B364 road designed to take timber out through Peru, and the hydroelectric projects;
- paying little attention to the interests of the indigenous people who lived in small numbers throughout the forest;
- paying little attention to the need for conservation programmes.

Recent changes in government have led to a re-evaluation of the Amazon development. Subsidies have been withdrawn from ranchers and tax concessions ended. Speculators see investment in the Amazon as less profitable while strict anti-inflation measures have made it more expensive for investors and speculators to borrow money. The government is also attempting to improve the effectiveness of the surveillance services which are supposed to control forest burning and to ensure that native people are protected from miners and ranchers when there is a conflict of interests.

The effectiveness of the new policies is limited by:

- the vast amount of money needed to implement them;
- the lack of coordination between government agencies (when the central government withdrew subsidies INCRA, the colonisation agency, continued to pay them);
- and the size and remoteness of the region which makes it difficult to supervise and control.

Possible solutions

Solutions which have been put forward by the Brazilian government, international agencies and other interested groups include:

❶ The zoning of the Amazon into economic activity regions so that mining, ranching, etc, will only be permitted in parts.

❷ Establishing a National Park or a number of Parks which would conserve the unspoiled forest that remains (this has been done in Cameroon).

❸ Setting aside reservations for the native peoples.

❹ Establishing more carefully planned and managed economic activities, e.g. **selective logging policies** which would mean that only saleable trees were felled and were replaced by planting to give the industry permanence; and **new farming techniques** designed to replace ranching with crop production so that the need for new farmland is diminished.

❺ The establishment of tourism which would bring new income to the region and would also sensitise visitors to the need to conserve what remains of the forest (this is being developed in the forests of Costa Rica).

DIFFERENT PERSPECTIVES

The free market perspective

This sees the Amazon as one of the few remaining regions of vast and untapped economic wealth which could be created by the application of modern industrial and financial processes to the region. It argues that Brazil should use the development of the Amazon to create work, raise standards of living and meet its international debts, even if this means the disappearance of existing habitats and displacement of people.

The conservation perspective

Conservationists see the tropical rainforests and the Amazon in particular as important areas of the natural environment to protect for the future. They emphasise the need for effective management and control of rapid economic exploitation, and favour development plans to minimise effects on the ecosystem and people, and work towards international cooperation on conservation programmes.

The sociological perspective

Many sociologists are concerned with the protection of the traditional ways of life of indigenous groups in the Amazon and ensuring their welfare as miners, ranchers, etc. move into their lands.

The nationalist perspective

Prominent Brazilians resent the interference of other nations in issues relating to the development of the Amazon. They see the Amazon as their own business and reject well-meaning proposals by developed countries to inject finance needed to undertake some of the conservation programmes, e.g. Norway suggested a debt swap which meant that Norway would forget what it was owed if Brazil spent the equivalent amount on conservation. It is claimed that conservation pressure on Brazil is the result of the fact that developed nations covet the Amazon and wish to interfere in Brazil's affairs.

4.7   POLLUTION

DEFINITIONS

Acid rain	This is a somewhat misleading term: 'acid deposition' is more accurate as this form of pollution may fall as dust as well as precipitation. Normal precipitation has a pH of 5.6, whereas acid rain can have an acidity as high as pH 2.4. The acidity is caused by sulphur dioxide (SO_2) and nitrogen dioxide (NO_2). The process by which these gases form part of precipitation is discussed in detail later in this chapter.
Eutrophication	The nutrient enrichment of a body of water which frequently results in a range of other changes. Among these are the increased production of algae, the deterioration of water quality and the reduction of fish numbers. The enriching nutrients are usually phosphates and nitrates which reduce the oxygen content of water and lead to the death of aquatic

plants and other living organisms. This decaying matter falls to the bottom, increasing the silt layers and slowly filling up the lake. Eutrophication ages a body of water to the point where it cannot support life.

Global warming

The increase in the global temperature which results from the build-up of 'greenhouse' gases, for example methane and carbon dioxide in the atmosphere. Like the panes of a greenhouse, these gases let in solar heat and then trap it when it is reflected back from the earth's surface. This process has become popularly known as 'the greenhouse effect'. Carbon emissions from fossil fuels – coal, oil and natural gas – have increased the amount of carbon dioxide in the atmosphere, trapping more heat and causing global warming. Plants absorb carbon dioxide but as the rainforests are destroyed by burning, stored carbon dioxide is returned to the air and there is less vegetation to absorb CO_2.

Pollution by carbon dioxide from fossil fuels has increased global warming with a measured temperature increase of half a degree centigrade in the past 100 years. The consequences of global warming include melting ice-caps, flooding of low-lying land areas and the growth of deserts.

Ozone

A form of oxygen (O_3). At low levels near the earth's surface, ozone is produced by the action of very strong sunlight on air particles in the presence of nitrogen oxides and volatile organic compounds, including emissions from car exhausts and power stations. Ozone is a pollutant and a key component of photo-chemical smog. It can affect health with symptoms which include running noses, coughs and asthma. Research in the United States indicates that ozone may interfere with the body's immune system. Although ozone is most likely to occur in industrial areas, particularly in large cities, readings at monitoring stations during the July 1990 hot spell in England show that some rural areas were more heavily polluted than central London as a result of winds blowing the ozone pollution away from the cities.

The ozone layer is a zone within the atmosphere between 20 and 40 km above the earth's surface where ozone is at its greatest concentration. The ozone layer prevents most of the potentially damaging ultraviolet radiation from the sun from reaching the earth's surface, so protecting life forms and helping to maintain the earth's heat balance. (The difference between the amount of the sun's heat trapped in the atmosphere and that which is radiated back into space.)

Aerosols and refrigeration plants emit chlorofluorocarbons (CFCs) which, with halons and other industrial gases, set off chemical reactions in the atmosphere, destroying the ozone layer faster than it can be replaced. In 1985 British scientists discovered that there was a 'hole' in the ozone layer over Antarctica, supposedly due to pollutants such as

CFCs. Any increase in ultraviolet radiation is known to cause skin cancer in humans, hence the urgency at the present time to reduce the amount of CFC and other pollutant gases in the atmosphere.

Pollutants

Key pollutants include carbon dioxide, sulphur dioxide, oxides of nitrogen and chlorofluorocarbons. Apart from these gases toxic metals such as lead, copper and mercury are also responsible for pollution as are radioactive materials, oil, nutrients, hydrocarbons, heat and noise.

Pollution

The release of substances and energy as waste products of human activities which result in changes, usually harmful, within the natural environment. Pollution is caused by people and can harm living organisms as well as reducing the amenity value of the environment.

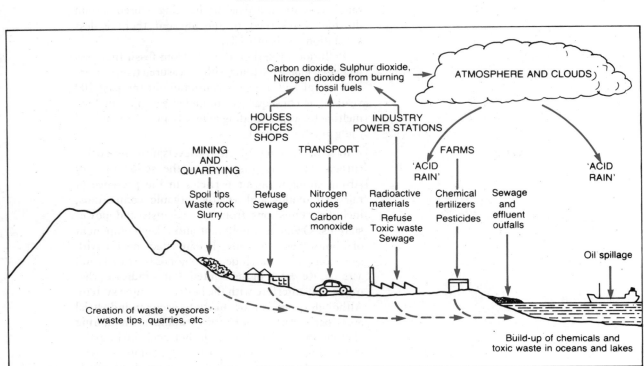

Fig. 155 Main sources and forms of pollution

AIR POLLUTION

Gas emissions

Pollution of the air is the result of the emission of gases such as carbon dioxide, sulphur dioxide and nitrogen dioxide. These gases are found in high concentrations, particularly in cities, as the result of the burning of fossil fuels and their derivatives. In addition there are particulates in the air. These take the form of dusts such as fine particles of clay or limestone. Also present are effluents from industry in the form of volatile compounds such as fluorocarbons. Metals such as lead also pollute the atmosphere.

Table 22 shows the types of air pollutants and their source as measured in the United States in 1986. Air pollution in the US is estimated to cause up to 50 000 deaths a year and cost £24 billion in health care and lost working days.

Table 22 *Air pollutant emissions by pollutant and source, 1986*

Pollutant	Source % by pollutant			
	Transportation	Fuel combustion	Industrial	Miscellaneous
Carbon monoxide	70.0	11.8	7.4	10.8
Sulphur oxides	4.2	81.1	14.6	0.1
Nitrogen oxides	44.0	51.8	3.1	1.1
Volatile organic compounds	33.3	11.8	40.8	14.1
Particulates	20.6	26.5	36.8	16.1
Lead	40.7	5.8	22.1	31.4

(Source: Statistical Abstract of the United States, 1989)

About 75% of the lead in the air is derived from lead in petrol while 85% of the carbon monoxide is also emitted by road vehicles.

The role of industry and power generation as major air polluting agencies is evident from the table below which shows that in the European Community the industrialised countries have the highest amount of air pollution.

Table 23 *Air pollution in EC countries*

Air pollution 1987	000 tonnes
Germany (Fed Rep)	2 969
UK	2 439
France	1 652
Italy	1 570
Spain	937 *
Netherlands	560
Portugal	303
Belgium	371
Denmark	266
Greece	217 *
Irish Republic	68
Luxembourg	22

* 1980
(Source: OECD)

In the UK power stations are responsible for 71% of the sulphur dioxide, 32% of the nitrogen dioxide and 33% of the carbon dioxide emissions. By comparison road transport is responsible for 1% of the SO_2, 45% of the NO_2 and 18% of the CO_2.

Acid rain

Sulphur dioxide and oxides of nitrogen are released into the atmosphere in large quantities as a result of burning fossil fuels, particularly coal and oil. About 50% of the gases fall in the immediate area of the discharge as dry fallout – microscopic particles which do not cause acid rain. The remaining gases combine with water in the atmosphere. Negatively charged sulphate ions cause water in the atmosphere to become enriched with positively charged hydrogen ions which then falls to the ground as acid precipitation. The pollutants drain into the earth and release poisonous metals such as aluminium, cadmium and mercury from their compounds in the soil.

Trees use stocks of nutrients such as calcium and magnesium as a defence mechanism against acidity but these nutrients become depleted in acid rain conditions and the trees are prey to attack from ozone pollution, fungus, insects and disease. Some species of trees are more sensitive than others to air pollution. In West Germany, 7.7% of the country's trees have been affected by acid rain. Of these 75% are fir, 41% spruce, 26% beech and 15% oaks.

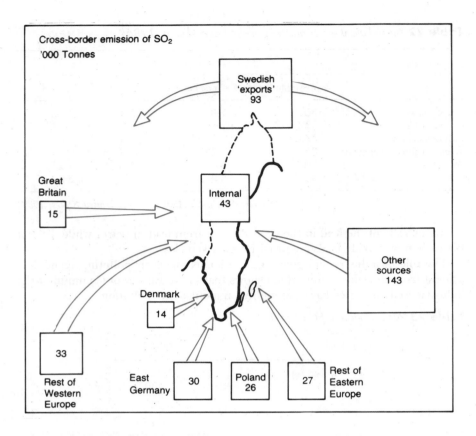

Fig. 156 Sulphur dioxide pollution in Sweden

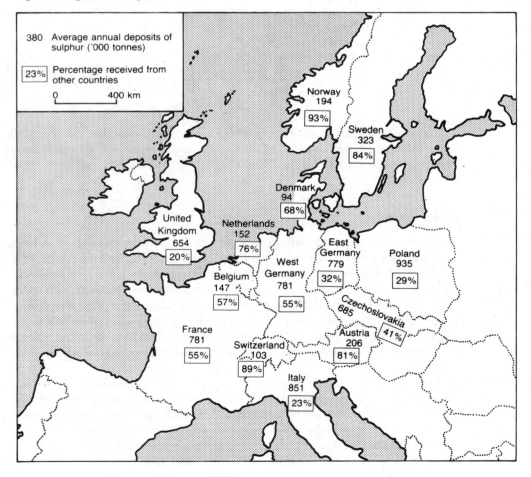

Fig. 157 Sulphur deposition in Europe — 1987

Acids and metals in the soil move in solution to the nearest lakes and streams where they concentrate. The combination of low pH values in the water and the increasing concentration of metals (notably aluminium) affects most aquatic species and insufficient food results in the death of fish and other living organisms. The process is complex, much depending on local soils, geology and the size and shape of the water body.

Buildings are also affected by acid rain. The Acropolis in Athens, the Taj Mahal in India and the Statue of Liberty in New York harbour are all being eaten away by industrial smog – sulphur dioxide in the air mixed with acid dust and water droplets.

Old-fashioned and inefficient sites and power stations in Eastern Europe are responsible for high levels of air pollution in neighbouring countries. The belief in the early 1980s that Swedish acid rain was mainly caused by Britain has been proved wrong, as Fig. 156 shows. Nevertheless, Britain is responsible for a considerable amount of cross-frontier pollution and has not joined the other industrial countries of Western Europe and Scandinavia in agreeing to at least a 30% desulphurisation programme for its power stations, although it has made its own counter-proposals.

WATER POLLUTION

Pollution of rivers and lakes by acid rain was described in the previous section because the underlying cause was atmospheric pollution by gas emissions. Rivers and lakes are also particularly vulnerable to two other types of pollution: (a) plant nutrients (b) toxic waste.

Plant nutrients

The enrichment of rivers and lakes by plant nutrients such as nitrates and phosphates is partly caused by run-off from agricultural land where these chemicals are used as fertilisers. It is also caused by effluent from sewage works. The annual human release to sewage is about 630 gm of phosphorus and 5 kg of nitrogen per person per year. Added to these are phosphates from other sources such as detergents. Sewage effluent is a rich fertiliser, stimulating the growth of algae and other photosynthetic organisms and leading to the over loading of plant nutrients in rivers and other water bodies which in turn leads to the over-production of algae. This forms a green scum on the water surface and decays to add organic matter on the lake bed. Some blue-green algae produce toxic substances which are poisonous to animals and people. In coastal waters the discharge of untreated sewage into the sea close inshore is a further source of pollution. Beaches are affected and Britain will have to spend large sums of money to improve many coastal areas to the standard set by the European Community.

Toxic wastes

Effluent from industry and sewage can be deadly. Some metal treatment processes produce an effluent containing cyanide and although pollution laws in many countries are strict, accidents do happen killing fish and aquatic plants over a wide area. Some toxic materials can become concentrated in organisms and passed on to form further concentrations in the higher members of the food chain. DDT became concentrated in coho salmon introduced in the Great Lakes. Mercury has also become concentrated in fish in some lakes, often because compounds of mercury used on seeds as fungicides have been leached out of farmland into rivers and lakes. Lead is yet another toxic pollutant liberated by car exhausts as well as industrial processes.

Oil spillage is usually associated with accidents to tankers at sea but waste oil from industry and shipping is also a pollutant in many rivers and lakes. Fig. 158 shows the extent of pollution in the rivers, canals and estuaries controlled by the

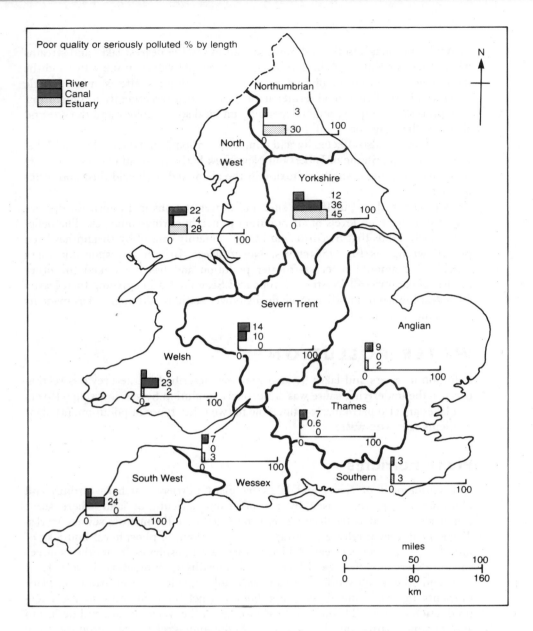

Fig. 158 Water authorities for England and Wales: river, canal and estuary pollution, 1985 (Source: River Quality in England and Wales, 1985, a report of the 1985 Survey, HMSO)

ten water authorities in England and Wales. The highest percentages of pollution are in the Midlands and North where industry has inherited the legacy of the industrial revolution.

Pollution of an ecosystem

The Norfolk Broads have their own distinctive fresh water ecosystem developed in the lakes (Broads) which were made by excavations for peat in the Middle Ages. The area is a mosaic of reedswamp, grazing marsh and open waters linked by six rivers and surrounded by arable land. In this century the area has suffered from extensive pollution with only four of the 52 Broads still supporting their former wealth of plants. The basic cause of the deterioration of the Broads, as Fig. 159 shows, is nutrient enrichment of the rivers and lakes by sewage effluent and fertilisers. The situation has been exacerbated by the growth of tourism with 250 000 visitors each summer. Many of the tourists' interests underline the need to check pollution and large sums must be spent to restore the Broadland

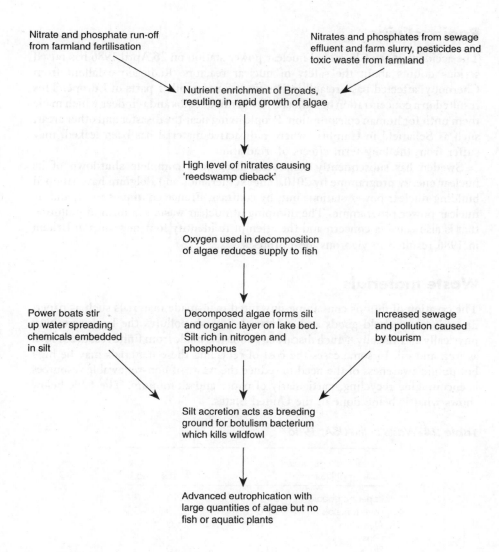

Fig. 159 *The effects of pollutants on a Broadland ecosystem*

ecosystem. One example of what can be done is Cockshoot Broad which has been dredged to remove silt and cut off from the River Bure to keep out further pollution. Aquatic plants have flourished and the water is clear and clean. Elsewhere scientists are working with water fleas which eat the algae and help clean the Broads.

OTHER SOURCES OF POLLUTION

Noise

Noise is recognised as a major environmental pollutant and prolonged exposure to noise levels in excess of 80 decibels is considered a hazard to mental, physical and social well-being. The decibel scale which measures the intensity of a sound is logarithmic so that the noise of a heavy truck rated as 90 decibels is 10 times that of the noise inside a small car rated at 80 decibels. In Britain two-thirds of the complaints about domestic noise concern the loud playing of music and the barking of dogs. The persistent noise of motor vehicles on main roads and motorways is the cause of most noise pollution and the main target of legislation and pressure groups such as the Noise Abatement Society.

Radioactivity

The accident at the Chernobyl nuclear power station on 26 April 1986 has raised serious doubts about the safety of nuclear reactors. Radioactive fallout from Chernobyl affected pastureland in Britain and many other parts of Europe. This resulted in a concentration of radioactivity in milk, lambs and reindeer which made them unfit for human consumption. People living near the disaster and other areas, such as Sellafield in Cumbria where radioactive material has been leaked, may suffer from the long-term effects of irradiation.

Sweden has subsequently committed itself to a complete shutdown of its nuclear energy programme by 2010. The Netherlands and Belgium have stopped building nuclear power stations but, by contrast, France continues to expand its nuclear power programme. The dumping of nuclear waste is a form of pollution that is also causing concern and the attempt to identify four new sites in Britain in 1986 resulted in vigorous local protests.

Waste materials

The creation of dumps containing unwanted man-made materials such as paper, discarded household goods and industrial rubbish pollutes the landscape both physically and visually. Much discarded rubbish is made from finite resources such as iron and oil. In some cases the cost of recycling these materials may be high but public awareness of the need to reduce the waste of non-renewable resources is encouraging recycling, particularly of paper and aluminium. The table below shows what is being done in the United States.

Table 24 *Waste in the USA, 1986*

Gross waste generated (millions of US tons)		% recovered
Paper and board	64.7	22.6
Ferrous metals	11.0	3.6
Aluminium	2.4	25.0
Glass	12.9	8.5
Plastics	10.3	1.0

(Source: Statistical Abstract of the United States, 1989)

GENERAL CONCEPTS

- **Pollution is a form of environmental degradation** which can result from natural phenomena such as a volcanic eruption, but is made, in the vast majority of cases, by people acting thoughtlessly, deliberately or in ignorance. Pollution usually has a harmful effect on living organisms and some forms of pollution such as radiation can cause illness and death.
- **Ecosystems are complex organisations** with interdependent components and pollution of one part of an ecosystem can set up a chain reaction which disrupts the stability of the whole system.
- **Pollution is an international problem** since some forms of pollution such as acid rain may be generated in one country but transferred in the atmosphere to other countries some distance away.
- **Pollution is also a global problem** because the preservation of the ozone layer which is threatened by the build-up of harmful gases is worldwide and one of the long-term effects is to break down protection from ultraviolet rays.
- **Many pollution problems are political issues.** Governments must decide between conflicting interests, for example, the farmers' need to

increase output by using artificial fertilisers and the polluting effects these fertilisers may have on drainage basins and ecosystems. Governments must also decide on the allocation of public money to meet the high costs required to check or prevent pollution. For example, the cost of building sewage outfalls some distance out to sea to prevent beach pollution or the cleaning of emissions from power station chimneys to limit the escape of SO_2 and NO_2.

International diplomacy is also an important aspect of global pollution issues. There is some conflict between the rich nations and the developing countries as to the phasing out of CFCs and other industrial gases. Developing countries want to expand industry and manufacture refrigerators on a large scale even though CFCs and other industrial gases are involved. Money from the more developed countries is available to help find suitable alternatives but how the money will be shared out, and persuading developing countries to cooperate, is a contentious issue. The role of the multinationals in increasing pollution in the Third World was highlighted in 1984 when a deadly gas escaped from a tank owned by the Union Carbide Corporation at Bhopal in India, killing over 2500 people.

Case study: Copsa Mica, Romania

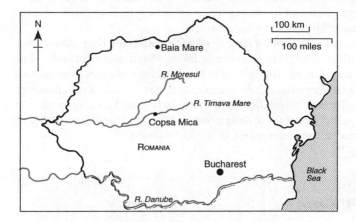

Fig.160 Copsa Mica, Romania

The collapse of Communism in Eastern Europe has revealed extremely high levels of pollution in industrial towns and regions. Out-of-date machinery and production methods are the main causes, together with a lack of environmental concern displayed by local officials and the state bureaucracy.

Copsa Mica is a small town with originally 7000 inhabitants in central Romania (Fig. 160). It contains two main factories on which local people depend for work. The Carbosin works produces rubber tyres for Dania cars. The IMMN works is a non-ferrous metal factory smelting ores from mountains near Baia Mare, 320 km to the north.

The IMMN works smelts lead, zinc, copper and cadmium. Together with the Carbosin works it emits 30,000 tonnes of pollutants into the air annually. Everything and everyone in the town is covered with black dust, even the farm animals. This is because the works lacks basic filters and both factories use worn-out machinery.

Most of the townspeople have fled. Factory workers are shipped in from towns 50 km away to work 4–6 hour shifts. Attempts to close the factories have been resisted because there is no other work.

A 1990 survey showed:
- the lead level in children's blood was twice the permitted level;
- children had low body weight;
- IQ tests gave unusually low results;

277

- one in three have bronchitic asthma;
- the rates of respiratory diseases and eye infections are two to three times above the normal;
- life expectancy may be as low as 43 years.

Milk and farm produce from farms within a radius of 30 km have been declared unfit for human consumption. Scientists have found that the lead and cadmium levels in the soil are more than ten times the permitted levels. In 1992 the World Bank and the EC called for International Aid for the region. It was estimated that £12 million would be needed for five years to remove the worst effects of the pollution.

DIFFERENT PERSPECTIVES

Growth of interest in the environment and lack of extensive research in the past has resulted in the publication of a variety of conflicting statements and reports. For example, until the late 1980s Britain was believed to be the main source of acid rain pollution in Sweden. Recent research by Swedish scientists (see Fig.156) has shown that the bulk of Sweden's sulphur pollution, which causes acid rain, comes from Eastern Europe. Our knowledge of the holes in the ozone layer is still in its infancy but this should not result in complacency about global warming since recent research suggests that the problem is more acute than was first thought.

When studying pollution and its causes try to obtain up-to-date material since our knowledge of the subject is increasing rapidly.

Human beings and other life forms have lived with pollutants throughout their evolution and have adapted to their presence at levels which occur naturally. For example, organisms are continuously subject to low levels of radiation from natural sources but the dosage is very small. Only in recent times as a result of urbanisation, industrial development and scientific discoveries have the levels of pollution become very high and in some cases dangerous to life. Any further addition to pollution levels increases the potential of biological damage.

Chapter roundup

This chapter follows the chapters on physical and human geography because it deals with regional and global issues which relate to what you have read already. For example, Unit 3.1 will help you to place Unit 4.3 on West Africa in a wider context while Unit 3.2 is also relevant. Unit 3.10 should be read in conjunction with Units 4.3, 4.4 and 4.5 in this chapter. Ecosystems were dealt with in Unit 2.10 and there is a close link between the concept of the ecosystem and the information in Unit 4.6. There are also links with other units which you should appreciate as you read this chapter.

Make certain you understand and remember the definitions which appear at the beginning of most units. These definitions are frequently asked for in the examination questions and the Chief Examiners complain in their reports of 'sloppy' explanations of such words as *overpopulation* and *global warming*.

There are numerous connections between the information in this chapter and topical events in various parts of the world. Read articles in newspapers and watch TV programmes which give you up-to-date examples of such features as regional problems, inner city issues, economic changes in the developing world and environmental issues such as exploitation and pollution. This chapter, like those before it, is relevant to the world around us. It will widen your horizons on a variety of current events which are taking place in your locality, in the UK or elsewhere in the world.

Illustrative questions and answers

1   Cameroon is a developing country in West Africa. It has a population of 11.1 million and a population growth rate of 2.6%. The GDP per capita is $1,190 US (UK £793). Life expectancy at birth is 53 years and there is an infant mortality rate of 98 per thousand (compare UK's 11). Cameroon is unusual in West Africa in that it does not have a primate city but has two major magnets for in-migration: the economic capital Douala and the political capital Yaoundé.

The figures on the maps (Fig.161) show the location of the two cities and features of migration to them.

(a) Outline the pattern of migration illustrated by these figures. (12)
(b) Discuss possible explanations for the pattern you identify. (12)

(in the style of the Joint Matriculation Board, A level)

Tutorial note

Do not be worried because you have never studied Cameroon in detail – very few people have! The information you need to answer part (a) is provided on the maps. The examiners want to test your powers of interpretation. To answer (b) you will need to know the reasons for internal migration, understand the core-periphery model and appreciate that Cameroon is a developing country. The allocation of marks should tell you that you must spend the same amounts of time on (a) and (b). However, before you start to plan out your answer, study each of the four maps carefully. Analyse what they show in terms of:
(i)   features common to both cities;
(ii) distinctive features that apply to one city only.

Suggested answer

(a) The features common to the pattern of migration for both Douala and Yaoundé are as follows.

1   Both cities receive migrants from all over the Cameroons. This is a reflection of their status as the two chief cities.
2   Both cities receive the bulk of their migrants from the south-west of the country. Their joint main catchment area forms approximately a quadrilateral area with the two cities on the western and eastern areas respectively.
3   There is a sharp fall in the number of migrants beyond the inner catchment areas.
4   In both cases in-migration is inversely proportional to the distance from the city of the division from which the migrants come.
5   Both cities receive the bulk of their migrants from the neighbouring administrative divisions.

(b) The possible explanations for the features described in (a) relate to the attraction of two major magnets to the rural hinterland of Cameroon.

There is no doubt that there are push-pull factors at work in this example of internal migration. 'Push' factors include the low standards of life in rural areas of developing countries such as Cameroon. Employment is difficult to obtain, opportunities for education and health care are very limited and living conditions are very poor. 'Pull' factors include the expectation of the immigrant that there are more job opportunities in the city, housing and health care are better and living standards are higher. These expectations may be unrealistic but immigrants, in the long term, may improve their living standards and benefit from the richer life that the city can offer.

In the Todara model the rural-urban movement is motivated by differences in

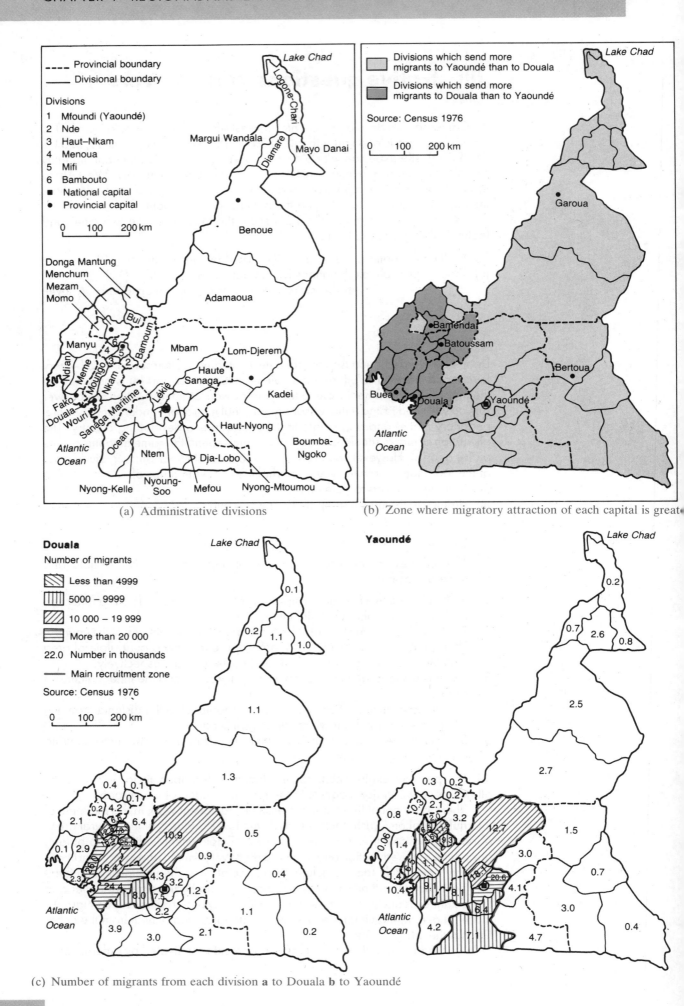

(a) Administrative divisions

(b) Zone where migratory attraction of each capital is great

(c) Number of migrants from each division **a** to Douala **b** to Yaoundé

Fig. 161 Cameroon

income between the formal wage earning urban dweller and the non-wage earning rural farm worker. This model may well account for some of the immigration but it can be criticised because it ignores the fact that many new immigrants survive in the city by earning money in the informal sectors of the economy.

The Mabogunje model was developed in relation to West Africa and consequently has significance for the Cameroon. The model recognises the socioeconomic factors which lead to migration and it also emphasises the complex nature of migration.

Myrdal's cumulative causation model also helps to explain the continuing growth of both cities. Having acquired particular advantages in the past as the economic capital (Douala) and the political capital (Yaoundé), new increments of growth and activity tend to be attracted to these centres because of their derived advantages.

One important factor which will influence the extent of the migration to either city is the flow of information, money and goods supplied by returning migrants. The attractions of the urban environment as experienced by their peers, will stimulate others to migrate. According to the Clarke and Kosinski model the overriding goal of the individual is to maximise his opportunities – first in the home area, but if this is not possible, elsewhere.

This spread effect helps to explain why the majority of migrants to both cities come from neighbouring administrative divisions. Information is more extensive and more easily obtained from areas close to the city. Distance is a fractional cost and information is disseminated more slowly and less frequently to the more remote parts of the country. It can also be argued that the cities complement each other. As the political capital, Yaoundé will have many government posts and associated service activities which will attract immigrants. As the economic capital, Douala is likely to be the chief focus for modern industrial and financial development. The concept of the primate city is replaced with one of a binary division as in Nigeria.

2   Study the sketch maps of an estuary in 1930 and 1985 (Fig. 162).

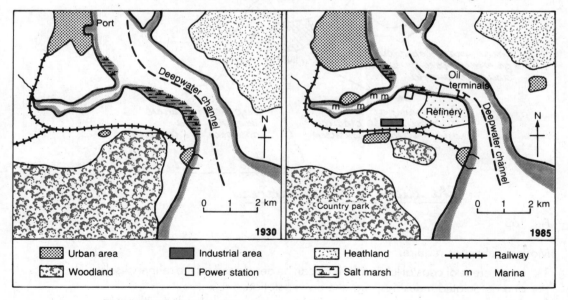

Fig. 162

(a) What have been the changes in land use in the area between 1930 and 1985?

(b) With the aid of a sketch map or diagram, explain the siting of the oil refinery.

(c) (i) What conflicts occur between refinery operation and

    1 marine activity;
    2 environmental conservation?
  (ii) In what ways might the refinery aid conservation in the area?
    (University of London School Examinations Board, A Level, June 1989)

Tutorial note

It is important that you do not make too many assumptions about the area shown on the sketch maps. Base your reasoning and arguments on evidence provided by the maps. Make certain your own sketch map is presented tidily, has a title and a scale.

Suggested answer

(a) (i) Reduction in the areas of both heathland and woodland with the major woodland area designated a country park by 1985.

  (ii) Expansion of the major urban area but the decline of its function as a port.

  (iii) Industrialisation of estuarine areas away from the major port – the oil refinery and deepwater terminals, the power station, a new industrial area.

  (iv) The appearance of leisure facilities – the country park and the marina.

  (v) The expansion of residential areas near major developments – the industrial estate and the marina.

  (vi) Significant reduction of the salt marshes, some of which have been used for the refinery site.

  (vii)Decrease in the land devoted to railway lines.

(b)

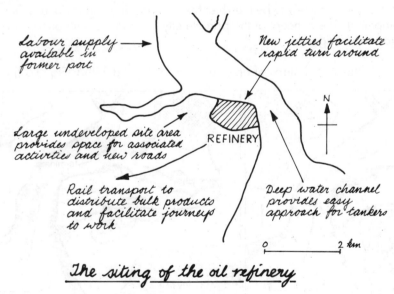

Fig. 163

Modern refineries require:

1 Large areas of coastal lowland which can be developed for the refinery itself and associated industries, e.g. the power station.

2 A deep water approach for modern large tankers heavily loaded with crude oil.

3 A transportation network to distribute the refined products and facilitate the journey to work from surrounding areas.

(c) (i)

1 Marine activity includes the movement in and out of oil tankers, the

movement of leisure craft to and from the marina and any fishing vessels that still use the original port. Any yachts or leisure craft will find large tankers a marine hazard. Conversely the tankers will have problems navigating in waters where leisure craft may occur in large numbers. These conflicts also apply to any fishing vessels or other craft using the estuary.

2   The building of the oil refinery took up a large area of salt marsh, effectively destroying part of an estuarine habitat. Industrial development may also have affected the scenic quality of the coastal area and housing development will also have destroyed rural habitats. Air pollution and waste emissions from the refinery and industrial centres may also cause conflict. The use of water for cooling and other industrial purposes may have created local water supply difficulties.

(c) (ii)

1   The oil company may be very sensitive to local opinion and possible bad publicity on environmental grounds. It may agree a carefully designed package that enhances conservation goals in the area.

2   Large industrial companies may sponsor conservation projects.

3   The disappearance of local open space may make people more concerned to preserve what is left.

4   Migrants to the area, attracted by the work available, may bring new energy to the work of local conservation groups.

5   Increased revenue from the industrial developments may provide local authorities with more income to undertake conservation programmes.

6   Users of the leisure facilities, such as the yachtsmen at the marina, will be anxious to conserve the area for their leisure enjoyment.

Question bank

1 (Time allowed: 15 mins)

Study the map and table below which shows Gross Domestic Product (GDP) per capita in 1976 and 1986 for the regions of the United Kingdom. The Regional GDP per capita figures are indexed to the UK figure (UK figure = 100).

		1976	1986
A	North	95.6	91.9
B	Yorks and Humberside	94.0	93.2
C	North West	96.4	93.5
D	East Midlands	96.0	96.1
E	West Midlands	98.1	90.6
F	East Anglia	94.7	100.8
G	South East	112.2	117.5
H	South West	90.8	96.1
J	Scotland	98.6	93.5
K	Wales	89.6	85.7
L	Northern Ireland	81.0	69.5
	United Kingdom	100.0	100.0

Fig. 164

(a) What name is commonly given to the general pattern illustrated by the data? (1)

(b) What **three** trends are identifiable in the data? (3)

(c) For **one** region where GDP per capita has increased, provide **three** supported reasons for the increase. (6)

(d) How might data such as that given above be seen as providing a misleading impression of regional differences? (5)

(The Associated Examining Board, A Level, June 1990)

Pitfalls

The examiners' report on this question speaks of some candidates being very repetitive in part (b), while others failed to read or understand what is meant by 'indexed' in the caption. In part (c) some students drifted away from discussing the GDP and gave all manner of reasons for the growth of the south-east, including the presence of night clubs! In part (d) you must appreciate how the data is presented and look at the map provided: these clues should help you to recognise some of the limitations of the statistics.

Points

You either know (a) or you do not. Do not be worried if you cannot answer this part of the question as it is only worth one mark. Look at the figures in the table when answering (b) and decide what trends they show. In (c) think carefully about what GDP really means. Do not confuse the term with standard of living. Part (d) can be approached with confidence if you recognise that the data is presented in per capita form and the figures apply to the regions of the UK.

2 (Time allowed: 45 min)

(a) Why do governments frequently wish to reduce regional inequalities? (9)

(b) With reference to any **one named** country which you have studied, discuss the problems which have to be overcome if a regional development policy is to succeed. (16)

(University of Cambridge Local Examinations Syndicate, A Level, June 1992)

Pitfalls

You must first decide which country you will take as your example when answering (b). If you do not have a considerable amount of information about the measures taken in one country, look for another question even though you can answer (a) reasonably well. Part (a) needs quite a lot of thought. It is not sufficient to say that the reasons for reducing inequalities between regions is to make all parts of the country comparable. You will need to plan this part of the answer carefully, in the manner shown below.

Points

Part (a) is best tackled by first describing the problems that arise in peripheral regions where development is limited, standards of living are low and out-migration creates problems for more affluent regions. Then describe the problems of core areas, including high costs, congestion, pressures on resources and a reduction in the quality of life. Do not forget that you are explaining the reasons for regional development from the point of view of the government which will be concerned about social, economic and political problems which can arise in peripheral and core regions because of the imbalance.

Part (b) could be answered taking the UK as your example. In this book there is a considerable amount of information about France and this could form the basis for your answer. Note that the question is only concerned with the problems which have to be overcome , so you must look carefully at backwash effects and similar factors.

3 (Time allowed: 40 minutes)

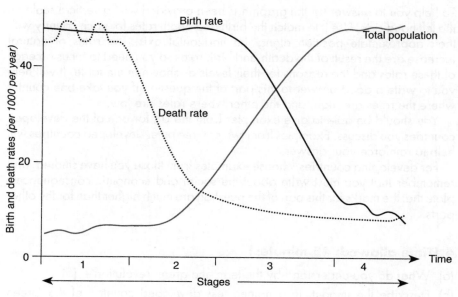

Fig. 165

Table 25

Country	Crude Birth Rate per 1,000	Crude Death Rate per 1,000	Natural increase
India	34	12	2.2
Nigeria	50	17	3.3
UK	13	12	0.1
USA	16	9	0.7

(a) Study Fig. 165 and Table 25 and match the four countries in the Table to particular stages in the graph. (4)

(b) With reference to any **two** countries shown in the Table, discuss the social and political factors which account for the differing rates of natural increase. (8)

(c) With reference to specific examples, discuss the social and economic consequences of the levels of birth rate in:
(i) developed countries, and
(ii) developing countries. (13)
(Total 25 marks)

(Scottish Certificate of Education, Higher Grade, May 1989)

Pitfalls

This question is about the demographic transition model and if your knowledge of this subject is very hazy, avoid it!

In part (b) you are asked to discuss the social and political factors . Do not wander off the point and discuss such things as drought or other natural disasters.

In part (c) you do not have to take the four countries in the question as your examples, although there is no reason why you should not if you have specific information about these countries. Note that you are asked to discuss the social and economic consequences of the levels of birth rate. Nothing is asked about the death rate so do not mention it.

Points

To help you to answer (a) the graph has been provided with a vertical scale on the left-hand side. Use it to match the birth and death rates for each country with their approximate position along the horizontal axis. The rates of natural increase are the result of the death and birth rates so you need to focus on each of these rates and the reasons for their levels as shown in the table. It will help you to write a good answer to this part of the question if you take one country where the rates are high, and the other where rates are low.

You should be able to give examples from the UK for one of the developed countries you discuss. Examples from two or three other developed countries will help to reinforce your answer.

For developing countries, choose examples from those you have studied, and remember that you must write about the social and economic consequences. Note that the marks for this part of the question are much higher than for the other parts.

4 (Time allowed: 45 minutes)

(a) What do you understand by the term 'the green revolution'? (5)

(b) Describe the impact, in a named less developed country, of the Green Revolution on:
(i) farming practices;
(ii) the organisation of farming. (5)

(c) With reference to specific examples, discuss the view that the Green Revolution has tended to increase rather than reduce the various inequalities in rural areas within less developed countries. (10)

(d) Discuss the detrimental environmental consequences of the green revolution in some less developed countries. (5)

(University of Oxford Delegacy of Local Examinations, A Level, June 1990)

Pitfalls

You are not asked to write down all you know about the Green Revolution so work through the question section by section making certain that you answer the question. The examiners' report said that some candidates confused the developed and developing countries. In part (b) most candidates were sound on farm practice but weak on farm organisation. Specific examples must be given in parts (b), (c) and (d) and you can lose marks for not providing some good examples.

Points

Tackle this question section by section. A short paragraph describing what is meant by the Green Revolution can be written in general terms, but the other three parts must avoid generalities and deal with specific examples.

Part (c) is the most important section since it is worth twice as many marks as each of the other parts. The question mentions inequalities within less developed countries, not inequalities between one country and another. Give specific examples where possible, e.g. the rural poor of India are just as numerous as before the green revolution.

Part (d) must include mention of pollution arising from the increased use of fertilisers, pesticides and herbicides. Effects on the soil, water supply and the danger from soil erosion should give you sufficient material to earn the five marks allocated.

5 (Time allowed: 35 minutes)

The Amazonian region of Brazil represents one example of an advancing agricultural frontier. Outline the causes of, and the problems associated with, such frontiers in the Developing World.

(The Associated Examining Board, AS Level, June 1990)

Pitfalls

The examiners' report emphasised that few candidates appreciated fully the reasons for this advancing agricultural frontier. Bland references to government policies were made, whereas the real reasons were ignored. Beware of questions about the tropical rainforests. Much has been written about these areas, many TV programmes have been made and articles have appeared regularly in the colour supplements to Sunday newspapers. Unfortunately this mass of information may hide some of the basic truths, or they may be ignored to make environmental points. As a result examiners have been inundated with half-truths and inaccurate statements and are concerned at the lack of depth in answers to questions of this kind.

The question gives the example of the rainforest in Amazonia but your answer should include examples from other parts of the world if you want to get high marks.

Points

There is an agricultural frontier here because of push factors in other parts of Brazil, particularly the north-east, where the land is poor and rainfall erratic. Population pressure is also important with the need to relieve overpopulation in other parts of the country. The government has created pull factors by developing a road network and providing cheap tracts of land to settlers. There is a belief that the region is highly fertile and can support a varied agricultural economy – this has proved to be false. Your answer should expand on these points and not focus on government policy which is really a response to social, economic and political pressures.

The second part of the question gives you scope to write about the problems and causes as they occur in other areas where agriculture is taking over land which has not previously been cultivated. This is happening in other rainforest areas such as northern Australia (Queensland), Malaysia and Indonesia. It is also happening in the tropical grasslands of Africa where small areas are being added to existing village farmland and areas irrigated which were previously left in a natural state. The causes and problems are similar to those found in Amazonia.

6 (Time allowed: 45 minutes)

For any *one* country in Europe (including the British Isles), the USA and Canada, Australasia, Japan and the USSR, discuss:

(a) the need for countryside conservation; (12)

(b) the ways in which this conservation may be achieved. (13)

(University of London School Examinations Board, A Level, June 1991)

Pitfalls

The examiners' report states that this was a popular question but the generally good answers to part (a) were not balanced with equally good answers to part (b). Few candidates appreciated that conservation can be achieved by a wide range of measures and the setting up of National Parks is only one answer to the problem. Do not be sidetracked into lengthy discussions about pollution or global environmental degradation. The question is about the countryside and that is the key word to remember when writing your answer. Remember that you must limit your answer to any one country.

Points

(a) Think of the various pressures being put on the countryside by groups such as developers, industry and others. You should be able to write about five or more such pressure groups using examples where possible.

(b) Think of the many ways conservation of the countryside can be achieved, you may be able to use examples from your own home area. The scale of the conservation need not be large, it can be as small as the action by a local council to preserve a piece of woodland from being cut down.

The marks are evenly divided between (a) and (b) so keep your answers for each part to roughly similar lengths.

7 (Time allowed: 45 minutes)

Paris drivers urged to walk or stay at home

With the Eiffel Tower half swathed in a yellow-brown smog and pollution readings at danger level, Parisians were urged last night not to drive their cars in the next few days.

The air of Paris has suffered from the calm sunny weather over Europe since the end of December.

According to meteorologists there is now a thick layer of warm air above a layer of rather colder atmosphere below, creating a fog that gets dirtier and dirtier.

Car exhausts are one of the worst offenders which is why a Government spokesman asked Parisian drivers to stay at home.

Fig. 166

(a) Read the newspaper report shown in Fig. 166 and explain the combination of circumstances which give rise to the situation described. (10)

(b) Briefly describe one other way in which air pollution in large urban/industrial areas can influence the local climate. (5)

(c) With reference to at least one urban/industrial area you have studied, discuss the acceptability of controls which have been or could be introduced to combat air pollution.   (20)

(Northern Ireland Schools Examinations and Assessment Council, A Level, May 1991)

Pitfalls

The question is in three parts but the weightings differ. You should avoid answering the parts as though they had the same weightings. Part (c) is particularly important since it carries half the marks for the question.

Part (a) does not ask you to write all you know about air pollution. It is concerned with one particular form, smog.

Part (b) asks you to describe one other form of urban/industrial air pollution which can influence local climate.

In part (c) you must refer to at least one urban/industrial area so a general answer about the need for smoke controls and other measures is not acceptable. You must link the controls with a particular locality.

Points

(a) Draw an annotated diagram to illustrate how smog forms and then write a short explanatory paragraph.

(b) The clues here are acid rain and noxious emissions, both of which may affect local climates.

(c) First of all describe controls which you know exist, such as Health and Safety Acts which control emissions from factory chimneys. Then extend your answer to controls by companies, such as some car manufacturers, which are being introduced to cut down air pollution and which you think should be reinforced by law. You may know of examples from other countries where the laws are stricter than they are in Britain. Do not wander away from air pollution to write about other forms of pollution which are the subject of controls. Remember that this part of the question, if answered well, can give you half the marks allocated for the whole question.

TEST RUN

In this section:

Test Your Knowledge Quiz

Test Your Knowledge Quiz Answers

Progress Analysis

Mock Exam

Mock Exam Questions and Answers

■ This section should be tackled towards the end of your revision programme, when you have covered all your syllabus topics, and attempted the practice questions at the end of the relevant chapters.

■ The Test Your Knowledge Quiz contains short-answer questions on a wide range of syllabus topics. You should attempt it without reference to the text.

■ Check your answers against the Test Your Knowledge Quiz Answers. If you are not sure why you got a wrong answer, go back to the relevant unit in the text: you will find the reference next to our answer.

■ Enter your marks in the Progress Analysis chart. The notes below will suggest a further revision strategy, based on your performance in the quiz. Only when you have done the extra work suggested should you go on to the final test.

■ The Mock Exam is set out like a real exam paper. It contains a wide spread of question styles and topics, drawn from various examination boards. You should attempt this paper under examination conditions. Read the instructions on the front sheet carefully. Attempt the paper in the time allowed, and without reference to the text.

■ Compare your answers to our Mock Exam Suggested Answers. We have provided tutorial notes to each, showing why we answered the question as we did and indicating where your answer may have differed from ours.

TEST YOUR KNOWLEDGE QUIZ

1 What is the mathematical association between two sets of variables called?

2 Give a definition for median.

3 What is the actual area where a settlement is built called?

4 Which way do winds rotate in an anticyclone?

5 What is the layer of the atmosphere nearest to the earth called?

6 What causes exfoliation of rocks?

7 List three agents of chemical weathering.

8 What is the weathered material called that lies above the bedrock and below the surface soil?

9 Define scree.

10 What does the term interception mean in the hydrological cycle?

11 What is the name given to that part of a stream's load which is moved along the bed of the stream?

12 Name four physical factors that may affect the lag time in a storm hydrograph.

13 Explain what is meant by bifurcation ratio.

14 What is the term used to describe the wearing away of material by ice, water or wind?

15 What is the surface layer of permafrost called that thaws during summer temperatures?

16 What is a pingo?

17 Why are houses in periglacial regions built on concrete stilts?

18 What is the difference between swash and backwash?

19 What is the name given to a small, seaward facing peninsula of shingle on a beach, linked to others by curving bays?

20 Is a ria caused by a positive or a negative movement of sea level?

21 What is the movement of particles by a series of jumps called?

22 List two ways in which moisture is responsible for weathering in arid areas at the present time.

23 Explain what the letters DALR stand for, and what the term means.

24 What is a local wind called caused by the heating of slopes during the day resulting in warm air rising up the slope?

25 Is air stable or unstable, if, when it is forced to rise it tends to return to its original position?

26 What are the sloping boundaries between air masses called?

27 Name two ways in which a microclimate can be modified by human action.

28 What is the process called in which material is washed down through the soil?

29 Name the soil-forming process in which leaching is dominant.

30 Is a soil with a pH factor of 8.0 alkaline, neutral or acid?

31 Name the type of soil which has developed in mid-latitude grasslands.

32 What term is used to describe the plants and organisms living near or above the surface of a soil system?

33 What term is used to describe each level in a food chain?

34 What is a biome?

35 Give the name of one phenomenon that may arrest a climax succession.

36 One of the principal features of an ecosystem is a one-way flow of ...?

37 Are carnivores secondary or primary consumers?

38 If the proportion of workers in a society is comparatively small, will the society have a high or low dependency rate?

39 Will the S or the J curve model result in a major rise in death rates and a rapid population decline?

40 What is intra-urban migration?

41 Who introduced laws of migration in 1885?

42 Which model argues that migration occurs according to the degree of attraction of a region or location and that the volume of migration depends on the populations of the two localities involved and the distance between them?

43 What does the expression the morphology of a settlement mean?

44 Name one factor which encouraged the nucleation of a settlement.

45 What is a central place?

46 What name is given to the minimum number of people needed to support a central place function?

47 What is the total trade value of a central place called?

48 What will the size of the second town in a series be, according to the Zipf rank-size rule, if the largest town has a population of 2 million?

49 If rank and size of towns is plotted on logarithmic graph paper the points when joined would form a...?

50 Which model of urban structure and growth considers that functional zones would develop around a number of nuclei of which the central business district is one?

51 What is the name given to the theory that considers efficiency in land use is measured by rent-paying ability?

52 Which one of the following categories will have the ability to pay the highest rents in a city – industrial concerns, high quality residential, large retail stores?

53 Give one problem associated with the inner city.

54 What is gentrification?

55 Give two reasons why cities in the developing world face problems which differ in scale and intensity to those of cities in the developed world.

56 What is the largest city in a country or region called?

57 Explain the law of diminishing returns in relation to agriculture.

58 Name four assumptions underlying Von Thunen's model of agricultural land use.

59 According to the Von Thunen model, which farm products would be located nearest to the city?

60 What would the zone nearest to the city in R Sinclair's analysis be called?

61 Name one way in which a government can influence what the farmer grows.

62 How can a slope be of advantage to a farmer?

63 What measures the degree of concentration of an industry in a particular area?

64 Name one type of industrial linkage.

65 Name two costs of production.

66 What is a line called that joins places with equal total transport costs?

67 Who introduced a model to explain the location of an industry or an individual firm?

68 What is a vertex (node)?

69 What does the beta index measure?

70 What is the name given to a path starting and finishing at the same point and traversing some or all of a network by the shortest route?

71 Name one of the factors put forward by Kansky which influences network patterns.

72 What factors is the gravity model based on?

73 Name one of the three principles identified by Ullman which help to determine the intensity of movement between locations.

74 Which form of transport has the lowest long distance costs?

75 What do the letters GNP stand for?

76 What does the cumulative causation model suggest about economic development?

77 What are the backwash effects of regional development according to Myrdal?

78 What two categories does the British government use for assisted areas?

79 Name one Urban Development Corporation.

80 Name one of the Partnerships set up in Scotland.

81 What do the letters ERDF stand for?

82 What is the name of the Board responsible for helping the Highlands and Islands?

83 Why has migration increase in France been most significant in the Midi?

84 Name one peripheral region in France.

85 Name one way in which the French government is tackling the core-periphery problem.

86 What is the meaning of 'death rate'?

87 What does the rank-size rule say?

88 Define optimum population.

89 What may cause a sharp fall in the death rate in Stage 2 of the demographic transition model?

90 Which one of these countries has reached Stage 4 of the demographic transition model: Nigeria, Japan, Thailand, Algeria?

91 What do the letters HYV stand for?

92 Give one way in which the environment has suffered as a result of the green revolution.

93 What name is given to a Brazilian shanty town?

94 Which region of Brazil has been the largest source of out-migration?

95 Name one way in which the Amazon rainforest region is being exploited.

96 What is the name given to the nutrient enrichment of a body of water which frequently results in a range of other changes?

97 Name one greenhouse gas.

98 Name one gas that is emitted as the result of burning fossil fuels.

99 Name one source which can overload rivers and other water bodies with nutrients.

100 How do car exhausts pollute the atmosphere?

TEST YOUR KNOWLEDGE QUIZ ANSWERS

The unit number in which the answer can be found is given in brackets at the end of the answer.

Award yourself one mark for each correct answer. Do not give yourself a mark if only part of the answer is correct.

1   Correlation (1.1)

2   Central value for an ordered series (1.1)

3   Site (1.2)

4   Clockwise (1.3)

5   Troposphere (1.3)

6   Daily heating and cooling causing the surface to expand more than the interior, setting up stresses which lead to the rock 'peeling' (2.1)

7   Hydration; oxidation; hydrolysis; solution (2.1)

8   Regolith (2.2)

9   Accumulation of rock fragments at the foot of a slope (2.2)

10 Capture of raindrops by the leaves, branches and stems of plants, preventing some of the water from reaching the ground (2.3)

11 Bedload (2.3)

12 Local geological structure; degree of slope; vegetation cover; amount and intensity of rainfall; extent of soil cover; nature of underlying rock; evapotranspiration rate (2.3)

13 The relationship between the number of streams in one order and the number of streams in the next order (2.4)

14 Corrasion (2.5)

15 Active layer (2.5)

16 A dome-shaped isolated hill with a core of ice (2.5)

17 So that foundations can penetrate into the permafrost layer which is always frozen (2.5)

18 Swash is the rush of water up a beach from a breaking wave. Backwash is the flow down the beach after the swash has reached its highest point (2.6)

19 Beach cusp (2.6)

20 Positive movement (2.6)

21 Saltation (2.7)

22 Dew promotes chemical decomposition of the rock. Moisture promotes crystallisation and then expansion occurs, breaking down the rock (2.7)

23 Dry adiabatic lapse rate – the rate at which rising unsaturated air cools, or subsiding unsaturated air warms (2.8)

24 Anabatic wind (2.8)

25 Stable (2.8)

26 Fronts (2.8)

27 Changing vegetation pattern; urban development; water control (2.8)

28 Eluviation (2.9)

29 Podsolisation (2.9)

30 Alkaline (2.9)

31 Chernozem or black earth (2.9)

32 Biomass store (2.9)

33 Trophic level (2.10)

34 One of the major terrestrial ecosystems of the world (2.10)

35 Flooding; fire; human interference (2.10)

36 Energy (2.10)

37 Secondary (2.10)

38 High (3.1)

39 J curve (3.1)

40 Migration from one part of a city to another part (3.2)

41 Ravenstein (3.2)

42 Gravity model (3.2)

43 The form (shape) of the settlement (3.3)

44 Cooperative system of working land; defence; water supply; dry site; scarcity of building materials; planned village (3.3)

45 A settlement which provides one or more services for people outside it (3.4)

46 Threshold population (3.4)

47 k value (3.4)

48 One million (3.4)

49 Smooth curve (3.4)

50 Harris and Ullman model (3.5)

51 Bid-rent theory (Ratcliffe theory) (3.5)

52 Large retail stores (3.5)

53 Economic decay; low-grade housing; high crime rate; depopulation; few job opportunities (3.5)

54 The improvement of older properties and areas by well-off people or developers (3.6)

55 Urbanisation is occurring very rapidly; lack of wealth and skilled labour; lack of advanced technology (3.6)

56 Primate city (3.4)

57 At a certain point in production, additional units will yield proportionately smaller units of output and the additional cost incurred will be greater than the additional revenue received (3.7)

58 An isolated state; one central city as sole market; uniform plain; plain inhabited by farmers who supply the city; farmers aim to maximise profits; cost of transport directly proportional to distance (3.7)

59 Vegetables and fresh milk (3.7)

60 Land speculation (3.7)

61 Tariffs; import quotas; subsidies (3.7)

62 If it faces the sun temperatures can be higher (3.7)

63 The location quotient (3.8)

64 Vertical, horizontal; diagonal (3.8)

65 Labour; entrepreneurship; capital; energy; raw materials; transport; land (3.8)

66 Isodapane (3.8)

67 Weber (3.8)

68 A location on a network such as a road junction or a station (3.9)

69 The connectivity of a network (3.9)

70 A circuit (3.9)

71 Relief; shape; size; population; degree of economic development (3.9)

72 Population and distance (3.9)

73 Complementarity; intervening opportunity; transferability (3.9)

74 Water transport (3.9)

75 Gross National Product (3.10)

76 That development leads to an increase, rather than a decrease in the differences between regions (3.10)

77 Capital and people move to the thriving regions so other regions are worse off (3.10)

78 Developed Areas and Intermediate Areas (4.1)

79 London Dockland; Trafford Park; Teesside; Tyne and Wear; Black Country; Cardiff Bay; Bristol; Leeds; Central Manchester; Sheffield (4.1)

80 Dundee; Edinburgh; Glasgow; Paisley (4.1)

81 European Regional Development Fund (4.1)

82 Highlands and Islands Enterprise (4.1)

83 Climate; new industries; overseas immigrants from Algeria (4.2)

84 Southern Brittany; Corsica; Massif Central; Pyrenees; North-East; Lorraine (4.2)

85 Redistribution of industry; modernisation of farming; improving communications; grants (4.2)

86 Number of deaths per year per 1,000 of population (4.3)

87 The size of settlements is inversely proportional to their rank (4.3)

88 The population of a country which, with the given resources and skills produces the greatest economic welfare (maximum income per head) (4.3)

89 Improved health care: better hygiene; better food supply; new medicines and drugs (4.3)

90 Japan (4.3)

91 High Yield Variety (4.4)

92 Pollution of rivers by chemicals; soil erosion; salination (4.4)

93 Favela (4.5)

94 North-East (4.5)

95 Commercial cattle ranching; timber; HEP; minerals (4.6)

96 Eutrophication (4.7)

97 Methane; carbon dioxide; nitrous oxide; chlorofluorocarbons (4.7)

98 Carbon dioxide; sulphur dioxide; nitrogen dioxide (4.7)

99 Agricultural land (fertilisers, pesticides); sewage; detergents (4.7)

100 By emitting lead and carbon dioxide (4.7)

PROGRESS ANALYSIS

Place a tick next to those questions you got right.

Question	Answer	Question	Answer	Question	Answer	Question	Answer
1		26		51		76	
2		27		52		77	
3		28		53		78	
4		29		54		79	
5		30		55		80	
6		31		56		81	
7		32		57		82	
8		33		58		83	
9		34		59		84	
10		35		60		85	
11		36		61		86	
12		37		62		87	
13		38		63		88	
14		39		64		89	
15		40		65		90	
16		41		66		91	
17		42		67		92	
18		43		68		93	
19		44		69		94	
20		45		70		95	
21		46		71		96	
22		47		72		97	
23		48		73		98	
24		49		74		99	
25		50		75		100	

My total mark is: out of 100

ANALYSIS

If you scored 1–25

You need to do some more work. You are not yet ready to take the Mock Exam because you do not have sufficient knowledge or understanding of the syllabus content. Starting at Section 2, Chapter 1, look at the list of units at the beginning of each chapter and revise those units on which you scored poorly in the test. When you consider you have completed your revision, get a friend to ask you questions (not necessarily those in the Test) and if you are still weak on some units, look at them again. You should then attempt the Test Your Knowledge Quiz again.

If you scored 26–50

You are getting there, but you must do some more work . Go through the list of units at the beginning of each chapter and mark those which you could not answer questions about correctly in the Test. In addition, look through the Practice Questions at the end of each chapter and the Points which accompany them. Go over some of your weak topics with a friend and then attempt the Test Your Knowledge Quiz again.

If you scored 51–75

You are nearly ready to attempt the Mock Exam, but to get the best out of it, brush up on those units which the Test shows you have not fully understood. Also look at the Practice Questions at the end of each chapter and check those questions which relate to the subject areas you do not feel confident about. You should then be ready to go on to the Mock Exam.

If you scored 76–100

Well done! You can tackle the Mock Exam with confidence although you will first need to revise some of the units which let you down in the Test Your Knowledge Quiz. Reassure yourself that there are no gaps in your knowledge and then set aside a time to do the Mock Exam.

LETTS SCHOOL EXAMINATIONS BOARD
General Certificate of Education Examination

ADVANCED LEVEL
GEOGRAPHY

Paper 1
Time allowed: 3 hours

THURSDAY 2 JUNE, AFTERNOON

Answer FOUR questions, TWO from Section A and TWO from Section B.
All questions carry equal marks.

Candidates are strongly recommended to read through the paper before attempting the questions.

Candidates are reminded of the need for good English and orderly presentation.
Credit will be given for the use of relevant sketch maps and diagrams.

Section A

1 Fig. 1 shows the fluctuations in temperature over a period of 24 hours in July at two locations in New York City – central Manhattan Island which is part of the central business district, and Kennedy Airport in the outer suburbs. The map shows these locations in relation to the built-up areas of the region.

Describe and suggest reasons for the differences in temperature which occur between these two urban locations.

(in the style of the Welsh Joint Examination Committee, A Level)

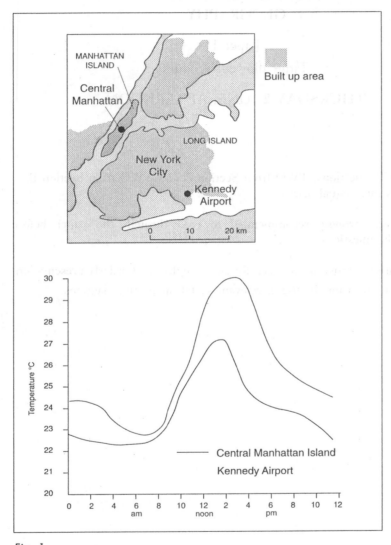

Fig. 1

2 (a) Study the map of coastal changes shown in Fig. 2.
   (i) Describe and explain the patterns of erosion and deposition along the coastline in the period shown. (10)
   (ii) At present the dredger dumping zone is in grid square F5. Giving reasons, suggest a better location. (5)

 (b) Assess the effectiveness of methods (other than groynes) used to combat either coastal erosion or estuarine flooding. (10)

(Northern Ireland Schools Examinations Assessment Council, A Level, May 1991)

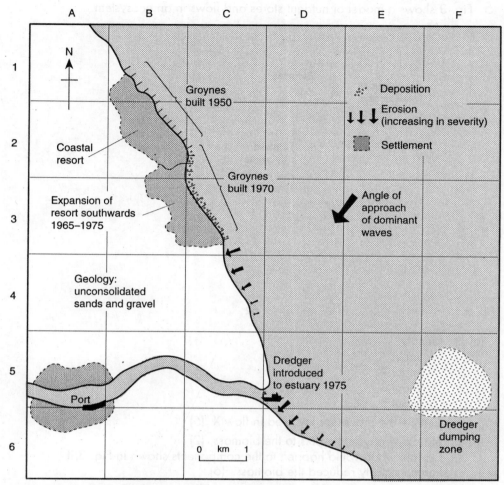

Fig. 2 Coastal patterns of erosion and deposition 1970–1985

3 (a) By using **fully labelled diagrams only**, describe the characteristics of the profiles of:

    (i) podsol soils and

    (ii) chernozem (black earth) soils. (10)

  (b) Choose **one** of the soil types named in (a) above. Identify the soil you have chosen and explain how its profile characteristics are related to climate, vegetation and other physical conditions. (8)

  (c) For **either** the podsol soil type **or** the chernozem (black earth) soil type show how human activities have led to upgrading of the soil in some localities but downgrading of the same soil type in other localities. You should identify the soil you have chosen before you write your answer. (7)

                     (Joint Matriculation Board, A Level, June 1990)

4 (a) Briefly describe and explain the origin and character of the following land surface:

    (i) reg;

    (ii) hamada. (5)

  (b) Explain the mechanisms by which sand particles are set in motion and transported by the wind. (10)

  (c) Describe and explain the landforms that are created by the deposition of wind-blown sand. (10)

(University of Oxford Delegacy of Local Examinations, A Level, June 1991)

5 Fig. 3 shows a model of nutrient stores and flows in an ecosystem.

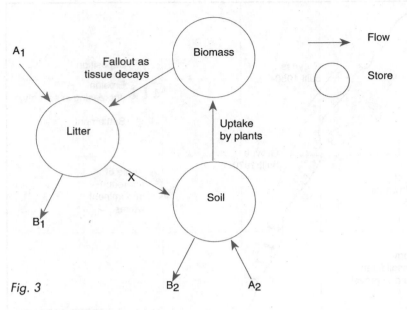

Fig. 3

(a) (i) Identify:
   input A_1
   input A_2
   input B_1
   input B_2 (4)

  (ii) Outline the processes involved in flow X. (5)

(b) (i) State *two* physical inputs to the biomass. (2)
  (ii) Explain what would happen to the components shown in Fig. 3 if human activity reduced the biomass. (6)

(c) Explain why the sizes of the various stores differ in each of:
   (i) a coniferous forest;
   (ii) a deciduous forest. (8)

   (University of London School Examinations Board, A Level, June 1990)

Section B

6 Table 1 refers to Fig. 4.

Table 1

Country	GNP per capita ($US)	Birth rate per 1000 of population
Switzerland	15 455	11.9
Belgium	10 800	12.7
USA	8 612	16.2
Japan	8 460	13.7
Portugal	2 000	17.1
Mexico	1 800	34.0
Paraguay	1 038	39.8
Peru	655	41.0
Sudan	320	45.8
Pakistan	280	36.0
Zaire	127	46.8
Bangladesh	85	47.4

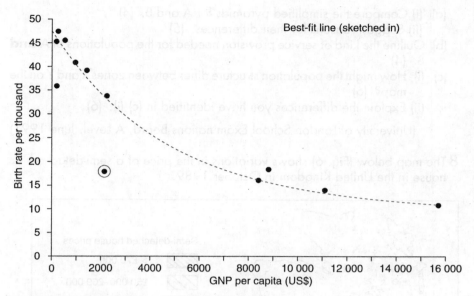

Fig. 4 Relationship between birth rate and GNP

(a) Identify the country ringed on the graph. (2)

(b) State whether the country's birth rate is higher or lower than that predicted by the best-fit line. (2)

(c) Describe the relationship between birth rate and per capita Gross National Product shown in the table. (9)

(d) Explain why there are marked differences between the birth rates in developed and developing countries. (12)

(in the style the Joint Matriculation Board, A Level)

7 Study Fig. 5 which shows (a) urban land-use zones, and (b) simplified population pyramids for permanent residents for two areas in a coastal town.

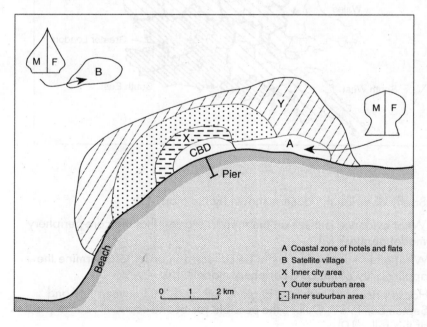

Fig. 5

(a) (i) Compare the simplified pyramids for A and B. (4)
   (ii) Suggest reasons for their differences. (5)

(b) Outline the kind of service provision needed for the populations at A **and** B. (4)

(c) (i) How might the population structure differ between zones X and Y on the map? (6)
   (ii) Explain the differences you have identified in (c) (i). (6)

(University of London School Examinations Board, A Level, June 1991)

8 The map below (Fig. 6) shows variations in the price of a semi-detached house in the United Kingdom in October 1989.

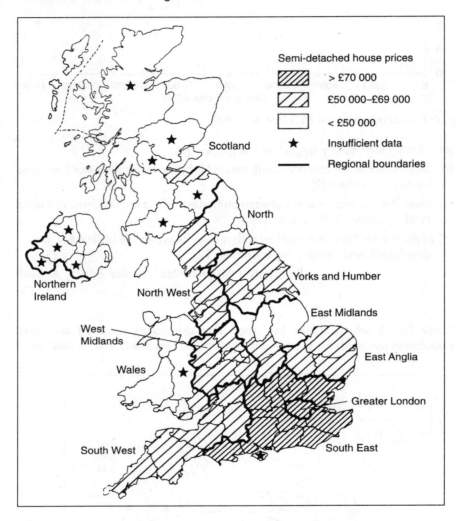

Fig. 6

(a) Briefly describe the pattern shown by the map. (5)

(b) What evidence is there on the map to suggest that the core-periphery model applies? (5)

(c) What other information might be collected in order to determine the applicability of the core-periphery model? (5)

(d) House prices in South-East England fell by 4.3% between July and September 1989. Outline the possible social and economic consequences of this fall. (10)

(The Associated Examining Board, A Level, June 1991)

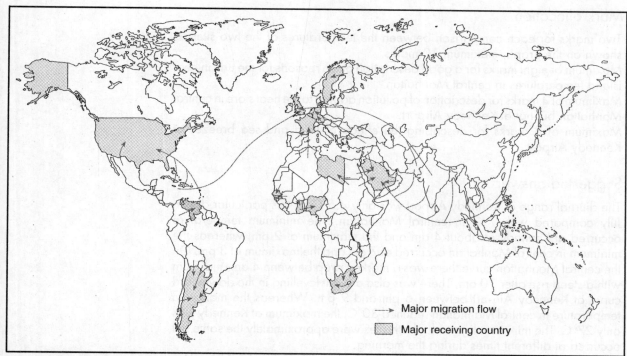

Fig. 7 Labour migration flows, 1960–90

9 (a) Study Fig. 7.
For any **one** of the major migration flows shown, describe

    (i)   the type of work undertaken by the migrant workers in the host country;
    (ii) the benefits which immigrants can bring to the host country;
    (iii) the social and economic problems which may arise in the host country as a consequence of large scale in-migration. (11)

(b) (i) For any one **developing** country which you have studied, suggest the **push** and **pull** factors which have caused the large internal migration to cities. (8)

    (ii) With reference to a **named** city in a **developing** country, describe the urban problems caused by rapid in-migration. (6)

(Scottish Certificate of Education, Higher Grade, May 1991)

10 (a) Examine the causes and consequences of *the greenhouse effect*. (15)
   (b) Discuss possible measures which might be taken to reduce the effect. (10)

(The Associated Examining Board, A Level, June 1991)

MOCK EXAM SUGGESTED ANSWERS

1 Tutorial note

The answer should be in two parts. The first of these should be fairly short and should describe the differences in the temperature patterns shown on the graphs. The second should explain as fully as possible why the two graphs are so different for urban environments which are only about 20 km apart.

The most systematic way of dealing with the second part of the answer is to explain at length the three main factors responsible for the development of an urban heat island. Kennedy Airport is also closer to the coast than central Manhattan – which means that there is another factor which can keep temperatures down.

Mark allocation

Two marks for each comparison between the temperatures at the two sites as shown on the graph, maximum 10 marks.

Maximum of eight marks for a good description of the reasons for the urban heat island temperatures in central Manhattan.

Maximum of 4 marks for description of pollution adding to the heat store in central Manhattan but not at Kennedy Airport.

Maximum of 3 marks for describing the effects of land and sea breezes at Kennedy Airport.

Suggested answer

The diurnal range at Kennedy Airport was only 4.5°C on this particular day in July compared with 7°C in central Manhattan. The minimum temperature occurred at Kennedy at about 4 am and the maximum at 2 pm, whereas the minimum in central Manhattan occurred at 7 am and the maximum at 3 pm. On the central Manhattan curve there was a marked drop between 4 am and 7 am with a steep rise after 10 am. There was also a slight levelling in the downward curve at Kennedy Airport between 6 pm and 9 pm. Whereas the maximum temperature in central Manhattan reached 30°C, the maximum at Kennedy was only 27°C. The minimum figures for both sites were approximately the same but occurred at different times during the morning.

The graph indicates that central Manhattan is part of the urban heat island for New York City, whereas Kennedy Airport in the outer suburbs is on the edge of the heat island and more open to oceanic influences.

One factor responsible for an urban heat island building up in central Manhattan is the direct production of heat from buildings and industry. These forms of heat are present in July in New York as heat extracted from the buildings by air conditioning systems and heat from car exhaust systems.

A second factor involved is the heat-conserving properties of brick, bitumen and stone in the densely built up area of Manhattan Island. The surfaces of the skyscrapers and other buildings absorb the heat, and turbulence from local winds distributes it as it is re-radiated from the surfaces. The building materials act as giant night storage heaters, delaying the loss of heat after dark.

The third factor is the amount of dust and other air pollutants such as car exhaust fumes in this large urban area. These particles scatter some of the short wavelength sunlight back into space and also absorb heat from the city surfaces. This has a blanketing effect, holding close to the surface at night the heat stored in the buildings during the day. These factors will be less evident on the edge of the built up area at Kennedy Airport.

Furthermore, Kennedy Airport is close to the oceanic influences of the Atlantic and will therefore be influenced by land and sea breezes in July. During the daytime air will rise over the land, drift out to sea, cool, become denser and sink forming high pressure contrasting with the low pressure over the land. Cooler air from the sea will be drawn ashore by the low pressure and reduce local temperatures. At night the reverse happens with a breeze from high pressure over the land area blowing out to sea where low pressure forms.

2 Tutorial note

There is uneven distribution of marks with (a) (i) and (b) having by far the largest share of the total. Part (a) (i) requires not only a description, but also an explanation of the patterns of erosion and deposition along the coastline. One key to the answer of this part and the other parts is the direction of the longshore drift, indicated by the arrow showing the angle of approach of the dominant waves. Longshore drift is also the key to part (a) (ii).

Part (b) gives you a choice of describing the effectiveness of methods used, so descriptions of the methods used should be kept to a minimum.

Mark allocation

(a) (i) Maximum 5 marks for describing the pattern of erosion in the built up area in the north, the area to the south north of the estuary and the area to the south of the estuary. Maximum 5 marks for giving reasons for this pattern.

(a) (ii) Maximum 2 marks for explaining where you would relocate the dumping zone and maximum of 3 marks for explaining why.

(b) Maximum of 3–4 marks for three methods fully assessed, maximum 10 marks.

Suggested answer

(a) (i) The dominant waves approach the coast from the north-east and therefore any movement of material along the coast by longshore drift will be from north to south. Erosion is likely to be rapid because the geology of the area shows that it is unconsolidated sands and gravel which are easily removed by wave action. The only section of the coastline where erosion is naturally checked is just north of the river estuary where the outward flow of water from the estuary will slow down, or halt the movement of material southwards. The estuary itself is kept clear by dredging otherwise the deep water channel would constantly change as material was deposited in it from the north. Human attempts to check erosion can be seen along the stretch of coast fronting the coastal resort. The older part of the resort in the north was protected by groynes built in the 1950s but there is no evidence of deposition. The expansion of the resort southwards resulted in the building of more groynes which have collected considerable deposition behind them. As a result, deposition to the south has been checked and erosion is at its maximum. The same occurs south of the estuary where, with deposition checked in the estuary, erosion is at its maximum to the south of it.

(a) (ii) Material dumped by the dredger would be of most use on stretches of coastline where erosion is heaviest. Because of longshore drift the present dumping ground will not affect the coastline on this map. I would dump the material in square C1 or C2 where it would be swept towards the coast and add material in front of the resort or just to the south where erosion is severe.

(b) Methods used to check coastal erosion are:

❶ Dumping large quantities of sand, shingle and other rocks on the beach area. This may be effective in checking the energy of the waves close inshore but it can have a detrimental effect on the section of coastline from which the material has been removed.

❷ Adding drainage pipes to unstable areas of cliff so that water flowing through the rock is less of a lubricant. This method will slow up cliff slumping but if the cliff displays instability, frost and even burrowing animals may cause erosion, giving drainage pipes a limited usefulness.

❸ Building sea walls, a method which is expensive and of limited value since a wall seems to increase the concentration of high energy waves.

❹ Planting marram grass to stabilise coastal sand dunes.

❺ Erecting brushwood fences or planting coniferous trees to check sand removal.

Methods (4) and (5) have a limited use since they can only take place on areas of the coast where sand dunes have been formed by the wind.

❻ Constructing breakwaters. These have a limited usefulness since they will check longshore drift material and reduce wave energy at one point but further along the coast erosion will not be affected.

Methods used to check estuarine flooding are:

❶ Sea walls – Effective but costly to erect, e.g. Canvey Island in the Thames estuary.

❷ Thames Barrier – Protects area above barrier which includes the lowland areas of London, but very expensive to erect and gives no protection further down estuary.

❸ Using estuarine marshes as infill for city rubbish – Raises marshes above flood level but can destroy local ecosystems.

❹ Dredging estuary – Provides deeper channel for tidal water but must be carried out regularly at considerable cost.

3 Tutorial note

It is far too easy to spend too much time drawing the diagrams for part (a) and leave yourself insufficient time for the rest of the question. You should have spent no more than 20–25 minutes on (a) but during that time you should have produced two neat and fully annotated diagrams.

In each of (b) and (c) you should have identified your choice of soil first. Your answers to each part of the question and the sub-sections should be clearly identifiable.

Mark allocation

Maximum of 5 marks for each soil profile diagram. Ignore any additional paragraphs or sentences, since the examiners want only fully labelled diagrams.

Maximum of 8 marks distributed with a maximum of 3 for climate, 3 for vegetation and 2 for other physical conditions.

Maximum of 3–4 marks for examples of upgrading, maximum of 3–4 for examples of downgrading, overall maximum 7 marks.

Suggested answer

(a) (i)

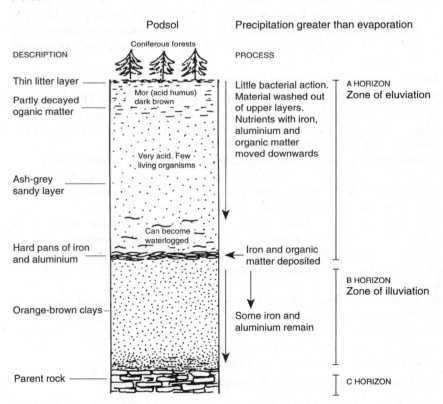

Fig. 8a

(ii)

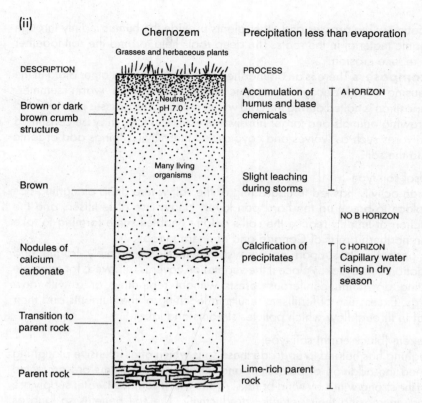

Fig. 8b

(b) Podsol soil type

Climate Winters are long and cold with temperatures as low as −30°C. Over six months the mean temperature is below 6°C. Summers are short but there are long hours of daylight and days are relatively warm, 10–15°C. Precipitation is light, heaviest in the summer because of convectional rainstorms. Total precipitation is between 250 and 450 mm. This is a region with precipitation during most of the year exceeding evapotranspiration so that there is a downward movement of water through the soil, leaching out organic matter, bases and other chemicals.

Vegetation Coniferous trees are adapted to this climate and form the main and almost only layer of vegetation. Plants forming ground cover are those requiring little sunlight which can live in the acid conditions. They include mosses, lichens and wood sorrel. Pine needles decompose very slowly in these conditions and give an acid mor humus with most nutrient in the litter. As evapotranspiration is lower than precipitation the nutrients are leached down. Conifers require fewer nutrients than deciduous trees and can tolerate the poor soil conditions.

Decomposers The cold climate and soils discourage earthworms and bacteria so there are few organisms to enable decomposition to take place. Animal droppings are also rare because few animals live in these forests and birdlife is also limited.

Chernozem (black earth) soils

Climate The range of temperatures is high with summers in the low 20s°C and winters of −15°C or lower. Three quarters of the precipitation falls in summer and averages only 500 mm annually. The clear skies give a large diurnal range and the ground is snow-covered between October and April, although falls are light. The grasses die down in the autumn and form a turf mat, decaying in summer to cause a rapid accumulation of humus in the soil. Leaching is almost non-existent except in the early spring snowmelt and during summer thunderstorms. In the late summer there is upward capillary action bringing bases near the surface.

Vegetation This consists of grasses, herbaceous plants and some trees near water courses. The grasses and other plants provide the humus mainly through the organic material in the roots. The deep roots help to bind the soil together and so reduce erosion.

Decomposers There is an abundance of earthworms and other biota in the soil causing rapid decay of organic matter during the warm summer. Decomposition is halted during the cold winter months. The grasses provide food for burrowing animals and larger herbivores which, in turn, may be consumed by carnivores such as wolves and coyotes. All these living things add organic matter to the soil.

(c) Podsol soil type

Human activity has led to upgrading of the soil where deep ploughing has taken place to break up the hard pan layer. Heavy use of fertilisers and the introduction of lime to reduce the soil's acidity enables some farming to take place in northern areas of Canada and northern Europe.

The podsol soils support an ecosystem which is extremely fragile and degradation quickly takes place if the vegetation cover is removed, for example by cutting down the coniferous forests without replanting area with new seedlings. Excess use of fertilisers results in leaching of the nutrients and their removal in throughflow which pollutes streams and lakes.

Chernozem (black earth) soil type

Ploughing has helped to upgrade these soils which after intensive ploughing may need the addition of potassium and nitrates. Many farms are protected against the strong winds by wind-breaks. Areas with insufficient water supply are irrigated, increasing their potential productivity. The soil benefits so long as salinisation is controlled. Degradation has been brought about by soil erosion, particularly wind erosion which removes the nutrient-rich A horizon of the soil. This has been held in check by using dry farming methods to preserve the moisture content and retain plant nutrients.

4 Tutorial note

The examiners report states that candidates were frequently confused or ignorant of the origin and nature of 'reg' and 'hamada'. Some of your descriptions in (c) are best reinforced with sketches although a sketch should never duplicate a written description since marks are only awarded once.

Mark allocation

Five marks for part (a), the maximum possible for two good descriptions.
In (b) 3–4 marks for each mechanism with a maximum of 10.
In (c) 2–3 marks for each of the major dune types with a maximum of 10.

Suggested answer

(a) (i) Reg is a desert plain covered with small pebbles, particularly well developed in the Sahara. It was formed by the progressive removal of fine material by the wind, leaving behind a pebble-strewn desert pavement. Originally, over much of the Sahara, during a wetter climate, the pebbles were transported by water from the surrounding highlands and deposited with sand, clay and silt on the lowland plain. The lighter materials have been blown away leaving the hard pavement and the pebbles.

(ii) Hamada is an extensive flat, rocky surface in the desert from which sand has been removed by the wind. This bare rocky surface is subject to weathering which displaces surface layers by exfoliation and fractures of rock by salt weathering. While the finest particles are removed by the wind, larger pieces of rock remain on the surface.

(b) The mechanism by which sand particles are set in motion requires a number of conditions to be met. These are: strong winds coming from a constant direction and blowing steadily for a long period of time; little or no vegetation; a dry and unconsolidated surface; particles small enough to be transported.

Wind transports the material by three processes: suspension, saltation and surface creep. Suspension requires a strong wind and very fine particles which are lifted well clear of the ground and carried considerable distances, e.g. Saharan dust reaching southern Britain.

Saltation is when sand particles are bounced along, having been lifted a few centimetres by the wind. These particles are larger than those carried in suspension. Coarse sand and pebbles are pushed along by the finer material moved by saltation. They are too heavy to move without some assistance. This process is called surface creep.

(c) Deposition of wind-blown sands results in a number of landforms which include barchans, seif dunes, longitudinal dunes, parabolic dunes, transverse dunes and star dunes.

Barchans are crescent-shaped and usually form around an obstacle such as a dead camel or a bush. The horns point downwind and are formed because the edges of the dune moves faster than the centre because there is less sand to move. Barchans move forwards by saltation and surface creep of the sand. Seif dunes are linear in shape and form in the direction of the prevailing wind. Longitudinal dunes are formed by winds cutting troughs in the desert floor and piling the sand in ridges on either side of the trough. Parabolic dunes are shaped like a hairpin with the rounded nose pointing downwind. Transverse dunes resemble ocean waves and form where sand is very plentiful. Star dunes develop where wind direction changes at certain times, causing the dunes to resemble starfish.

5 Tutorial note

This is a structured question based on the nutrient flow model. In the examination this question would be answered in an answer book which is set out with lines on which to write your answer for each part of the question. Sufficient lines are provided so there is nothing to be gained by writing answers of excessive length.

Mark allocation

One mark is awarded for each answer to (a) (i). Five marks are awarded for outlining the processes in answer to (a) (ii). One mark each is awarded for naming the physical inputs into the biomass (b) (i).
A maximum of 6 marks are awarded for the explanation asked for in (b) (ii).
A maximum of 4 marks are awarded for (c) (i) and 4 marks for (c) (ii).

Suggested answer

(a) (i) Input A_1: nutrients in rainwater.
Input A_2: nutrients from weathered rock.
Input B_1: loss of nutrients in run-off.
Input B_2: loss of nutrients by leaching.

(ii) As litter decomposes, nutrients in the litter are released and enter the soil. Decomposition in the litter layer provides humus which in turn provides the food for soil microorganisms. These help to break down the organic matter.

(b) (i)

❶ vegetation
❷ excrement of animals

(ii) If human activity reduces the biomass there are fewer nutrients available to enter the soil via the litter layer and the soil as a result will be less fertile. Removal of biomass which forms a soil cover, e.g. cutting down trees in the rainforest, may result in soil erosion and removal of nutrients in the soil by leaching or run-off. The soil is rapidly reduced and impoverished.

(c) (i) Coniferous forests produce a relatively small store of litter. The trees produce needle-like leaves and cones which decompose very slowly because of the cold climate and lack of decomposers in the soil. Soil stores of mineral nutrients are small because formation is difficult. The biomass store consists mainly of trees, with hardly any other vegetation to decompose and provide nutrients.

(ii) Deciduous forests have a larger biomass store, derived from leaf-fall and a range of other vegetation. The soil store is large and includes worms and other decomposers which provide organic matter. The litter store is also large because bacterial action and the decomposition of dead vegetation are sufficiently active to break down the material which accumulates each autumn.

Section B

6 Tutorial Note

This data-response question tests your ability to interpret statistics and give logical reasons why the birth rates in developed and developing countries differ greatly. You should set out your answer in four parts, (a), (b), (c) and (d) with each part clearly labelled.

Mark allocation

(a) and (b) two marks each.
(c) Three marks for each good point fully described, total 9 marks.
(d) Four marks for each good point fully explained, total 12 marks.

Suggested answer

(a) Portugal.

(b) Portugal has a birth rate lower than that predicted by the best-fit line. It is 17.1 per thousand, whereas the best-fit line predicts approximately 30 per thousand.

(c) The chart shows there is an inverse relationship between the birth rate and the GNP per capita. The higher the birth rate, the lower the GNP per capita. Two countries which are placed in the correct order on the GNP hierarchy table, are out of order in the birth rate hierarchy. They are Portugal and Pakistan, both of which have birth rates lower than would be expected when their GNPs are taken into account. Whereas birth rates for the first five countries on the table are relatively similar, those for the other countries rise rapidly from 34.0 to 47.4 per thousand of population.

(d) A number of social and economic factors account for the marked differences between the birth rates in developed and developing countries.

Poverty and malnutrition The poorest and most undernourished people tend to have the highest birth rates. This sets in motion a vicious circle: high birth rates lead to poverty which in turn results in malnutrition.

Knowledge The more educated the people, the more likely they will know about and adopt birth control methods. Better-educated people have a higher degree of social awareness and a wider choice of action. In Brazil, mothers with secondary education have, on average, 2.5 children whilst those without have, on average, 6.5 children. The literacy rate in the developed world is much higher than in the developing world.

Belief Some religions encourage large families and denounce birth control. Muslim countries, for example, have high birth rates. The social belief that the elderly members of a family will be looked after in old age by their children encourages large families. Such beliefs are common in developing countries.

Political and social pressures In Hindu society it is the custom for girls to marry at puberty and to have large families. In developed countries these social pressures are less evident and tend to be replaced with economic pressures which encourage people to spend their money on goods and services thus limiting family size.

Demographic structure The age-sex structure of a country is highly significant. Countries with a high proportion of young adults will have high birth rates. As a result of dramatic decreases in the infant mortality rates in the 1950s and 1960s, many developing countries have a high percentage of young adults. Developed countries with low birth rates have a greater proportion of older people, many of whom are women beyond child-bearing age. This in turn can lead to further reductions in the birth rate.

7 Tutorial Note

The most difficult part of this question is (c) since it is concerned not with the main features of the inner city, but with its population structure. The examiners' report noted that answers to (c) tended to comment on housing and urban conditions and so marks were lost.

Mark allocation

(a) (i) Four marks are awarded for a comparison of the two population pyramids. No marks if each is described separately and there is no comparison.

  (ii) Five marks are given as a maximum for three suitable reasons.

(b) Four marks are awarded for two or three good points explaining what service provisions would be needed.

(c) (i) Two marks are given for each difference, giving a maximum of 6 marks.

  (ii) Two marks are awarded for each good explanatory point, maximum 6 marks.

Suggested answer

(a) (i) Whereas pyramid A indicates that the bulk of the population is middle-aged or old-aged and that there are proportionately fewer teenagers or people aged 20 to 40, pyramid B indicates a population containing many teenagers and people in the 20 to 40 age range, with fewer people who are middle-aged or of pensionable age (i.e. over 60).

  (ii) In a coastal zone containing a number of hotels and flats there will be a resident population of older people, many of whom have retired and want to live close to the sea. These families will have grown-up children living elsewhere, so the proportion of young people will be low.

   In the satellite village there will be young married people who may work in the coastal resort or locally in the village. These families will have children so there will be a larger population of young people with fewer in the higher age brackets.

(b) The population at A, because of their age, will need extensive medical care. Some will be unable to carry out maintenance work on their flats so the services of carpenters, decorators and plumbers will be needed. Those who are incapacitated in some way will need nursing and other social service provision such as meals on wheels.

The population at B will need schools for their children and leisure facilities for the young people. Bus services into the town will be required, as well as some local service provision such as a post office, a general store and a health centre.

(c) (i) Zone X is an inner city zone whereas zone Y is an outer suburban zone. Zone X will have a population structure with the higher percentage of young people with families and old people. Those of middle age will be less in evidence but there may be a high student population because of cheaper accommodation.

Zone Y will have a different population structure. The outer suburbs attract the upwardly mobile and those older people who can afford the higher housing prices in this zone. The pyramid will bulge outwards for those of working age and since these age groups will also have children attending schools and colleges, there will be high proportions in these age bands.

(ii) The differences occur because the inner city zone is one where economic, social and environmental conditions pose problems and often people living there cannot afford to move elsewhere for a variety of reasons. Some are single-parent families, some are elderly people living on a state pension, some are low-income manual workers and some may be overseas immigrants with no capital available for better accommodation.

This contrasts with the outer suburbs where houses are larger and many are detached or semi-detached. There is little evidence of deprivation and living costs are higher than in the inner city. Amenities are good and the density of housing low, particularly at the urban-rural fringe. The people living in this zone will be able to afford mortgages, or be owner-occupiers of their property. They will have sufficient earnings to incur the increased transport costs of the outer suburbs and they, with their children, make up the bulk of the population in this zone.

8 Tutorial note

A blow-by-blow account of house prices throughout the UK is not required and would be a waste of time. The map shows three broad bands and these should be described since they form a pattern. Some exceptions within these bands could also be noted.

The evidence on the map for a core and periphery is to be found in the shading for the South-East contrasted with the low house prices at the periphery.

In (d) it is easy to fall into the trap of talking about the recession and its effects rather than about the fall in house prices and their effects on various groups of people.

Mark allocation

Five marks are awarded for describing the three elements in the pattern.
Five marks are awarded for noting that the core consists of the South-East because of high prices, and the periphery consists of areas like Wales.
Two marks are awarded for each additional piece of information provided its usefulness is described – total 5 marks.
Two marks for each consequence, if its inclusion is justified – total 10 marks.

Suggested answer

(a) The pattern on the map consists of three broad areas, based on the prices of semi-detached houses. The first area is Greater London and the South East, which has the highest prices. The second area stretches from Cornwall across to East Anglia and north-west to Cumbria. Houses here are in the middle price band. The third area includes most of Wales, parts of Northern Ireland , the East Midlands, the North and parts of Scotland. There are exceptions to these broad categories in the East Midlands and the Lothian region of Scotland.

(b) The evidence on the map that there is a core area is the consolidation of high prices in London and the South-East with no similar prices in other parts of the country. The periphery can be identified by a price band of less than £50 000, as in Wales, Northern Ireland and North-East England. Again, there are exceptions to this simplified model in the East Midlands.

(c) Other information to help determine the applicability of the core–periphery model are land values, the employment structure, migration rates and unemployment rates. Land values help to identify areas of high land value; employment structure locates areas with high rates of employment and migration into regions providing further evidence of a core. By contrast, high unemployment rates and high out-migration, coupled with low land values, could further identify the periphery.

(d) The social and economic consequences of a fall in house prices would be felt by the building industry and estate agents who lose customers and money when prices fall. Furthermore, people having to sell would face a loss on the original price they paid and other people who would like to sell would be deterred by the fall in prices. The general effect would be stagnation of the property market with a reduction in the number of houses being bought and sold. There would also be a reduction in the number of houses being built resulting in unemployment for bricklayers, carpenters and others employed in the building industry.

9 Tutorial note

Selecting one flow from all those on the map can be difficult. It is worth spending a few minutes considering which flow to write about since there are a considerable number on the map. The more specific you can be when answering (a) (ii) and (iii) the better, but some of the points you make will be applicable to many immigrant groups.

In part (b) the country chosen does not have to be the one chosen for part (a). Furthermore, the city chosen for (b) (ii) can be from yet another developing country. The choice is very wide and your answers should make it quite clear which migration flow/country/city you have chosen.

Mark allocation

(a) (i) Two marks are awarded for describing two or more types of work.
   (ii) Three marks for describing at least two benefits.
   (iii) Six marks are given for describing at least three social and economic problems.
(b) (i) Maximum 4 marks for push factors, maximum 4 marks for pull factors.
   (ii) 2 marks for each urban problem fully described, total 6 marks.

Suggested answer

(a) (i) I have chosen the movement of immigrants from Pakistan and India to the UK between 1960 and 1980.

These immigrants have taken up a variety of jobs in this country. A number moved into the textile towns such as Bradford and worked as mill operatives. Others set up small businesses and shops in parts of large cities, such as the Southall area of London. Most work taken by the immigrants was unskilled or semi-skilled and included jobs in transport (bus drivers and conductors) and operatives in the clothing industry (East London).

(ii) One benefit of this migration was to reduce the labour shortage in both industry and in the service sector, especially in transport services. Most work undertaken was poorly paid and unattractive to members of the host country. Cultural benefits include the introduction of new foods, music and sports to to the UK — immigrants have enriched the quality of English cricket.

(iii) There are a number of problems which arise as a result of this in-migration. They are:
- resentment towards immigrants when unemployment rises among host workers;
- the tendency for migrants to form ethnic groups which do not mix with indigenous population and to be a drain on local services such as health care;
- the fact that religious differences may cause hostility, e.g. the Muslim attitude to certain aspects of British society, such as marriage;
- some immigrant groups may feel they are the object of racial discrimination, particularly with the growth of ethnic ghettos;
- racial tension which can erupt between different immigrant groups, e.g. the riots in Burnley and Huddersfield in July 1992;
- the tendency for workers in the host country to feel they should have priority treatment in jobs and other economic advantages.

(b) (i) The developing country I have chosen is Bangladesh where the main movement of migrants is to Calcutta. The push factors which encourage this movement are:
- rural poverty and overpopulation;
- lack of basic services such as a piped water supply;
- lack of health care and hospitals;
- high unemployment rate often disguised as underemployment;
- few economic prospects for young people;
- lack of educational facilities.

Pull factors are:
- the perception of greater opportunities in Calcutta;
- the prospect of better education and health facilities;
- the chance to acquire simple accommodation with basic facilities such as electricity and water supply;
- the evidence of a higher standard of living to which immigrants can aspire;
- the evidence provided by in-migrants from rural communities who report back to their villages of the advantages of Calcutta and send home money obtained in the city.

(ii) The city I have chosen is Rio de Janeiro with a number of urban problems caused by rapid in-migration. These are:

- The growth of shanty towns (favelas) on the steeper slopes of the city where land is too steep for normal housing developments. These favelas lack basic services such as a supply of fresh water and are breeding grounds for disease.
- High unemployment among in-migrants leading to the growth of the informal sector, such as street trading, which can have illegal aspects, e.g. trading in drugs.
- The growth of crime, especially amoungst the young. Rio is particularly threatened by street crime carried out by youths and children.
- The strain on social services such as health care which are unable to deal with the influx of migrants.
- The inability of city services such as water supply to cope with the demand.

- Inadequate public transport to deal with demand; the road network is poor and poorly maintained due to lack of resources and capital expenditure.
- Rio's inability to deal with migrants has led to a 'two worlds' mentality by some of the original inhabitants. The prosperous live behind high fences protected by armed guards and feel threatened by the poor in-migrants who, for their part, see the rich residents as part of a privileged and alien society.

10 Tutorial note

Questions about the environment always encourage some candidates to make irrational statements which are not supported by facts. Some newspaper articles have been very sensational about the greenhouse effect, over-dramatising the situation to attract attention. Ignore such articles and confine your reading to reliable scientific accounts. The examiners' report states that 'sensational language was in inverse proportion to the marks gained.' Part (b) was apparently 'an even greater licence for the sensationalists.' Environmental causes were featured which have nothing to do with the greenhouse effect, such as removing lead from petrol. Again, a rational approach is needed, devoid of popularist gestures.

Mark allocation

(a) Seven marks are allocated for a detailed examination of the causes, including the naming of the greenhouse gases.
Eight marks for describing the effects. It is probably easier to reverse the answer and deal with the effects before explaining the causes.

(b) Ten marks are allocated on the basis of 2–3 marks for each measure, fully explained and justified.

Suggested answer

(a) The greenhouse effect is the result of the increasing build up of certain gases in the atmosphere. The most significant of these gases is carbon dioxide which constitutes 50% of all the greenhouse gases. The other greenhouse gases are methane 18%, chlorofluorocarbons (CFCs) 14%, ozone 12% and nitrous oxide 6%. These gases trap heat from the sun in the earth's atmosphere that would otherwise radiate back out to space. Incoming short-wave radiation from the sun is able to pass through these greenhouse gases, but long-wave infra-red radiation from the earth's surface is either absorbed by the gases or re-radiated to earth. These gases are responsible for keeping the planet warm, provided they remain at their original level. Unfortunately the level of these gases in the atmosphere has dramatically increased in recent years, producing the greenhouse effect. That is, the gases act like the panes of glass in a greenhouse, trapping the sun's heat and maintaining higher temperatures than would otherwise be the case.

The results of the greenhouse effect centre around slow changes in the climate which will increase average temperatures over the earth's surface. This overall effect is known as global warming. Scientists disagree about the pace of this global warming but they do agree that there is a slow rise in the earth's temperature which will result in a rise in the sea level as the ice caps melt. The increase in temperatures in the 1980s may, or may not be the result of the greenhouse effect. What is known for certain is that the earth's atmosphere is changing with, for example, concentrations of carbon dioxide in the atmosphere 25% above the pre-Industrial Revolution level.

The increase in the level of carbon dioxide in the atmosphere is the result of the increasing consumption of fossil fuels and the burning of rainforests. Methane levels have increased because of leaks of natural gas, more widespread animal rearing and rice cultivation. Chlorofluorocarbons are produced by solvents, aerosols, air conditioners and coolants for refrigerators. Nitrous oxide is released in large quantities when fossil fuels and forests are burned and also when fertilisers are used. Industrialised nations are responsible for more than 90% of human-generated greenhouse gas emissions.

(b) The problem is very complex and cannot be solved by one country alone. If, for example, Brazil stopped burning sections of rainforest, there would not be a dramatic drop in the volume of greenhouse gases. The problem is best tackled by international diplomacy and this began in 1988 with the setting up of the Intergovernmental Panel on Climatic Change (IPCC). This was set up by the World Meteorological Organisation and the United Nations Environmental Programme to report on global warming with a view to establishing a basis for international cooperation. The Montreal Protocol which came into force in 1989 called for all nations to halve their CFC emissions by 1998. Subsequently it was decided that CFCs should be phased out by the year 2000. So far, 55 states have signed and ratified this protocol but Brazil, China, India and Korea have not.

The problem is made more complex because it is the richer industrial nations that are causing the increase in greenhouse gases. These countries of the developed world contain 23% of the world's population but are responsible for 70% of emissions from the burning of fossil fuels. The effects of global warming will not discriminate between developed and developing countries and the latter are fully aware which nations are responsible for the problem. Developed countries, such as Japan, have the scientific and industrial resources to develop fossil fuel-saving technologies to sell to the rest of the world, but progress is slow with the industrial giants such as the USA and Japan dragging their feet. A report commissioned by the Dutch government suggests that developed countries should cut their emissions from the burning of fossil fuels by 20% by 2005, by 50 % by 2015 and by 75% by 2030. Developing countries should stabilise their emissions by the year 2010, allowing them to rise by only double their present levels as they continue to industrialise. So far there is no international consensus on what should be done.

INDEX

321